VISION THE STORY OF BOEING

Always, it seemed, the path of progress
was a problem to be solved. Always it was
the hard path to take. But the effect
of every vision was another chapter
in the 50-year saga of man's progress
in the sky . . . into space.

VISION

The Story of Boeing

A Saga of the Sky and the New Horizons of Space

by HAROLD MANSFIELD

POPULAR LIBRARY • NEW YORK

Published by arrangement with Duell, Sloan and Pearce,
New York, this book includes a condensation of the
original VISION by Harold Mansfield and a major extension of that story by the author. Portions of dialogue
from BILLION DOLLAR BATTLE by Harold Mansfield included with permission of David McKay Company, Inc., New York.

"*What is that proverb that ye have had—
The days are prolonged, and every
vision faileth?*

*They shall no more use it as a proverb . . .
Say unto them, The days are at hand,
and the effect of every vision.*"
                              —The prophet Ezekiel

1

At old Dominguez Ranch, a few miles south of Los Angeles, the rainy sky had cleared and it was California-warm. The atmosphere was charged with anticipation and mystery. Twenty-five thousand people packed a grandstand to the top rails, while other thousands were milling about the edges of the grassy field, eying in wonderment the latest Curtiss, Bleriot and Farman flying machines that were stealing attention from the balloons and dirigibles.

It was January, 1910, and America's first international aeronautical tournament.

William E. Boeing of Seattle was among the spectators at the meet. Tall, mustached, with intent eyes behind thin-rimmed glasses, he had the air of a distinguished college professor. He was moving toward the landing area where a Farman biplane was approaching low. It was a machine larger than the others, with four wheels instead of three, two vertical tail-planes at the back and a wide cloth-covered horizontal surface well out in front of the wings. As it bounced to a stop, its peppery motor idled down. The motor was a rotary type; fastened behind the lower wing, it spun around with the propeller, cylinders and all. When the aviator stepped down from his perch on the wing and walked toward the crowd, Boeing was out in front.

"Monsieur Paulhan, my name is Boeing," the visitor from Seattle said. "I like your machine. I like the way you fly it."

"*Merci*, Monsieur Boeing." The Frenchman clicked his heels and did a quick bow. Boeing asked him more about the Farman. Would it be possible for him to take a ride in it? "*Oui* Monsieur," said Paulhan, but added that it couldn't be done until tomorrow after the endurance competition.

Boeing walked over to his motorcar and drove off. Next afternoon he was back, joining in the crowd's roaring applause as Paulhan completed forty-seven laps around the 1.6 mile course. Glenn Curtiss had dropped out at ten times around and Charles Hamilton at twelve. At the first opportunity Boeing asked again about the flight. "*Oui*, Monsieur Boeing." Paulhan would be glad to take him—a little later. Boeing waited and watched while various dignitaries went up in the machine with Paulhan.

Another day was much the same. Every time he thought he was about to get a flight, someone with special priority would arrive. The flashing-eyed Frenchman was a great favorite. Hoping to make a more definite arrangement, Boeing visited the aviator at his hotel, but learned that the $10,000 cross-country event was on the next day's program.

The course was to Lucky Baldwin's ranch, twenty-three miles away, and back. When it came time for the birdmen to start, a breeze had come up. This was a dangerous thing; a gust from the side might throw them. All balked but Paulhan. He twirled a scarf about his neck and climbed onto his place on the wing. The Farman lifted, lurched, then steadied into the wind. The crowd shouted. Some pursued along the country road on horses, motorcycles and automobiles. In one of the racing motorcars, Madame Paulhan was praying aloud and crying. Paulhan winged along at a height of 1,000 to 2,000 feet, turned successfully over the Baldwin Ranch, and made his way back to the field in an hour and two minutes. When he arrived the yelling crowd burst out of the grandstand and onto the field. Two men hoisted the birdman to their shoulders and the pressing, shouting thousands bore him happily off the field.

After Paulhan's triumph, Boeing didn't see him again. The wide-spreading wings of the Farman, on which the visitor from Seattle had pictured himself aloft, were crated and hauled away. Cleanup crews swept the litter from Dominguez Field.

Bill Boeing didn't mention his disappointment to anyone, but it left a mark. He returned to Seattle, not knowing that Paulhan, too, had departed in a seething mood. The French aviator had been summoned to defend himself in court against the Wright brothers.

When Wilbur and Orville Wright had first taken up the challenge of flying, they had found one of the keys to the art in the bicycles they built for a living. If they turned a corner on a bicycle without leaning into the turn, they would spill. It was the same with the flying machine. They found that by pulling down on the trailing edge of the outside wing in a turn, they could make the machine bank properly. This became their basic patent. The court decided that the "aileron" devices which Paulhan and Glenn Curtiss had hinged to the trailing edges of their wings were a violation of the Wright patent. The Frenchman returned to Paris to try to build a plane without these devices, with a wing instead that was limber at the back, like trailing feathers on a bird.

In America, as in Europe, the zeal of competition was fanning an adventurous faith that the flying machine would yet be important. The new publication *Aircraft* summed it up:

> *You cannot tether time nor sky.*
> *The time approaches, Sam must fly.*

When the noisy excitement of the Los Angeles air meet was recreated nine months later at Belmont Park, New York, Paulhan was not there, but Glenn Curtiss was on hand to defend the Gordon Bennett trophy he had won at Reims, France, the year before.

Among Curtiss' fans at the meet was a Navy lieutenant named Conrad Westervelt. A couple of years earlier he had watched all day while Curtiss tested the wind with his finger and finally, in the still air at dusk, hopped two hundred feet. Westervelt, an engineer, was serving as junior officer in the Navy Construction Corps in New York; he obtained permission to represent the Navy Department at the Belmont Park meet. Enthralled, he watched LeBlanc of France take ten speed events with a Bleriot monoplane. With other spectators he gasped at the flying skill of the French aviator Latham in a 100-horse-power Antoinette racer. Claude Grahame-White of England won the Gordon Bennett trophy. Ralph Johnstone, who flew to 9,714 feet in a 30-horsepower Wright Flier, was the only American to set a world's record. Lieutenant Westervelt reported that aviation's progress was astounding. The Navy should watch closely the developments in Europe as well as in this country.

Advanced to assistant naval constructor, U.S.N., Westervelt was sent to Puget Sound Navy Yard and then to the Moran Shipyard in Seattle. At Seattle's University Club, a host introduced him to Bill Boeing.

"I expect you could give me a few pointers," said Boeing, pleasantly. "I have a boat under construction that isn't doing so well right now."

Westervelt and Boeing, both bachelors, found many interests in common. Bill Boeing also had studied engineering, in Sheffield Scientific School at Yale. Weekends they played bridge, cruised up the Sound in Boeing's yacht, talked about things mechanical. Westervelt came to know and appreciate some of the thoughts that were going on in Boeing's active, restless mind. If others thought him aloof, it was because they didn't understand his background, Westervelt decided. Boeing had been a lone operator since boyhood. His German-born father died when Bill was eight. His Viennese mother continued to bring him up in strict fashion. But with a spirit of independence and a supply of funds, he was on his own at an early age. The family had large holdings of timber and iron ore in Minnesota's fabulous Mesabi Range. As part of his upbringing young Bill went to school away from home, both in America and Switzerland.

When his mother remarried, Bill didn't hit it off well with his stepfather. In 1903, a year before he was to graduate from Yale, he decided the time was ripe to move west and acquire timber of his own. He was twenty-two then. His hunch proved a good one.

It was this desire to do things, Westervelt thought, that explained Boeing's outfitting of expeditions to Alaska, his purchase of the Heath shipyard on the Duwamish Waterway—in order to finish building a yacht—and his interest when a flier named Terah Maroney brought a Curtiss-type hydroplane to Seattle. Westervelt and Boeing talked about airplanes and discovered a bond of interest in memories of the two great aviation meets of 1910. "Let's see if we can get a flight with Maroney," Boeing proposed.

It was July 4, 1914. "I've been wanting to do this for a long time," Westervelt admitted to Boeing, on their way out to Lake Washington. "Isn't this a day for it?" The sky was blue. The Olympic Range behind them and the long Cascade skyline ahead were the rim on a bowl of beauty. At the edge of the lake, Maroney was ready to take them up. The plane was nosed into a board ramp, its pusher propeller idly flailing the air. The two straight wings were covered with muslin on the lower as well as the upper side. Below was a sledlike float. The engine was hung between the two wings, its tall radiator almost making a back to the pilot's seat.

"Would you like to go first?" Westervelt asked.

Boeing climbed up beside Maroney on the front edge of the lower wing and steadied his feet on the open footrest that reminded him a little of a shoeshine stand. A mechanic in overalls was pushing the machine to head out into the water. Maroney gunned the engine in short spurts. Boeing adjusted the goggles he had been given, then used both hands to hold on.

The taxiing out was jiggly, vibrant with noise. The

race down-lake was a prolonged drive for take-off speed, wind in the face, water rushing at them. Boeing tightened his grip. The water began to get less bumpy. He felt a shake and a boost; there was a surge of power against the small of his back. The din of the motor filled his ears as the water dropped away.

In another minute the whole landscape was tilting up beside him and he realized they were banking and turning away from the lake. Boeing looked down upon Westervelt and the tiny group on the shore. They seemed like something detached, a detail in a picture. Maroney was winging straight over trees and housetops, still climbing, attaining an altitude of perhaps a thousand feet. Boeing settled more comfortably in his seat. He felt a certain mastery he had been seeking. It all seemed right, the hourglass shape of Seattle below, with Puget Sound and the Olympics in the distance, unrolling before him. Man was meant to fly.

When they got back Westervelt was eager for his turn, and he, too, was filled with enthusiasm after the flight.

More flights with Maroney cultivated the seed that was growing in Boeing's mind. "There isn't much to that machine of Maroney's," he told Westervelt one day. "I think we could build a better one."

Westervelt hid his surprise. "Of course we could," he agreed.

Westervelt wrote to Jerome Hunsaker, who had established a wind tunnel and the country's principal store of aviation technical information at Massachusetts Institute of Technology, and to others. What could they tell him about the theory of stability and control, the Wright patents, now available for use, weights, stresses and motors? With the aid of his naval engineering tables, he studied strength requirements. He took a tape out to Maroney's ramp and measured the supporting members of his plane, then took the figures home to check the stresses. "My gosh," he told Boeing. "There isn't any reason why this thing should hold together. The strength of the parts is just about equal to the load they have to carry."

Herb Munter, the local exhibition flier, was getting a new plane ready for flights, down on Seattle's Harbor Island. Westervelt and Boeing had decided to talk with him. Munter's headquarters was a fifty-foot shiplap hangar on the dredged-up sand flat. They found Munter inside working on his craft.

"What type of machine are you building?" Boeing asked.

"It's a Munter."

Boeing looked up uncertainly and then fixed his eye on a wing-rib. "You design this yourself?"

Munter's pride was evident. He brushed back a shock of red hair. "This is my fourth."

"Where are the others?"

"Washed out."

"You built them all here?"

"No, the first two I built at home in the kitchen. Mother helped me. On those we went by a picture of the Curtiss in *Aerial Age*, but the last two have been my own. Main thing is to make them so they're easy to take apart for crating. We're on the move a lot. See how this comes apart? It's going to be a honey."

"Did you study engineering?" Boeing asked.

"No, I went to high school, nights."

Westervelt turned to look out the hangar door, the top half of which went up with pulleys, the bottom half lying down to form a ramp to a plank runway about three hundred feet long, twelve feet wide. "You take off from here?" he asked.

"Sure," said Munter. "Works fine. So long as the wind is blowing in the right direction."

"Do you think the public is interested in flying?"

"Mostly they come out to see if you're going to crash," Munter grinned. "I've built my show around that. I end up by diving straight at the ground. Then I pull up just high enough so the tail doesn't hit."

"Isn't that rather terrifying?"

"It's not bad. The thing won't go any faster straight down than it will in level flight. About forty or forty-five. But I let 'em think it's tough."

Was that all there was to aviation—risking your neck like a trapeze performer? Bill Boeing was asking himself. The possibility of building a pleasure airplane for his own use intrigued him. But he felt restless about other things developing in 1915. Across the world the Triple Alliance had swept all of Europe into a mortal struggle. The great liner *Lusitania* had been sunk by a German U-boat, taking the lives of 114 Americans among the 1,153 who perished.

The unnatural contrast between peace at home and war across the Atlantic was disturbing to Boeing. Perhaps because of his schooling and frequent trips abroad, Europe seemed nearer to him. It was likely that America would be drawn in, he reasoned. He thought of the urgent effort that must be going into airplane development in the countries at war, and then of the plane in which they had been flying. Wasn't America falling behind?

One day, plans in mind, Boeing asked Herb Munter to join him and Westervelt for lunch. "We're going to get a group together to build some airplanes," he said. "Will you join us?"

"Sure."

They planned to start on two airplanes, to be called B. & W.'s for Boeing and Westervelt. They would get motors from the Hall-Scott plant in San Francisco. They'd put Ed Heath, down at the shipyard, to work on the pontoons.

Boeing wrote to Glenn Martin in Los Angeles. A few days later he told Westervelt: "I'm going down there to learn to fly."

At Griffith Park in Los Angeles, Bill Boeing was an earnest pupil. He went out with Floyd Smith, the instructor, at dawn each day while the air was quiet. Again about dusk it would be still enough for more instruction.

Boeing was enthusiastic when he returned from California, the owner of a $10,000 Martin seaplane. He formed an Aero Club to use the plane. Boeing watched while Munter made a flight with one of the club members, John Hull. Munter seemed to be banking unusually steeply over the lake. Suddenly the plane slipped and dived straight for the water. Boeing gasped as he saw it hit. Then it came up again to float motionless—wings on the water, tail in the air. A motorboat brought the two men ashore.

Munter was dazed and apologetic, said he felt the machine was heavy for its power.

"Forget the airplane," Boeing said. "The important thing is that you and Hull came out of it."

They repaired the Martin, but Boeing was more interested in his two new airplanes under construction at the Heath shipyard—the B. & W.'s. Meticulously he examined the grain of the wood that had been selected, and checked closely while Ed Heath fitted and glued it to form the pontoons.

"Keep them light," he cautioned.

The old shipbuilder seemed affronted. "Mr. Boeing, they're so light now, I'm afraid to open the door or they'll blow out."

The war in Europe was growing in intensity. The French, British and Germans were sending up aviators with machine guns. Airplanes diving on each other with raking gunfire, wings and fuel tanks bursting into flame, aviators turning into fiery torches as they plummeted to earth; these were the blazing new images of warfare in the air. Boeing and Westervelt knew the implications were grave.

Before the first B. & W. was finished, Westervelt was ordered to return to Navy duty in the east. Boeing was alone to see the machine readied for flight in June 1916. It was a crisp-looking craft there on the ramp at Lake Union, wings straight and pert, spruce struts gleaming with new varnish. Its 125-horsepower and its span of fifty-two feet were identical with those of the Martin, which had been a great aid in determining dimensions, but it was lighter and its wing section was different.

Inside the hangar, Boeing kept looking at his watch. "Where is that Munter?"

Superintendent Jim Foley said he was sure he would be along soon.

"I'll take it out myself," said Boeing.

He got in, taxied out to the middle of the lake, swung around to head north and gunned the Hall-Scott full out. The plane gathered speed. It skipped along for a time, throwing a good deal of spray. Then Boeing lifted it into a quarter-mile straight-away flight low over the water and set it down again. When he got back to the ramp, Munter had arrived. "Taxi it around and try out the controls," Boeing said, eying Munter. "That's all I want you to do. Don't fly it."

Munter taxied for several days, wondering if Boeing was afraid to let him fly. One day when he was practicing small hops off the water he concluded it was time for action. He hauled back on the stick, roared into the air and winged across the city to Lake Washington. Boeing rushed over. "Don't ever do that again unless I authorize it," he ordered. Then he looked at the airplane with pride. "How was it?"

"Great."

The twenty-one men working for Bill Boeing gained zeal from the sight of their B. & W. in the air. Boeing's view of the future developed sharper outlines, less confused with the question of war or peace. One day the airplane would be accepted as a means of transportation. It was time to incorporate a company. He asked his attorneys to draft the broadest possible charter, one that would allow them to manufacture airplanes or other products, operate a flying school and "act as a common carrier of passengers and freight by aerial navigation."

The articles were drawn—July 15, 1916.

Engineer T. Wong, a young Chinese graduate of Massachusetts Institute of Technology, whom Bill Boeing had hired, had new ideas for the next plane which they called Model C. Wong had a passion for study. At M.I.T. he was fascinated by the work of Gustave Eiffel, builder of the Paris tower, whose writings Jerome Hunsaker had translated. Eiffel had measured wind forces to learn their effects on his tower structure. With a flat plate tilted in various ways, he'd learned about the loads on a plane surface with air rushing by it, and that was what an airplane was. It was a delicate balance of forces in four directions: the pull of the propeller against the drag of the machine through the air; the lift of the wing against the downward pull of gravity. The wind lifted the wing as it would lift your hand when you'd hold it out of a moving car and tilt it upward, or as it pushed against Gustave Eiffel's flat plate. Wong wanted to apply some of Eiffel's calculations in designing the new Model C for Mr. Boeing.

"We've learned some things that the Wright brothers didn't know," Wong told general manager Foley. "Now we know how to make a plane inherently stable, so it will return to normal if it is forced off balance in any direction."

"That's the way it should be," said Foley.

"We don't need a vertical fin on the tail to stabilize it, because if we tilt the wings up—that's called dihedral—you can tip the plane one way or the other and it will come back level. We can also do away with the horizontal stabilizer by staggering the top wing ahead of the lower one, to give a broad surface. Then we'll balance the elevator, put part of it ahead of the hinge line, so it will be easier to move. The part in front of the hinge will catch the wind on the opposite side and help the pilot." Foley couldn't see any flaws in Wong's concepts. Model C went from theory to form.

The plight of the Allies was growing more desperate. It appeared that America could not stay much longer on the sidelines if its friends were losing. Commander Westervelt wrote that the Navy would surely be buying some school machines. The chance for a contract would be good if the Model C could meet Navy requirements. Bill Boeing told the men to finish it as fast as they could, but to make it right.

Everyone was at the hangar for the first flight of the "C," November 23, 1916. The day was bright and cool, and there was a low wind from the southwest. All was in readiness, but Herb Munter balked. For the past week, following Boeing's instructions, he had been taxiing the plane and taking short jumps off the water. He was unhappy about the controls. "You can't fly a plane with that tiny rudder and no stabilizer on the tail," he insisted.

Wong was polite but firm. "The controls have been thoroughly proved out." He turned to Boeing with reassurance. "The model has been in the wind tunnel for six hours. Mr. Munter will feel differently about it when he gets it in the air."

Foley looked sharply at Munter. "You're not the engineer, you're the driver."

"I know something about airplanes and it doesn't look right to me," Munter persisted.

Bill Boeing, impatient, interposed. "It's just something new that you've got to get used to. Let's get going."

Munter lifted the airplane off Lake Union without trouble. He climbed to about two hundred feet. He knew he'd have to turn promptly to the right to stay over water while trying things out. He pushed the rudder pedal cautiously. "Better not try the aileron yet," he thought. "One thing at a time." If he got into too steep a bank, it would be hard to right it again without a stabilizing fin.

The plane banked itself, without aileron. "Wong's dihedral did that—the uptilt of the wings," Munter thought. He shoved the stick to the left to decrease the bank with opposite aileron. Instead, it went into a steeper bank. Muscles and mind straining, he jammed his foot hard on the rudder pedal to straighten it out. The turn tightened instead. He had a sinking feeling. "Why did I give in?"

He could see he was running out of lake, Queen Anne Hill ahead. If the plane banked any steeper, he would spiral into a spin and wouldn't have enough altitude to pull it out. He thought of the hole he had made in the lake before.

Munter was pushing now with all the strength of his arms and legs. His body against the machine. He was leaning and pressing and urging, almost out of the narrow cockpit. He thought he felt a favorable response. The plane was slowly beginning to straighten. He pressed harder. It was straightening out. He headed down and slapped the unruly craft onto Lake Union with a solid smack.

Herb Munter taxied back to the ramp and climbed out, wrenched off his helmet and stomped over to the waiting group. "Put on some more rudder and some fin," he demanded of Wong.

"It has enough." The engineer's look was critical of the pilot.

"You'd better take it out again and get used to it," Ed Gott, Bill Boeing's cousin suggested.

"I'll take it out again when you've made the changes," Munter said. He was shaking.

"But there is no reason to change it," Wong insisted. "You have not given it a full trial."

"I'm telling you. If I'm going to fly it, it's going to stay right here till you do what I say."

2

The days of the first World War saw the old shipyard on Seattle's Duwamish Waterway surrounded by a business-like cluster of buildings. The Model C design had been altered and improved and finally was accepted by the Navy as a training plane. The war gave the plant a brisk, brief market, but afterward a postwar slump all but closed its doors. Two young Scandinavians from the University of Washington engineering school led the remnant group that kept it going: Phil Johnson as production manager and Claire Egtvedt as chief engineer.

For a time they built furniture. They built a three-place flying boat—the B-1, designed by young Egtvedt and his assistant, Louis Marsh. When it was completed and sent to Lake Union for test, there were bets, half in jest, that it wouldn't fly, but Bill Boeing refused to join. "I think the boys have done a good job," he said.

Egtvedt and Marsh were anxious to see if the water would break cleanly along the sides of the B-1's hull. The two engineers got in the back seat to watch while Eddie Hubbard, the new test pilot, taxied. "It's coming clean," Egtvedt noticed as Hubbard gathered speed. The big Hall-Scott engine was deafening now, and Marsh was gesturing wildly. They hadn't expected to fly, but the boat had popped right out of the water. Hubbard looked around with a grin. He was continuing to climb. They reached about three hundred feet when the engine coughed—then sputtered.

"The pump! The pump!" Marsh shouted. The fuel pump driven by the engine had slipped out of gear and the engine wasn't getting any gas. The two passengers strained in a futile effort to assist Eddie, who was reaching for the hand pump with one hand while battling to hold the stick forward. The strength of one arm wasn't enough. The horizon was dropping, the nose coming up. It was evident that Hubbard couldn't handle the sudden load on the elevator. With the heavy fuel tanks down in the hull and the propeller up high behind the wings, the airplane wanted to nose up when the power was cut off.

Pushing hard with both hands, Hubbard was able to lower the elevators enough to bring the nose back down and momentarily release one hand for the pump. They heard the engine catching hold. But instantly the surge of power reversed the forces and sent the airplane rocketing downward. When Hubbard got the nose back up, the engine again began to die. Again they humped and roared downward. Three or four times they rocketed and dived. Finally Hubbard put it down on the lake. Wet with perspiration, he just sat there for a while. "We can fix the fuel feed, but that elevator. . . ." He shook his head.

"We went too much by the Curtiss boat, I guess," Egtvedt said. "This is a different airplane."

Back at the plant they looked into the difficulty, realizing that they didn't yet understand everything about control surfaces. The problem was that an elevator had to be made longer to be more effective, but the longer you made it, the more force the pilot had to overcome. Wong's balanced elevator was one solution, but it had proved too tricky, too touchy. There had to be another way. Claire Egtvedt stared at the dozen elevator doodles his pencil had been making. He started to toss them all in the waste basket, then looked back. One of the sketches, upside down, got him thinking. Why not make the elevators wider instead of longer? That would provide the area for the lift that was needed, but the controls wouldn't be as hard for the pilot to move. Suddenly it seemed odd that no one had thought of it before. Elevators had always been long and narrow.

Revisions and testing of the B-1 continued, along with work on two smaller planes, one of them a land plane. But Ed Gott, now the general manager, announced unhappily that all the machines under construction wouldn't bring in enough to pay the overhead. The furniture business was helping to keep a work force together, but unprofitably.

"We can't stay in the aircraft business unless we can get production orders from the government," Gott wrote to Joe Hartson, who had established an office in Washington.

Hartson's reply was a counter-offensive. "The plant has got to get busy and design something we can sell."

Gott wrote back that they couldn't develop a new airplane in time to do any good. "Get hold of an established design the government is planning to buy," he instructed Hartson, "and we'll bid on that. We can sell something they want quicker than something we have developed."

"I don't agree with you," Hartson replied. He said he had been in to see the Army and Navy again and again. He had shown the Navy the B-1 drawings. "A small-size Curtiss boat?" they had asked, derisively. He had sought an Army experimental contract. "What claim have you to one?" Colonel Hall in the supply office had asked. "What have you developed except the C-type trainer? What successful land machines have you designed? Who is your designer? What experience has he had with military requirements? What original ideas has he come up with?" Hartson had found himself out of answers.

As fall turned to winter of 1919, spirits in the front office were as downwashed as the steady rain that drained into the Duwamish. Boeing was advancing money from his personal account almost weekly to meet the payroll. One day Gott could stand it no longer. He took the books in to Boeing. "Do you think we should close up shop? We're going to finish the year $90,000 in the red."

Boeing had been carrying on the fight within himself. He had lain awake nights thinking about it. He didn't like to start something and not finish it, but he had to face the facts. Possibly they could close down the airplane part of the business and keep on with other work until conditions were better, he had thought. But that would mean losing the start they'd made. The thing that concerned him most was the men at the plant—young fellows like Johnson and Egtvedt and Marsh, trying to make a go of it.

"I'd hate to break up the organization," he told Gott. "But we can't keep on like this indefinitely. If we can't get some business with an assured income . . ." he paused a long while, ". . . we'll have to close."

Hartson wired that there was a chance to get a contract remodeling fifty wartime de Havillands.

"We'll take it only if it's certain there's a profit in it," Gott wired back, "not just for the sake of staying in the aircraft business. We've decided to go out of business unless there is an assured opportunity."

Hartson negotiated zealously and a contract to rebuild the DH's was drawn. Phil Johnson, superintendent, organized the shop force to hit the job hard. To make the de Havilland remodeling a financial success, the emphasis had to be on manufacturing. Overhead was slashed. Engineering was down to two men.

Sensitive, eager Claire Egtvedt, who'd been dreaming about better airplanes from the time he took his first rides with Herb Munter and Eddie Hubbard, was languishing, even rebelling, under the system.

"If we only had a chance to do something on our own . . ." he lamented to his one-man staff, Louis Marsh.

"Looks like our chance is running out."

Claire Egtvedt's thwarted hopes and dreams followed him home at night. "Isn't it right to advance the product?" he would ask himself. "Shouldn't we be doing something about this instead of just going down with the tide?"

He went to see Ed Gott and found Boeing with him in his office. The time was now; he was going to say what was on his mind, no matter what the consequences.

"We are building airplanes, not cement sidewalks," Egtvedt began. The conviction in his own voice gave him confidence. "If you want to build cement sidewalks and just do work requiring a minimum of engineering, then you can do away with engineering. Do away with it. Just mix the materials, pour them into a form and collect your money. But if you want to build and sell airplanes, you first have to create them. That takes research and development and testing and engineering. The airplane isn't half what it ought to be. Can't we hire a few engineers and try to build a future?"

Ed Gott seemed about to answer when Boeing spoke, nodding. "I think Claire is right."

Boeing's support put a spring in Claire Egtvedt's step, but as time passed there was still no way found to get original designs into production. McCook Field at Dayton, Ohio, where Army planes were bought, had its own ideas of what it wanted. With payroll dwindling the men at the Seattle plant were glad enough to get some three-wing armored attack planes and a standard biplane pursuit to build from designs furnished by the Army.

At Selfridge Field Egtvedt watched the young pilots go through mock combat games in the pursuits, one winging over and diving with motors, props and wires screaming, the other whipping down on to his tail and dog-fighting across the sky. Hangar talk was vivid afterward. Egtvedt heard the men blame their airplanes when they came out on the short end of a duel.

"If you were designing a new pursuit, what things would you consider most important?" he asked them.

"Think about what we have to do," one of the pilots answered. "We have to pursue the other fellow, outdodge him, turn inside him. When you're in a dog fight, speed and maneuverability are everything. The boys at Mc-Cook hang on a lot of equipment that doesn't mean a thing. It just loads down the airplane. What we want is an airplane stripped for action."

Claire Egtvedt sat in a Pullman car, watching landscape go by, thinking about the Army pilot's comments. He had time to consider. What interfered with speed on the pursuit? The bracing wires between the wings. Their shrill whistle showed how badly they needed to be out of the way. How about a thicker wing instead? Fokker was using one. It could be made strong enough to support itself, at least partly. You could get rid of the wires. You could make the lower wing short, just use it to brace the upper wings at the middle.

Maneuverability, the pilots wanted. How fast could an airplane turn? How fast would a pilot dare turn it, when he knew it would pull apart? Wouldn't metal tubing help, instead of wood? They could build a real pursuit, Egtvedt was convinced, if they only had the chance. His pencil made eye-satisfying, free-hand ellipses, wings, bodies, as he moved with his thoughts across Iowa, Nebraska, Wyoming, homeward.

"We've got to design our own pursuit," he told Marsh when he got home. "I have some ideas." They got started with them, between times, just between themselves, calculating loads, arrangements, structures.

The Army had called for no new design competition. The plane would simply have to be good enough to sell itself. The more Egtvedt thought about it, the more right it seemed. The Army could not refuse it if it were the best.

When they got far enough along, a meeting was set to present the idea to Bill Boeing. With hope in his heart Egtvedt went to Boeing's uptown Seattle office to make his proposal. Ed Gott was also present. "We are learning about pursuit planes," he began. "When you see the young fellows in the Air Service up there, rolling and diving and dog-fighting, you realize that they have to have a superb airplane. What we're building is far from what they need. We know how to build a much better airplane than that." Boeing's eyes were kindling. Ed Gott was thoughtful. Egtvedt continued, hoping to gain support from Gott, to impress Boeing more.

"Mr. Gott has often pointed out that the rules governing military design competitions are unsound. You get a job building an experimental model to Army specifications and someone else may land the contract to produce it. Even if it's a successful design, you can't look forward to anything." He noticed Gott was nodding. "You don't get out the best design because you don't have the incentive, and you can't stray very far from the specifications. What I'd like to do is to go out on our own to build the best pursuit we can. Our own pursuit, with our own money. It will be entirely up to us, then, to get the maximum in performance and efficiency and general utility for the purpose—to make it really a pursuit airplane."

Boeing was on his feet, looking out over Elliott Bay. The Olympic skyline, spectacular in winter, was in full view, but his eyes narrowed as though focusing on a point out beyond, as though seeing what he had wanted to see all along.

Egtvedt sought to keep up the momentum. "We would go to all the sources available," he said, "here and abroad, to get information and data. We wouldn't have to put in all the contrivances and devices that the Air Service thinks up. It would be designed for one purpose only—combat work."

Boeing didn't even ask how much the project would cost. He turned about. "That's exactly what we should do," he said emphatically. "Do it on our own. Keep it secret. Develop the best pursuit that can be built. Then we'll take it back to Dayton and show them what it will do."

The experimental PW-9 pursuit of 1923 was the start of a long line of Boeing Army pursuit planes and Navy carrier fighters. By 1926 Egtvedt and his enlarged staff of engineers had developed a still more advanced fighter powered by an air-cooled engine—the Pratt and Whitney Wasp. With radial cylinders surrounding the propeller shaft, the Wasp packed much more power for its weight than the old water-cooled motor. The pursuit plane business was becoming outstandingly successful.

But in the rush of production activity, only Eddie Hubbard, the former test pilot, had carried forward Bill Boeing's original hope, expressed in the 1916 charter, of "acting as a common carrier of passengers and freight by aerial navigation." Hubbard had been using the B-1 flying boat they had built after the war to carry mail by air between Seattle and Victoria, British Columbia. More recently he had moved south to California where there was more flying activity.

"If we could get Eddie Hubbard back up here," Phil Johnson suggested, when the company was ten years old and Bill Boeing was in a reflective mood, "we could start a passenger airline around Puget Sound—Seattle, Victoria, Vancouver, B.C." Johnson was president then; Bill Boeing, chairman. The world war was a nightmare forgotten. The postwar slump was a thing of the past and the country was breathing deeply, stretching its arms for economic expansion. "The business of America is business," President Coolidge had said. Johnson's notion appealed at once to Boeing who asked him to write Hubbard. But they could get no commitment from the pilot.

It was several months later, in the fall of 1926, that Hubbard appeared in Seattle, bursting with an idea of his own. Johnson was away and Hubbard went to Claire Egtvedt, confiding that he didn't want to talk about a Puget Sound airline, but about something much bigger. The Post Office was going to put its Chicago to San Francisco airmail route up for bids for private operation on November 25, Hubbard revealed. He was extremely excited. "This is the opportunity of a century, Claire. I've got all the figures on mileage and pounds of mail carried. If you can produce some mail planes I know we can operate them successfully."

Egtvedt, taken aback, reminded his old friend that he was talking about a huge undertaking. "It's a lot of country. The distances are great, as you know. You'd have winter blizzards to contend with, and all that."

"We could do it."

"You'd have to fly at night. Are the beacons in all the way?"

"Every twenty-five miles." Hubbard said he had talked with the airmail pilots.

Thinking of the airplanes that would be needed, Egtvedt found himself tumbling fast. "We could modify the 40, I expect." That was an experimental mail plane they had just built for the Post Office department. "Probably we could make room for a couple of passengers and still have space for the mail."

They got down to performance details. Hubbard thought the 40 would do, if it had more power. "Let's get away from the Liberty motor," he said. "It's a dodo for sure."

"How would you like an air-cooled motor?" Egtvedt asked, his spirit of adventure quickening. The new air-cooled Wasp was two hundred pounds lighter than the Liberty. They could allow that much more for mail.

Hubbard was ready and eager, trusting Egtvedt's judgment. He was sure they could get the operating costs down to well under what the Post Office allowed for carrying the mail.

"We'll have to talk to Mr. Boeing," Egtvedt said, coming back to reality. "Have you ever discussed anything like this with him?"

"No, just local flying, but Mr. Boeing's pretty game, you know."

"Let me work on the design end. If you'll work out the personnel and maintenance costs, I'll get you something on the operating cost of the plane. We can put our figures together and then we'll have something to show Bill. No use going up there without the answers."

A few days later Hubbard and Egtvedt went to Boeing's office armed with a fat file and an idea fairly walking under its own power. They laid it all out. Boeing was silent quite a while. His forehead was wrinkled. "This is something foreign to our experience."

"I've logged 150,000 miles on the Victoria route without trouble," Hubbard said, "and made money at it."

"I think you're talking now about something far different. This is over the whole western half of the country. You've got mountain ranges and winter storms to contend with. It would be a mighty large venture. Mighty risky."

They went over it all again. When there was nothing left to say, Egtvedt and Hubbard departed. "It was a good try," Egtvedt said.

But there was a disposition in Bill Boeing that didn't show behind his stern look. It had strong roots, tenaciously grown in rocky soil. It went back to the phrase he had inserted in their original articles of incorporation, and to the fact that he liked to finish what he started. For years they had talked the utility of the airplane, while the public had no inclination to listen. Here was an opportunity at last, it appeared, to offer the airplane as a public service.

Bill Boeing knew he had the resources. By now his men had built a good reputation. If anyone could, they could go at it with success and safety as the goal. He found it hard to avoid acknowledging this, as he tossed through the night. By morning the idea had gained command. He was up for an especially early breakfast. Bertha Boeing knew something was astir. "What's on your mind, Bill?" she asked guardedly, never wishing to pry too deeply into the privacy of his business mind.

"Maybe we'll bid for the Chicago to San Francisco mail route." Boeing looked at his wife. "What would you think of that?"

"Why not? It will develop a market for planes."

"It will be a hazardous thing. Big."

Egtvedt got to the plant at 7:30 A.M., bringing back the stack of paper that had seemed so alive the day before. The telephone operator hailed him. "Call Mr. Boeing right away. He's been trying to get you for half an hour."

When Egtvedt got Boeing on the phone, the boss's voice was quick. "Get Hubbard and come on up here. I want to talk some more about that proposition of his. It kept me awake all night."

They hurried to the uptown office. Boeing wanted to go over the figures again, wanted to know about the bond that would be required and to compare Hubbard's costs with the Post Office figures. The Post Office would allow up to $3.00 per pound for the first one thousand miles and thirty cents for each additional one hundred miles. The figure Egtvedt and Hubbard had come up with was $1.50 per pound for the first thousand and fifteen cents for each additional one hundred miles. There was a vast difference, but that was the way it had come out.

"Those figures look all right to me," said Boeing finally, decisively. "Let's send them in."

On January 28, word came that they were the low bidders—extremely low. The nearest bid was $2.24. Harry S. New, the postmaster general, doubted that theirs was a reliable bid. Other companies had assured him, he said, that the mail could not be carried for such a low figure, and he didn't want a bankrupt carrier on his hands. He said he'd have to have a $500,000 bond to insure performance of the contract. Resolutely, Bill Boeing personally underwrote the bond and the contract was signed.

The plan called for the building of a fleet of twenty-five planes, to be ready on the line in five months, by July 1, 1927. The men dug in, a dream within their reach.

It was while the Model 40 mail planes were being built that Charles A. Lindbergh headed out over the Atlantic for Paris in his Ryan monoplane. The suspense that built up in the thirty-three and a half hours of his silent crossing was cracked suddenly when his silver wings appeared in the Paris twilight. The floodlights and the acclaiming thousands at Le Bourget Field, on May 21, 1927, awakened the world to flight.

In Seattle the race to build the mail planes finished with a sprint. On June 30, all twenty-five planes were gassed up and waiting along the line, ready for the official start, the midnight transfer of the mail at Omaha from a Post Office de Havilland to the new airline—Boeing Air Transport System.

Next day a plucky Chicago newspaper woman, Jane

Eads of the *Herald and Examiner*, was to be the first passenger on the new line. She was the center of attraction at the Chicago airfield—in high heels, knee-length business suit, feather boa and felt cloche—headed for the clouds. At 9:30 P.M., on July 1, in the harsh white of arc lights, Pilot Ira Biffle helped Miss Eads up on the step pad of the lower wing and through the low door to the tiny cabin between the two wings. Biffle jazzed the motor twice and pushed out into the black.

Jane Eads' heart palpitated as she began her role of trail blazer in a new form of transcontinental travel. The pilot, out of sight and out of hearing in the open cockpit behind, seemed far away. Alone in the night, behind the constant drone of the motor, cutting the darkness at ninety-five miles an hour, Jane found companionship for a time with a thin crescent moon beyond the left wing. Now and then a sparkle of light drifted by in the black below. She wasn't sleepy. She turned the switch on the glazed dome light in the ceiling. It was cozy, the sea-green of the little walls broken by a sliding window on either side. She let in the cool air. This was fun, she thought.

Later the crescent disappeared and Jane began to feel rocky. The plane tilted and tipped, then dropped as in a hole. She wasn't sure if it was supposed to act this way. Then with a hard jolt she realized they were landing. At Iowa City she admitted, "I was scared."

They passed over Des Moines without coming down. A city without buildings, just strings of jewels. The flight over western Iowa was under a canopy of stars. It seemed strange that the sky should be lighter and more real than the earth below. The plane flew straight and steady into the western night. The changeless roar of the engine was strong, sweet music now to Jane Eads' ears. How odd, how wonderful, she thought, to be settling for the night up here. She found the leather-cushioned seats just large enough to curl up on, kitten fashion, and it was peace.

The landing jolts of Omaha awakened her. Reporters were there to interview *her*. "I could fly forever," Jane glowed. "I love it." She transferred to a new plane, piloted by Jack Knight. Shoving off at 1:45 A.M. Knight wished her "a merry trip" and she called back gallantly, "Same to you—and a *safe* one."

Before morning the air grew choppy. Great flashes of lightning lit up the sky. The cracking streaks seemed to be breaking all about them. The plane was being lifted and thrown about. Jane put her head on her knees and tried not to think about falling. Then it ended as suddenly as it had begun. There was a yellow fringe on the horizon behind, which grew and flooded the earth with a golden glow. She remembered how a pilot had told her he never knew why the birds sang so sweetly until he saw his first dawn from the sky. They came down at North Platte, then lifted again for Cheyenne, with the sun setting fire to the edge of the clouds on the horizon ahead.

Out of Cheyenne, past the bald, rippling foothills, she could see in the distance the snow-crested magnificence of the Medicine Bow range. Hugh Barker, the new pilot, pushed the mail plane higher and higher. Jane grew drowsy and her legs were heavy with the altitude and the bumping. The road seemed as rocky here as it was below. They skimmed past Elk Mountain and into Rock Springs.

A veteran now of the ups and downs and the vast, changing topography of the states, Jane flew on past the white flats of the Great Salt Lake country, the forbidding waterless gulches of Nevada, the ultramarine blue of Lake Tahoe, the yellow hills beyond. Suddenly the hills opened into San Francisco Bay. Twenty-three flying hours after leaving Chicago, Jane Eads put her feet on California soil, like an explorer who had discovered a new world—air transportation.

3

The new airline made money in its first month, and in its second and third. The public interest, aroused by the Lindbergh flight and now by a sky trail to California, was ringing the cash register. There was no serious trouble. But winter was harder going. Snow piled deep at Cheyenne, Salt Lake City and Rock Springs; blizzards tried to sweep the plains free of commercial airplane intrusion. Over the Sierra Nevada hump the clouds hung low.

The pilots were getting the weather by telegram, but storm centers could pull in front of them on the way, or behind them. All they could do was get down under, follow the railroad tracks, watch intently for known valleys and passes through the mountains. Decisions were constantly being pressed upon them—alone with the mail, their $25,000 airplane, perhaps a passenger, and their own hide. Look for a place to sit down, or chance it? Bill Boeing and Phil Johnson came to dread the ringing of the phone in the night. There had been no tragedy yet.

"I'm sure you could give your pilots the weather by shortwave radio," Thorp Hiscock, Boeing's brother-in-law, said one night at dinner with Johnson and Boeing. "With a two-way telephone they could get it from each other." Hiscock had a ranch in Yakima, Washington, but most of his waking hours were spent tinkering with radio.

33

"Could you build it?" Johnson asked him.

"Just put me to work."

When Boeing consented, Hiscock went to work in a shed at the plant and erected a tall pole for an experimental aerial. The Bell Laboratories were consulted. They were getting started on the problem, but were not too hopeful of two-way communication because of the noise and interference of the airplane's engine.

"We'll work at it," Hiscock said. He put a shortwave receiver on a truck to cruise away from the plant while he broadcast records of the comic Two Black Crows, because they offered voice dialogue instead of music. Bill Lawrenz, his helper, drove the truck farther and farther away as Thorp tinkered. Lawrenz listened all the laughs out of the somber comedians. Late at night, maybe up in the Cascade mountains or down near Portland, Oregon, he'd hear Hiscock sign off: "I'm going home now, Bill." Lawrenz, who couldn't talk back, would wheel around to spend the rest of the night getting home. "It's for science," he'd console himself.

Later they installed a shortwave set in a mail plane and Eddie Allen, a Boeing Air Transport pilot, took Lawrenz's role as guinea pig. They moved from Seattle to Oakland where equipment was available. They tried every kind of shielding for the engine's interference without much luck. One day Allen didn't show up at the hangar. The hangar crew thought he was sick, but when they didn't locate him at home, they sent out a missing persons alarm. He was found next day sunning himself on a beach. "I've run out of ideas," Allen explained. "It's quieter here to listen for a new one."

By perseverance the two-way radio was perfected and, with the help of Western Electric, installed on the line.

Finding that the route was not paved with gravestones, more and more passengers sought tickets. The crawl-in box cabin of the Model 40 was admittedly inadequate. They went to work on a big tri-motored biplane powered by Wasps. It would carry eighteen passengers in luxury, with window curtains and leather chairs.

First the single-engine 40s, then the big 80s, along with the competitive Ford trimotors, gained a romantic fame. The pursuit plane business was going well. Claire Egtvedt, now general manager of the plant, with Johnson devoting his time to the airline, considered gratefully the long way they had come. Yet the fabric-covered biplanes were already beginning to seem old and slow. Egtvedt had a feeling that they had scarcely begun to meet the challenge of the sky.

In the spring of 1928 Egtvedt was pausing on a walkway in San Diego to enjoy the surroundings for a moment before going to see Admiral Joseph Mason "Bull" Reeves aboard the aircraft carrier *Langley*. A delightful breeze was rustling the pepper trees and palms along the bay shore. There was a familiar music in the air: the singing of Wasp motors in the tiny Boeing biplane fighters cutting scallops in the sky. It was concerning these that Egtvedt was paying San Diego one of his regular visits.

On the carrier Commander Gene Wilson, the Admiral's senior aide, met Egtvedt and went with him to the Admiral's cabin. Reeves, commander of aircraft squadrons, Battle Fleet, extended his usual hearty handshake. They sat at a long green baize-covered table, beyond which a metal bulkhead was covered with sea charts. "Wilson tells me the F-4 is looking good," the Admiral said. The F-4 was a new model fighter they had designed that could carry a 500-pound bomb underneath. Egtvedt wanted badly to sell the Navy a new order of them.

"We were happy the way the ship turned out," Egtvedt said. "A fleet of them would make a real striking force, wouldn't it, Admiral? We think it would be a good deal more versatile than torpedo planes." Up to now carrier fighters had been used only to protect the fleet. If they could be used as an attacking force with 500-pound bombs, they'd become much more important, he felt.

"Bull" Reeves was a scholar of naval science. "Striking force? Do you know what striking force really is?" he challenged Egtvedt. "Let me tell you about it." He lowered his voice with measured assurance. "Your 500-pound bomb won't penetrate deck armor. A sixteen-inch projectile from a battleship's turret delivers 60,000 foot-tons of striking force at a single point. A flight of thirty-six F-4s can deliver eight tons of bombs, if it can get past enemy fighters. A battleship delivers eight tons of projectiles every time it fires a round from all its turrets, and it can keep on firing. Two hundred rounds each from four two-gun turrets is 1,600 tons of steel. Multiply that by the force of the projectiles striking at 2,000 feet per second and you get nearly 100,000,000 foot-tons of destructive force. One battleship."

Egtvedt reeled a little under the weight of the figures. Here was a man who played a big game, it was evident, and who knew how to play it for keeps. "I'm not belittling your product," "Bull" Reeves continued, seeking to put Egtvedt at his ease, "but I wanted you to see its place. The fighter plane is primarily to keep our ships from being bothered by enemy planes. It has an important job. If it can carry a 500-pound bomb, so much the better, but there is nothing in the aircraft line that can pack the punch of a dreadnought. The airplane just isn't as effective a weapon as those we already have in the fleet. It isn't a dreadnought."

The furrow in the Admiral's forehead had melted. "Now back to the F-4. If it turns out to be what Wilson says, we're going to want plenty of them. It'll be a more effective weapon than what we have. Any time you can make an airplane more effective, there's a use for it."

Egtvedt was glad for that last remark. But he left the carrier rudely awakened. The airplane wasn't a dreadnought, he was admitting. It wasn't as effective a weapon as those the Navy already had. Yet he wondered. He thought back to the time when General Billy Mitchell had taken the opposite view, envisioning the life and defense of the nation as one day dependent on the airplane. As best he could, with the equipment available, Billy Mitchell had set out to prove his contention. His opportunity had come in volunteering for the job of disposing of a group of captured German ships after World War I. He said he could do it with bombs dropped from the air.

The Navy had turned out in full force for that exercise, expecting to see the dreadnoughts ride serenely through Mitchell's fireworks, but the ships went to the bottom. Two years later, September 5, 1923, with the smoke scarcely cleared from the furor that followed their sinking, Egtvedt had been invited to watch a second such demonstration by General Mitchell. This time the exercise was being played down by Washington, simply as a means of disposing of the battleships *Virginia* and *New Jersey*, in accordance with the Covenant on Naval Armaments of February 1922.

Reveille was sounded aboard the transport *St. Mihiel* at 5:30 A.M., on the day Egtvedt watched the bombing demonstrations. The morning was foggy, but after mess it showed signs of breaking. There was a buzz of excitement on deck. Civilian guests in small groups were speculating as to the outcome of the day's events.

"What's our position?" George Tidmarsh, Egtvedt's companion, asked an officer. Neither sea nor sky was visible.

They were told it was off Cape Hatteras, a hundred eighty miles from Langley Field. By 8:30 the fog had thinned enough to reveal the battleships on the horizon. In a few minutes more the sun burned hot on the deck.

"Great day for Mitchell," someone was saying. The General was to lead the attack personally. Eyes were watching the sky for him. General Pershing, General Patrick and other high officers were on the bridge. Two blimps carrying photographers approached at low altitude and circled pompously.

At nine o'clock the drone of engines signalled the first attack. Six Martin bombers, big biplanes, were headed for the *New Jersey* at an altitude of about 10,000 feet. They were flying single file, spaced a considerable distance apart. The announcer said they carried 600-pound bombs.

Eighteen bombs were dropped. Four of them hit the deck with an eruption of smoke. One or two dropped into the water close to the *New Jersey*'s hull. This was

considered the most destructive point of aim because of
the effect of the water pressure on the hull. A boat went
over to check the damage which was minor. Then seven
more Martins approached at 6,000 feet altitude, each
carrying a 2,000-pound bomb. All sent up fountains of
water two hundred yards astern.

"They'd have to do better than that in war," Egtvedt
observed to Tidmarsh beside him. The *New Jersey* was
a sitting duck, yet they'd missed her. An artillery major
nearby said he could easily have shot the bombers down
with anti-aircraft.

"Look, though," said Tidmarsh. "She's beginning to
list." Now they could see a hole torn in the side amid-
ships, flooding some of the *New Jersey*'s thirty-three
water-tight compartments. The bombers went back to
refuel and reload.

Just before noon the third attack by the string of seven
Martins, this time with two 1,100 pound bombs each, approached at 3,000 feet. They passed up the *New Jersey*
and centered on the *Virginia*, sitting proudly with her
massive stacks and bulwarks. Before the spectators were
set for the new inning the bombs were dropped and a
tremendous belch of black smoke enveloped the battleship, pluming upward in a column 1,500 feet high. The
thunderous report was echoed by a chorus of exclama-
tions from the *St. Mihiel*'s decks. When the smoke
cleared, the *Virginia* looked like a toy ship that had been
kicked by a heavy boot. The precise handiwork of its
superstructure was swept away. All three stacks and
both masts were gone. A lone crane and a turret stood
watch over a deckload of junk. In the *Virginia*'s distress
another bomb plunged deep alongside, shaking her to the
heart. She heeled over, bathing her wounded side, then
kept on rolling. In a rush of foam her keel came out of
the water. Yard by yard the Atlantic claimed her.

In the afternoon another flight finished off the *New
Jersey* and sent her hunting the depths for her companion. A Navy Department representative said it was an impressive demonstration of coast defense. "Obviously they
wouldn't have the range to touch a fleet at sea," he added.

Claire Egtvedt remembered that dramatic episode of 1923, as he brooded over Admiral "Bull" Reeves' comments now five years later. It was true that the sinking of the *New Jersey* and the *Virginia* had been at very short range and under ideal conditions, without opposition. "Bull" Reeves had pointed up the limitations of aircraft. Yet to Egtvedt the Admiral's words were a sharp irritant that would remain until the truth of his claim was dissolved. They simply hadn't yet built what Billy Mitchell called "air power."

"I have an idea, Claire," said Eddie Hubbard, now operations vice-president of the Boeing airline, when the two men were sharing a hotel room after the 1928 Los Angeles Air Races. "Why shouldn't we go entirely to metal when we build our next transport? We have to line the mail compartment with metal anyway, so the mailbag locks won't tear the fabric. We have to put metal plates up front for accessibility to the engine controls. Why not go metal the whole way, nose to tail?"

Hubbard's quick hope and confidence were born of gallant hours in the open cockpit, alone in the sky where there was room for open thought. It was this stimulus that Claire Egtvedt needed. Egtvedt laid a piece of stationery on the dresser, drew the front view of a wing, long and slender, his imagination at work. "If the body's going to be metal, the easiest way to make it is perfectly round," he said, sketching. "Set it here on the wing. Here's an airplane with minimum drag." He had drawn a circle for the body, on top of the single wing. That was all there was to it, a low-wing monoplane. "It gets rid of all the wires and bracing on the wings."

To Hubbard it looked too simple. "Where's your landing gear?" he asked.

"You could pull the gear up into the wing after you get off the ground. Dragging that thing through the air costs more than all the mail you carry."

"Do you think you could build that?"

"It's only a question of whether we could afford the cost of working it out." The corrugated-metal "flying

washboard" surface on the Ford and the German Junkers
trimotors wouldn't do for this plane, Egtvedt felt. It
would have to be a smooth metal skin. But without the
corrugations there would have to be more stiffening on
the inside. They would probably have to use thicker
metal for the skin and make it carry part of the load. No
one had much experience with this kind of structure. "It
will depend a lot on how big an airplane we'd try to
build," Egtvedt said. "If it gets too costly we could never
do it."

Hubbard was encouraging. He said the trimotor was
too big. "In bad weather we leave it in the barn and take
out the 40s. I'd rather have smaller planes and more of
them—more frequent flights—more flexibility."

When Bill Boeing later saw the monoplane sketch he
was highly interested. The cleanness of the design appealed to him. He wondered if they could get to work on
it as a secret project, as they had done with the pursuit
plane, and bring it out as a surprise. Egtvedt listened,
fairly jumping inside. He said he'd have the engineering
department investigate.

The chief engineer then was A. N. "Monty" Monteith, a man of stature both physically and professionally,
author of the textbook on aerodynamics used at West
Point and many universities, and regarded as one of the
most surefooted engineers in the business. But Egtvedt's
proposal had him shaking his head. "I don't think we
could do it. I don't think it'll have the strength."

Monteith's reticence was due to a long concern on his
part over internally braced monoplanes with the wing
supported by structure inside. When he was with the Air
Service he had watched his friend Lieutenant F. W.
Weidermeyer fall to his death as the center section support gave way on an experimental plane with such a
structure. He had seen the wing of another monoplane
begin to flap and fail the time Harold Harris made the
first parachute escape at McCook Field in 1922.

"We just don't know enough about it," Monteith said.
"It may be all right on a slow airplane but when you get
to higher speeds, it's an unknown."

Monteith wanted to lead the race as much as anyone, but he was acutely conscious that the chief engineer was the one responsible if the new idea didn't work. "Keep it simple," he had written in his textbook. "Then there's less chance for something to go wrong." Things like retractable landing gear, he said, would add to the speed, but they were also an invitation to trouble. It was better to know you had a landing gear out there to come down on. But he knew also that the airplane business lived on advancement. That was his conflict inside.

The all-metal idea would take time to develop, Monteith concluded. Instead he proposed that they get under way with a six-passenger transport not quite so advanced —a monoplane, but with a high wing so it could be braced externally from the body.

But the new idea for a fast, low-wing monoplane was growing, nonetheless. Egtvedt's talk with Bill Boeing had been well timed. The Kelly Act had put the five-cent airmail stamp into use. Air transportation was taking on a big look. Boeing felt it was time to build up more engineering and research, so he authorized construction of a new building with a big area allotted to engineering. When a preliminary design study was begun on the all-metal low-wing proposal, its simple, smooth lines quickly won the hearts of the engineers from the more conventional high-wing design that they had under way.

Then two shocks hit in quick succession. In Salt Lake City Eddie Hubbard was rushed to the hospital with an internal disorder and died on December 19, 1928. Seven days later Claire Egtvedt was taken to the hospital critically ill. Finally he began to recover, but he would not be at his desk for some time.

Meanwhile the new airplane called "Monomail" was steadily coming into being, first on the drawing boards, then in metal. The high-wing project was dropped. There was something irrepressible about an idea that was right. Bill Boeing took inspiration from the progress he could see. "We must not dismiss any novel idea with the cocksure statement that it can't be done," he said in an interview. "We are pioneers in a new science and a new industry. Our job is to keep everlastingly at research and experiment, and let no new improvement pass us by. We have already proved that science and hard work can lick what appear to be insurmountable difficulties."

Monteith was supervising the Monomail's break with tradition. After all, it was an experimental ship, Monty told himself; why not make the most of it?

The new plane had been a well-kept secret until the wings and body were taken to be assembled on the field, a mile down the highway. Then Seattle was astir with interest. Fans crowded the fenced-off area. The plane didn't look like other airplanes. Somehow it looked as an airplane should, its builders thought: something meant to fly. Its body was slender, smooth, round, resting neatly on a silver wing, a wing turned slightly up, slightly back, outstretched for flight.

Employees brought their families to look. Painted there boldly on its side was the word once mysteriously murmured through the plant: *Monomail*. Now it was something real.

Seeking the best pilot to fly the plane, Monteith had chosen Eddie Allen. Meticulous Eddie, an engineer himself, studied the ship carefully. He seemed concerned about the propeller. He climbed into the cockpit and called down to a mechanic in his gentle, high voice, "I'm going to try a couple of runs at this setting, then I'll be back." The blades of the metal propeller could be adjusted on the ground, and he was trying to determine the best pitch. He taxied down the runway, then back. "Set it two degrees flatter," he instructed.

When he was ready for takeoff, everybody watched. He started to roll, picked up speed and raced for the end of the field. There was a screeching of tires and a cloud of dust as he stopped short. "I think we'd better run some more static thrust tests," he said, almost apologetically, when he got back.

They tied the airplane to an anchor and used a spring scale to measure the strength of its pull. The dilemma was painfully clear. The whistle-clean airplane was capable of great speed in the air, but to get this speed the propeller blade would have to take a big bite of air with each turn. They'd have to set the pitch of the blade steep. But when they did that on the ground, the propeller would just blow the air sideways. The plane wouldn't take off. To get enough power at low speed required a flat pitch. But that wasn't good for flying.

After the tests Eddie agreed on a compromise setting. On May 22, 1930, with the Hornet engine roaring her loudest, the Monomail sailed into the air. Down from the flight Eddie climbed out nodding and smiling. "It's as smooth as it looks," he said to reporters. Then he drew Egtvedt aside. "It's a pity, though, Claire. This airplane really wants to get up and go, but you just can't get the power out of the propeller."

The testing went on. After some weeks Slim Lewis, chief pilot of Boeing Air Transport, came up from Cheyenne to try the plane. Monteith and some others were watching him from a rooftop at the plant when he tried some steep banks, pouring it on. They saw him pull up sharply.

Monteith clasped his hands to his head. "Oh, no, he wouldn't dare." Up, up and over on his back went Lewis, in a loop. "It won't stand that," cried Monteith, his long legs covering in seconds the stairs and the distance to his car. Commercial airplanes weren't meant for stunting. He raced to the field, skidded to a stop in the gravel by the hangar and jumped out, waving his fists at the sky.

"How're we going to get him down?" he demanded of John Wilson, the chief inspector. Lewis pulled up into another loop. Monteith came down with two powerful arms on top of John Wilson's slight shoulders, shouting, "We've got to get him down!" Helplessly they watched Lewis do a third loop. Then he came down, grinning until he caught the looks of his audience. "Well," said big Slim Lewis, "my boys have to fly all kinds of contraptions that you fellows put together up here. I want to be sure they're good and sound before I let 'em fly 'em."

Inspection showed a few popped rivets on the metal fairings at the wing root, but no real damage. The internally braced wing structure was proved. A few weeks later Lewis took the plane on down to Cheyenne, Wyoming, enthusiastic. But he hadn't reckoned seriously enough with Eddie Allen's findings concerning propeller limitations. When he took off in Cheyenne's rarefied air 6,000 feet above sea level, he barely got over the tree tops at the end of the field. The Hamilton Standard propeller people had started to develop a controllable propeller that could take off at one pitch and be shifted to another in flight, but Monty didn't think that was the answer. It would add weight—and something else to go wrong.

The propeller men had another solution, a smaller propeller turning at a faster speed. Then the pitch didn't make so much difference. But Eddie Allen still felt throttled.

4

Always, it seemed, the path of progress was a problem to be solved. Always it was the hard path to take. The old way, the familiar way, was the easy path.

It had been disturbing to the pilots on the line when the big trimotor had put them inside a closed cockpit. Fliers of the purple twilight, they liked the breath of the night on their faces. They wanted to be able to look out, to lean over the edge and follow the railroad or the fence row. This attitude was so strong that it was decided to build one of the trimotors with an open cockpit. A place was made for the two pilots atop the square nose.

It was a sun-baked day in July 1930 when pilot Clair Vance ferried the new plane to Oakland with Fred Collins, assistant sales manager, as co-pilot. Collins flew over the Siskiyou mountains, then Vance said he'd take over. Collins, sun-drowsy and well fed at Medford, Oregon, leaned on his arm for a nap. His peace was shared by the half-dozen men relaxing in the armchairs of the eighteen passenger cabin. Harold Crary, a publicity man who didn't relax easily, went forward and climbed up the ladder to the skyroof cockpit to see what was doing. He found both Collins and Vance bowed and limp, the sun blazing down on the backs of their necks, the big airplane droning on. Crary shook Fred Collins vigorously by the shoulders. Fred waved a sleepy arm to the left. "He's flying it."

"Nobody's flying it," cried Crary, beating Vance on

the back. The stable trimotor hadn't noticed their neg-
lect. But the pilots decided the closed cockpit was better after all.

With such trial and error, idea and test, the airplane
was rapidly changing its shape, and the streamlined
Monomail was the biggest change yet. Hobbled with its
own propeller problem, the Monomail was not celebrated,
yet it had opened the view to other new ideas: a twin-
engine monoplane B-9 bomber which jumped speeds in
the bomber field from a placid 100 miles an hour to 185,
then a twin-engine monoplane transport which promised
equal speed on the airways. The transport, called Model
247, finally incorporated the controlled-pitch propeller
that Eddie Allen had sought, enabling it to shift into high
once it had climbed to its cruising altitude.

It was at noon on February 8, 1933 that the new ten-
passenger monoplane, silver-bright, lifted off Boeing
Field and winged out over Puget Sound on its first test
flight. The acclaim was instant, and the local pride was
great. "They'll never build 'em any bigger," said a trium-
phant Monteith.

There was, in fact, a law of "diminishing returns"
which said the bigger you made an airplane, the more
difficult the problem of structural strength, so that good
airplanes couldn't get much larger. There was another
rule of thumb that said if you doubled the speed of a
given plane, you'd need eight times the power, because
of the increased drag at the higher speed. It seemed evident that speeds were not likely to go much higher. But
the view that the gleaming 247 was the ultimate in the
monoplane design was shortly proved premature.

Deliveries of the revolutionary twin-engine transport
went first to United Air Lines, successor to Boeing Air
Transport and a corporate cousin, as part of the new
United Aircraft and Transport Corporation. While
United was gaining its advantage other airlines turned to
Douglas for a competing plane, and the later Douglas incorporated new features, a larger cabin. Beyond the first
seventy-five airplanes, there were no orders in sight for
the 247.

Then Government legislation dealt an unexpected blow as the new administration in Washington sought to discredit former Postmaster General Walter F. Brown's contracting of airmail routes. A law was passed prohibiting airmail contractors from being associated with aviation manufacturing companies. The big United Aircraft and Transport Corporation was ordered to split. Smallest of its remnants would be Boeing on the West Coast, low on orders, low on cash.

Everything suddenly seemed to be going backward that spring of 1934. Good men were laid off, profits down, transport and pursuit orders nearly finished. A new experimental Navy fighter and Army pursuit didn't sell. "The big planes take so much effort that we can't give the attention to pursuits," Monteith maintained. "We simply can't spread our design people that thin."

A twin-engine bomber competition had been won by Martin. There was no chance of getting back in the bomber business without a new model. Egtvedt wanted to build a new experimental twin-engine bomber and a matching twin-engine transport. But where would the money come from? When the legal and financial separation of United Aircraft was completed, the airplane plant would have just $582,000 cash, most of it needed to meet payroll and obligations for the remainder of the year.

Bill Boeing had retired from the company, bitter over the conduct of the legislative hearings that had preceded the corporate split-up. Claire Egtvedt was president, and completely wrung out. Yet the whole organization had been working from the heart; surely effort like that couldn't lead to failure, Egtvedt thought. This couldn't be the end of the line.

He looked out of his window across Engineering to the shops, thinking of the men there and the planes they had built. There was no notion of defeat in them. Some of them came in and suggested a plan of alternating work, one group on for two weeks, then off while the other group worked the next two—to preserve the staff. When the plan was put into effect, many of them came down on their time off and worked without pay.

Then Egtvedt got a call from Brigadier General Conger Pratt, chief of the Air Corps Matériel Division at Wright Field. The general asked if Egtvedt could come there personally for an important meeting on May 14. The matter was secret. He would rather not say more on the phone.

Brigadier General Conger Pratt had men on his staff who had a high goal in their hearts, as had George Leigh Mallory, the British mountaineer, who explained why he wanted to climb Mount Everest: "Because it is there." The Army Air Corps was made of men like Mallory. They wanted to fly high, into the challenge of the sky.

One of these was Leonard "Jake" Harman, who had left the University of Idaho to attend Army flying school. "I want to fly bombers," he said, when everyone knew that pursuits were the thing for a young fellow to get into.

"Why?" he was asked.

"Because they are air power." Jake Harman had been reading General Billy Mitchell. But when he got to flying Keystone bombers at Langley Field in 1929 he felt cheated. One day when Harman was pushing along over the landscape a pilot in a Ford trimotor passed him by with a pleasant wave. This was absurd, he thought; he couldn't even keep up with a passenger plane.

When the squadron commander sought Harman's help in brushing up on mathematics to enter Air Corps engineering school, and then suggested that Harman apply also, there flashed before him the hope that he might some day help get better bombers. "Would they take me, a lousy second lieutenant?"

"Put down a good reason and I'll see that you get in."

Jake Harman gave as his reason: "To see to it that the Air Corps gets some fast, long-range bombers." Major Hugh Knerr, who had been writing up the needs of bombardment aviation, encouraged him. When, three years later, Harman found himself the bombardment project officer at Wright Field, he thought he'd better try to make good that goal. New B-9 and B-10 twin-engine bombers were bringing higher speeds. Harman wanted next to go after more range.

Range was synonymous with size. To carry a bigger fuel load you had to have a bigger wing and a bigger airplane. The question of how big you could go became a favorite subject of speculation at the Field in 1933. Jan Howard, the chief engineer; his assistant, Al Lyon; Jimmie Taylor, chief of the aircraft branch; Hugh Knerr, head of the field service section, were all interested. Harman was in on the discussions.

Did the long-standing notion still apply—you couldn't make a plane much larger because you'd have to put so much weight into the structure that you'd end up with a white elephant? Now there were all-metal structures to work with; more strength. Could a pilot handle the control surfaces on a bigger plane? What about power plants? Normally you took what range you could get, after you found how heavy a structure was permissible and how large a power plant was available, and you didn't get much range.

Jake Harman had a suggestion. "Why not go at it the other way around?" he asked. If they wanted to get a long-range bomber, why not start planning on the basis of what was needed, instead of what they thought they could get? It was brash, perhaps, but he was hankering to give the concept a try, as were the others. They prepared a list of desired future bomber categories: 1) 75-foot wing span, 15,000 pounds gross weight (that took in the current B-9 and B-10); 2) 100-foot span, 40,000 pounds gross; 3) 150-foot span, 60,000 pounds gross; 4) 200 feet, 150,000 pounds; 5) 250 feet, 200,000 pounds; 6) 275 feet, 250,000 pounds; 7) 325 feet, 300,000 pounds, and so on up the ladder. It sounded fantastic, but who could say that it was? How could they ever know without setting up some projects to find out? Harman kept asking.

In the fall of 1933, Major Jimmie Taylor budgeted a project for a 5,000-mile bomber in category Number Three, skipping Number Two, reaching into the future as far as he dared. General Pratt sent the plan to Washington, recommending that Wright Field be authorized to put all its experimental money into this one project.

At Air Corps Tactical School in Montgomery, Alabama, a Billy Mitchell disciple named Hal George had been teaching strategic bombing to Air Corps officers. "Future wars will begin with air action," he lectured. "The enemy's industrial fabric will be a more vital target than his armed forces." In California Brigadier General Oscar Westover had been flying a trial mission in defense of the West Coast. "Modern bombers with speed and defensive fire can outstrip pursuits," he reported to Washington; "they can go it alone." In Washington Air Corps chief Benny Foulois took General Pratt's double-sealed secret envelope to a meeting of the General Staff, strongly endorsing the Wright Field proposal. "A plane with a range of 5,000 miles could protect Hawaii and Alaska," he said. "I think it is highly important that we undertake this as an experimental project." The General Staff agreed.

When Claire Egtvedt stepped into Conger Pratt's carpeted office in Dayton on May 14, 1934, it was as if he were going onto a ship headed for a foreign land. Nine or ten chairs flanked the General's desk. Various officers were arriving and sitting down, among them Captain Al Lyon, acting for Major Howard in the latter's absence. Egtvedt greeted C. A. Van Dusen of the Martin Company, who was among the industry representatives present.

"The purpose of this meeting," General Pratt began, "is to discuss a procedure under which the Air Corps will consider proposals for the construction of a long-range airplane suitable for military purposes, an airplane weighing about thirty tons, to carry 2,000 pounds of bombs a distance of 3,000 miles."

Egtvedt caught his breath. He looked over at Van Dusen who appeared equally startled. Captain Lyon was smiling over their surprise. The General continued: "Before I go further, may I ask if you gentlemen are interested in discussing such a project?" Egtvedt and Van Dusen both nodded.

"Good," said the General, and he proceeded to outline the preliminary data, including cost estimates, which the companies would be asked to submit by June 15 in order that a design contract might be awarded.

June 15 was just one month away. Egtvedt shut his eyes on a swirl of thoughts. Already he could see hazy outlines of a great thing taking form in the Boeing plant, a thing that no one would believe—a super airplane. He was resolved to win the competition.

Back in Seattle a secret area was set off in Engineering and a preliminary design was drawn for a 150-foot wingspan, four-engine giant monoplane labeled "Project A." The plane would be so different from anything yet built that there could be no leaning on old engineering. Everything would have to be started from scratch. Monteith was shaking his head over the plan, saying that a year or two earlier he would have thought such a study ridiculous. Like something in a dream the proposal went together to make the mid-June deadline.

On June 28, a design contract proved that it was no dream. Jack Kylstra was made project engineer. A place was set aside to build a full-scale wooden "mock-up" model of the control cabin and other parts, as required by the contract. If the mock-up and the design data looked good enough, there'd be a chance to build an experimental model of the plane.

The Wright Field people came out to consult. There were things in the design to tax the imagination: a wing with a passageway big enough to permit crawling out to the four engines in flight; six machine-gun turrets; a flight deck instead of a cockpit, with places for flight engineer, navigator, radio operator and two pilots; sleeping quarters for the crew; a 3,800-pound landing gear. Going all out, Harman and the Wright Field group wanted even a kitchenette with hot plate and percolator.

"There won't be any power left to fly the airplane

when we get through driving all this equipment," engineer Kylstra was protesting.

Lieutenant Bill Irvine suggested putting a gasoline engine in the back end to generate 110-volt electricity. "That ought to run your percolator," he jested. His idea went into the plans.

While the designing of the improbable "Project A" was getting started, United Air Lines was looking seriously at a Boeing proposal for a new twin-engine transport to compete with the Douglas DC-2s of other airlines. But the plane's performance wasn't good enough, they were contending. "Why not go to four engines?" United's Thorp Hiscock asked. The question reinforced a feeling on Claire Egtvedt's part that an inevitable trend was carrying Boeing into the business of big airplanes. The idea of a large transport and a bomber of parallel design appealed to him. When the design of a twenty-four passenger, four-engine transport was started, he suggested that the engineers keep in mind a bomber of equivalent size. It would be about halfway between their earlier twin-engine B-9 and the giant Project A.

Everyone understood that Project A was an experiment. Its purpose was to learn how to build a maximum size airplane, and it might be years before such planes could be built in quantity for Air Corps use. The present contract in hand called for design work only. They wouldn't know for another year whether a contract would be forthcoming to build even one airplane. Yet Project A had been so arousing, so agitating to the imagination, that it was hard to think any more of a twin-engine bomber. Again Egtvedt thought of "Bull" Reeves: *The airplane isn't a dreadnought.* The admiral's words were taking on a new meaning. The airplane could be a dreadnought, Egtvedt was now certain. He could see aluminum replacing the grey steel walls of "Bull" Reeves' cabin, the roar of Wasp engines out on long wings replacing the throb of the motors down in the heart of the carrier. He could envision a new kind of fleet, with dreadnoughts in the sky—eagles of American freedom. He had to shake himself. Was he dreaming?

A circular came in the mail from Wright Field on August 8, 1934. Specifications for the next production bomber: bomb load, 2,000 pounds; *required* top speed, 200 miles per hour; range, 1,020 miles; *desired* top speed, 250 miles per hour; desired range, 2,200 miles; a crew of four to six. Interested companies should submit bids for construction of up to 220 airplanes.

Claire Egtvedt read it through excitedly. To be eligible for the competition, a flying airplane would have to be submitted by August 1935—one year away. Thinking of the estimated performance of the four-engine transport they had been designing to submit to United, again Egtvedt was picturing a fleet of flying dreadnoughts for the Air Force. Preliminary design of the transport was well along and a few ideas had already been set down for a similar size "Model 299" bomber. He read the circular again. "Multi-engine," it said. That was the term the Air Corps had always used to describe the twin-engine category because occasionally someone would submit a tri-motor. He wondered if a four-engine bomber would be considered. Could they afford to build such a plane on speculation?

The stakes would be huge, Egtvedt knew. Such a decision could be catastrophic if the idea turned out to be unsound. He flew to Dayton to talk with Major Jan Howard, the engineering chief. "Would a four-engine airplane qualify?"

Major Howard looked up quickly, squinted, then smiled. "Say, now." He looked at the circular. "The word is 'multi-engine,' isn't it?"

Egtvedt flew back to Seattle and preliminary design work was started in earnest on the four-engine bomber. The plant situation was critical. Total employment was down to 600 from 1,700 at the first of the year. United Air Lines were uncertain now about a new transport. To build a big four-engine bomber for the Army competition would take all the company's manpower and most of its capital. The plant was operating in the red. The prospect of building "25 to 220" bombers loomed like a golden harvest, but the prospect of risking everything on one costly experiment hung like a menacing thunderhead over it.

Egtvedt asked Bill Allen, the company lawyer, to come down for a talk. He explained that there would be many unknowns in the proposed project. The design studies for Project A made that clear enough. "You know what little we have left here, Bill," he said. "I don't want to jeopardize the future of the company."

Bill Allen had a way of heading right for the point. "Do you think you can build a successful four-engine airplane in a year?"

Egtvedt looked over the roof of Engineering to the buildings of the plant. "Yes. I know we can."

On September 26, 1934, the board of directors voted $275,000 to design and construct the four-engine bomber Model 299, to be delivered to Wright Field for trials by the following August. The plant was reorganized on a one-job, maximum-effort basis.

Three-view plans were drawn: a streamlined monoplane measuring 103 feet in span and 68 feet in length, using four 700-horse-power Hornet engines. It was neither a low- nor a high-wing airplane; more of a mid-wing —a structure with strength and integrity. The results of one hundred hours of wind-tunnel testing were a tonic. The top speed would be at least 235 miles per hour; range, 3,000 miles. That news spurred the seventy-three engineers through their seven-day-a-week, long-hours schedule.

There were engineering controversies. Young Ed Wells, the assistant project engineer, was working on large flaps to be extended from the back of the wing to slow the plane in landing. "Let's don't stretch our luck," said Monteith, looking over Wells' drawings. "We won't need them. We'll have good brakes."

"We can leave them off," said Wells, a quiet, studious engineer, "but I wonder if we can afford to lose the performance." He laid out the comparative data showing that the plane could land and take off with 2,000 pounds greater load by using the device. The flaps went in.

By December a good share of the drawings were in the shops and men were pouring in the rivets. The board of directors dug for another $150,000 needed to finish the ship.

By the first of July, 1935, the body and wings, draped over with canvas because of military security regulations, were ready to go to Boeing Field. Newspapers spread rumors about a great "mystery ship." Almost simultaneously, in a secret double envelope, a contract came from Wright Field for construction of the even larger "mystery ship." Project A would become a reality.

The month of July in the Boeing Field hangar, getting the 299 bomber ready for flight, was rugged. Superintendent Fred Laudan checked in with the day shift, out with the night. In the final week there were no shifts; all worked as long as they could. Flight date was set for Monday, July 28. From Saturday morning everyone stayed to see the job through.

The ship came out in the light for taxi trials, a gleaming giant bristling with five machine-gun turrets. Newspaper reporters called it an aerial battle cruiser, *a veritable flying fortress*. Test pilot Les Tower sat in the instrument-filled control cabin, rehearsing his role.

Before sun-up on July 28, a cluster of men stood on the edge of Boeing Field, shivering a little in the morning mist, their hearts and the soles of their feet catching the rumble of four idling engines at the far end of the field. The rumble grew to a burning, firing roar and the big form was moving toward them down the runway, racing past them. Les Tower lifted her slowly, surely, over the end of the field. As though timed by a stage crew the sun popped over the ridge of the Cascades, its brightness glistening on the polished wings that streaked to meet it, and the 299 was a receding speck in the sky.

Claire Egtvedt shut his eyes and smiled. Design engineer Bob Minshall turned to Ed Wells who had been promoted to project engineer for the 299. "That's it, Ed. Great work."

On August 20, at 3:45 A.M., the Flying Fortress was

cutting the darkness toward the Cascade Mountains with a nonstop flight plan for Dayton. Test pilot Les Tower rode the controls over the mountains like a cowboy, turning occasionally with a grin to ask the engine man, Henry Igo, how the fans were turning. Two hours out Igo came up from his study of the temperatures and manifold pressures. "Let's give her the works." Tower put the propellers in high pitch and let the Hornets go to work.

Exactly nine hours after leaving Seattle they were coming down at Wright Field—two thousand miles nonstop at 233 miles an hour. Mechanic Bud Benton was dancing. "It's impossible. Unheard of."

Claire Egtvedt and Ed Wells, awaiting them at Wright, were under the cockpit door when they got out, to shake their hands and pat them on the back. Bud Benton wondered why there were so few people around.

"You're not supposed to be here," said Wells. "The field expects you two or three hours from now."

The days that followed were in high key. A twin-engine Martin B-12 and a twin-engine Douglas B-18 were in the competition, but all eyes were on the Flying Fortress. Pete Hill, head of Dayton flight test, was plainly impressed, even awed by the big fellow. He assigned Lieutenant Don Putt, a spirited young pilot who was enthusiastic about the plane, as project test pilot. The competitive evaluation began, according to the rules: speed, endurance, time to climb, service ceiling, structure and design, power plant, armament and equipment installation, maintenance, landing characteristics, utility as a type.

Preliminary flight test results looked excellent. Egtvedt and Wells were buoyant. Oliver Echols, who had taken Jan Howard's place as chief of engineering at the field, followed the plane's tests like a Yankee fan at the world series. Jake Harman wore a big grin. Brigadier General A. W. Robins, the new CO succeeding General Pratt, was cordial. The Flying Fortress would win the competition for sure.

One morning in October the tower crew at Wright Field watched the plane warm up for takeoff. The four engines gave their battle roar, the ship rolled down the runway, first slow, then slithering-fast, then lifted. The duty officer whistled. It was an impressive sight, watching the big ship clear the ground. The airplane was climbing steeply. Too steeply. "Hey, what's he doing?" The plane was heading straight up, falling off on a wing. The officer hit the emergency button. The plane was coming down, straightening out again now, almost but not quite enough. It was going to hit.

There was a belch of flame and smoke from the wing tanks as the 299 hit ground. Fire trucks streaked toward it.

Jake Harman, bombardment project engineer, in conference with General Echols, heard the sirens, heard someone say "299," raced out and hailed a field car, teeth set. Fire trucks were pouring foam on the burning plane, and a crowd was standing transfixed when Harman arrived. He scrambled with Lieutenant Giovanelli onto a flatbed truck. "Back it in there!" he shouted at the driver.

Pulling coats over their heads, with arms shielding their faces, Harman and Giovanelli dove from the truckbed into the furnace and dragged out Pete Hill, the pilot, and Les Tower. Don Putt, face gashed and burned, had jumped from the front end shouting something about "the control stand." Two other crew members scrambled out the back end. All were rushed to the hospital.

It was discovered that the ship had been taken off with the control surfaces locked. This was a new thing, having tail surfaces so big that they had to be locked from the cockpit against the whipping of the wind on the ground.

Major Hill died that afternoon—a bitter blow. Les Tower, who had been on the flight as an observer, was badly burned but expected to live. Putt and the others would be all right. General Robins telephoned Egtvedt in Chicago where he'd been trying to sell the four-engine transport to United.

"Oh, no. No," Egtvedt whispered. It was news the body couldn't bear. He headed desolately back for Dayton.

There was no airplane now for the final judging. The last item on the evaluation sheet—utility as a type—was all that was left, but that called for flights by operating commanders. The Flying Fortress was ineligible under the rules.

"There must be some justice in the world," wrote Treasurer Harold Bowman. "Maybe we can sell the design to England." He added: "Our bank account is overdrawn."

Les Tower rallied but he was taking the failure personally, blaming himself for not having discovered the oversight about the control lock. It took the heart out of his recovery. Egtvedt assured him that it wasn't his fault. Then word came that Tower was worse, Tower was gone—Les Tower. Losing an airplane was nothing like losing a man.

The debris of the wreck began to wash in. There were statements in Washington that this was more airplane than a human being could handle, and the rumor grew that the twin-engine Douglas B-18 would get the production contract.

Egtvedt clung to Dayton and Washington to see what could be done. He found the Air Corps was full of friends. Men like Tooey Spaatz and Hap Arnold insisted the Flying Fortress must be carried forward. Arnold was a brigadier general in command of the first wing of the new GHQ. Air Force, under the Army General Staff. Commanding general of the GHQ. force was Frank M. Andrews, and Colonel Hugh Knerr was his chief of staff. Knerr and Andrews took up the campaign for the four-engine plane. At Dayton Jake Harman wouldn't let go of the rope he was pulling. The new engineering head, Oliver Echols, who had been down at the Air Corps Tactical School getting a vision of strategic bombing from General Billy Mitchell's writings and from Captain Hal George, was of like mind.

The six hundred people left on the payroll in Seattle

were doing their Christmas shopping with a prudent peek at the bottom of the purse when the news came that the Air Corps had chosen the twin-engine Douglas B-18 for production. But it would also place a service test order for thirteen of the Flying Fortresses, plus a fourteenth to be built for structural tests. B-17, the new airplane would be called.

5

Douglas had won the production order; still, the building of the thirteen Flying Fortresses would be a sizable undertaking. Claire Egtvedt's thoughts were pulled far from engineering and design, as he considered the program ahead in 1936. There was a business to manage, contracts to be kept, stockholders expecting profit, not a $334,000 loss like that of the past year. Most trying of all, there was the problem of work for the future.

Egtvedt wanted mightily to capitalize on the four-engine idea with a plane that would put Boeing back in commercial business. It had looked for a while in the fall of 1935 as if United and American Airlines would both buy the four-engine transport. Then their interest cooled and they ended up putting money in a pool with other lines to help Douglas build an experimental four-engine landplane called the DC-4. This seemed to kill the chances of selling a domestic airliner.

Pan American Airways had just bought three Martin flying boats for their overseas routes. Their future requirements weren't clear, but their plans were big. Already they were pioneering the trans-Pacific route and beginning to think about the Atlantic. That would take big airplanes of long range and large passenger capacity. Egtvedt considered the possibility of doing something with a commercial adaptation of the Project A airplane—

the giant XB-15, but Pan American needed flying boats. He wondered if the Boeing plant facility was suited for building and launching huge flying boats. He wondered, too, if they could finance such a project.

The existing plant was not adequate for four-engine bomber production, and that requirement, Egtvedt knew, had to be taken care of first. He felt it was imperative that the company obtain a site next to Boeing Field, the King County Airport, for future expansion of land plane production, even if this required bank loans. Egtvedt devoted time with lawyer Bill Allen to the procuring of a Boeing Field site and the constructing of a new plant on it, and also to organizational changes necessary to handle the work ahead. In the process he established a service department to handle engineering contacts with the customer, placing Wellwood Beall in charge.

Beall was an exuberant young engineer who had been an instructor at Boeing School of Aeronautics in Oakland, then had joined the Sales Department. In 1934 he had received short-notice instructions to go to China to endeavor to sell some pursuits. He had called his fiancee, Jean Cory, in Oakland; four days later they were married and sailing on the *President Jackson* for Shanghai. The following summer Beall and Jeannie were at the Cathay Hotel in Shanghai at a cocktail party. The street sounds of singing coolies trotting up the Bund with cargo from the Wang Po river boats was in strange contrast to the excited comments at the party over a piece of unusual news. Captain Ed Musick had just flown a Pan American Sikorsky-type clipper to Midway Island; the rumor was that China and the U.S. would be linked by a regular air service before the end of the year.

"That's a lot of poppycock," Beall said to those around him. He was flashy with bow tie and trim mustache. "You can do a lot of things with airplanes as a stunt, but it will be ten or fifteen years before this sort of thing is commercially practical. Don't let anybody fool you." The guests were glad to be put straight, though a little disappointed. Beall didn't much notice the frown on his wife's forehead.

Not long after, the Bealls were headed back for the States. After a whirling year, all was suddenly quiet. Jeannie twitted Beall: "Isn't this boat kind of slow for an airplane man?"

"Well, peaceful anyway."

"You were sounding pretty authoritative at that cocktail party, about air travel to China being ten or fifteen years off."

"I don't think they can do it. I don't think they can get equipment that will do it," Beall said.

"Don't you think you might have to eat those words?"

That rebuke of Jeannie's haunted Beall as he undertook his new post as service engineer. "A lot of poppycock," he had told those people in the Cathay. Since his return to Seattle, Pan American had put the first of its three new Martins in service on the Pacific. Beall was walking out into the shops, possessed of an idea. "Maybe I can do something to correct that mistake." He walked past the receiving storeroom, where they were piling up stocks of structural aluminum tubing, some of it three inches across; past the machine shop, where a machinist was shaping a big piece of steel into a wing terminal; through the welding shop, idle now; the empty body shop; the anodizing and paint shops; into the big wooden assembly building on the Duwamish backwater, where the parts for the XB-15—Project A—were going together.

The wing shop had taken over the whole floor, to stretch the 149-foot span of the big experimental bomber between the balconies of the high, barnlike building. The main wing that would carry four 850-horsepower twin-Wasp engines was taking form. Beall looked into it through the inside structure toward the tapered tip. It was hard to believe. The "Ms" and "Ws" of the structural members, repeated dozen upon dozen, looked like some low attic braced for a heavy snow—a wing big enough to crawl through. Under the bracing was a heavy inner skin of corrugated aluminum to which was attached the smooth outer metal skin.

The people who said it wouldn't hold together with

its thirty-five-ton load should see those two wing spars that constituted the main lengthwise structure, Beall thought. They were built like bridge trusses.

"You like it?" asked Ernie Orthel, the wingshop foreman.

"It's weird and wonderful."

"Every morning when I come to work," said Orthel, "I tell myself, 'It's the wing of an airplane.' "

Beall returned to his office by the outside road, walking slowly, eyes squinting at a sky full of thoughts. There *was* a way he could correct his Cathay folly. Pan American needed big airplanes. Here was the plant that was building big airplanes—the world's biggest bomber. He could see those great wings flying to China, carrying not bombs but fifty, maybe seventy passengers.

In the days that followed Beall spent his spare time looking at data on Project A and adding things up. He went to Bob Minshall, now the chief engineer, with Monteith upped to vice president. "Why shouldn't we get into the flying-boat business—submit a Clipper design to Pan American?" he asked.

"We've already discussed that," Minshall told him. "Claire and I talked with Pan American about it last year." He showed Beall a letter dated February 28, 1936, from Frank Gledhill, the Pan American vice president and purchasing agent, asking if Boeing would be interested in submitting plans for a "long-range four-engine marine aircraft" built around engines of 1,000- to 1,250-horsepower.

"Great. That's right in the XB-15 class," Beall said.

"I know. But we can't do it."

"Why not?"

Minshall spelled out the problems—money, facilities, manpower. "Look at the date they want the drawings. We're up to our necks now." Minshall looked tired. Responsibility was putting furrows in his round, full face.

"I'd like to work on it, if that would help," Beall said.

"We've already written Gledhill that we won't be able to enter."

Beall went home disturbed. The prospect of a transoceanic flying boat based on the wings of the experimental bomber seemed extremely important. He tried to shrug it off; it was none of his business; he was supposed to be the service engineer. But the idea wouldn't be put off.

"What's bothering you?" his wife asked.

"Remember what I said about a commercially practical transocean airplane being ten years off?"

"Yes." Jeannie was matter-of-fact.

"I think we could build one now, based on the big bomber."

"You could?" She left Beall with his thoughts.

He got out some paper and began making layouts on the dining room table. Even if the project wasn't authorized, there was nothing to stop his working on it at home. He started with the bomber wings and tail. The bottom of the body would have to be a boat hull, with a step at the back to permit lifting the nose for takeoff. The sides could come straight up from the outer edge of the hull bottom to provide roomy passenger compartments, as in a ship.

Night after night Beall worked at it on his dining room table. A control cabin like the one in the bomber would give room for desks for the flight engineer and navigator and radio operator behind the pilots, occupying the space in front of the wings. They'd need a full deck below for the passengers—a two-deck airplane. Beall thought that sponsons, the short sea wings that Martin used on its flying boats, would be safer than wing-tip floats to stabilize the craft on the water. These could be big enough to contain the fuel tanks also.

After some throwaways, the sketch was beginning to take a positive form. Occasionally Jeannie would glance over Beall's busy shoulders. "It looks a little like a whale," she said. She had pictured it more round and sleek like the Flying Fortress.

"What's that?"

"I said it looks like it really should sail."

"Yeah, yeah."

Beall took the sketches to Bob Minshall, who seemed

impressed. Minshall said he'd talk with Egtvedt. When he reached Egtvedt in Dayton, suggesting an attempt to get an extension of the Pan American deadline, and Egtvedt approved, Minshall wrote at once to Gledhill of Pan American. Gledhill agreed to the extension.

With sleeves rolled high, they got into the details. The giant craft would be 109 feet long, with a wing span of 152 feet, much too large to be assembled in the plant, but the hull and wings would be built inside and assembled afterward on the ramp. There'd be space in the hull for seventy-four passengers and a crew of six. With a gross weight of 82,500 pounds, the airplane could have a range of 3,500 miles.

The general layouts and performance estimates for the big flying boat were complete by the time Egtvedt returned to Seattle in late April. He was enthusiastic over the progress that had been made. In two weeks he left with Beall and aerodynamicist Ralph Cram for New York, to show the plans to Pan American.

They found Frank Gledhill tremendously interested in the proposal. André Priester, the little Dutch dreamer who was Pan American's chief engineer, was smiling from ear to listening ear, and Egtvedt was shortly calling Bill Allen to join them for contract negotiations. In Pan American's high tower in the Chrysler building, then at night at the Barclay Hotel, they compromised problems of cost and performance guarantees. On June 21, 1936, a $3 million contract for six Model 314 Clippers was signed, with an option for six more.

While the meetings with Pan American were going on in the Chrysler building's high spire, a meeting of a different sort was taking place in the Munitions building in Washington. The officers of the Army General Staff were assembled: G-1, the general for Personnel; G-2, Intelligence; G-3, Operations; G-4, Supply. The Chief of the Air Corps was there, Major General Oscar Westover. His assistant, Hap Arnold was sitting on the sidelines with General Frank Andrews, head of the GHQ Air Force. Oliver Echols, the Air Corps engineering chief from

Dayton, was there and with him, Jake Harman. The meeting was for the purpose of discussing bombardment airplane procurement policy.

General Westover explained the bomber program. The Air Corps had a quantity of twin-engine Douglas B-18s on order and thirteen four-engine Boeing B-17s under construction for service test, he said. "This year we'd like to allocate funds for more B-17s."

"Isn't that the airplane that crashed in Dayton?" one of the generals asked.

"Yes, unfortunately we lost the first experimental plane."

"And the bigger one—the long range airplane—is that project still going forward?"

Oscar Westover squared in his chair. "Yes, we have the XB-15 airplane under construction."

"Why do we need airplanes that big?"

Westover looked at Colonel Echols and Echols nodded to Lieutenant Harman, who unwrapped the charts he had prepared and stuck them along the walls with pieces of masking tape. The charts compared the capabilities of bombers according to performance and size. The Martin B-10 was shown as a starting point, then the twin-engine B-18, the B-17 Flying Fortress, the XB-15—Project A, in Category Three of the development list made up in 1933, and finally the still bigger XB-19, an experimental project in Category Four which they had just asked the Douglas Company to design. Westover explained the added power of the bigger ships, their greater range, how increased speed enabled them to perform more missions per day and how a larger wing area enabled them to carry a larger load. No one interrupted, but there was a restlessness among the listeners.

One chart showed the big airplanes as troop carriers; the larger the shell of the plane, the more troops it could carry. The G-3 waved an arm at this chart. "Why haul people around in the air?" he demanded.

Westover faltered, as a man struck by a weapon he couldn't see. Before he had recovered, G-4 was concurring. "I guess that's a good question. Now I have a question I'd like to ask. Isn't it a fact that airplanes are getting too big for their metals?"

Westover turned to Echols. "Will you answer that, Colonel?"

Oliver Echols, a solid engineer, slow of speech but penetrating, rose to his feet. "I don't see that they are getting too big for their metals. At one time we built bridges out of wood. When we had to have bigger ones, we built them out of a low-grade iron. Finally we needed to get them still bigger, and we used high-grade materials, high-test cables. You decide what you need—what you want to do—and you can find the technical means of doing it."

"I still think they're getting too big for their metals."

Another general took issue with the 5,000-mile range of the XB-15. "That's absurd," he said. "The Navy will protect our shores. The Air Force should be confined to three hundred miles off shore."

General Frank Andrews came forward. "Gentlemen, I suggest we have a war game on paper so we can all see just what the big bombers can do." There was banter and confusion. The meeting was adjourned off-key.

G-4 prepared the report to Chief of Staff Malin Craig. Concentration on the big bombers was inconsistent with national policy and threatened unnecessary duplication of function with the Navy. No country had or was soon likely to have aircraft capable of attacking the United States. The twin-engine B-18 was equal to any mission assigned to the Air Corps and was much less expensive than the proposed four-engine ships.

True, there was no threat of war. The disturbing sounds from Europe and Ethiopia were dim and inarticulate. In Dayton Jake Harman was still simmering, a few months later, over the Washington rebuff when Oliver Echols called him in. "Look, Jake," the Colonel said, "I have an idea. We aren't going to get any more than thirteen B-17s for a while. We could make it fourteen, if we made a flying airplane out of the one that is supposed to be used for structural tests. I doubt if we need those tests. Why don't we use that airplane to put in turbo-superchargers for high altitude."

Harman thought it an excellent idea. The engine turbo-supercharger, developed by Dr. Sanford Moss of General Electric with the aid of Wright Field engineers, was a turbine wheel with many little paddles like a steam- or water-driven turbine, except that this one was to be turned by flaming exhaust gases which would take a torrid whirl through its blades, then emerge on the surface of the wing. The turbine was used to pump high-pressure air into the engines for higher power at thin-air altitudes.

"What would turbos do for the speed of the 17?" Echols asked.

Harman got out his slide rule and worked the numbers back and forth. "At 25,000 feet, maybe two hundred ninety miles an hour."

"Get hold of Claire Egtvedt and find out if Boeing will do it. I'll see if I can dig up the money."

In one corner of the Engineering Department at Seattle, a few drafting tables were separated from the rest by a glass partition and a door on which was stenciled, with an air of mystery, RESTRICTED AREA. PRELIMINARY DESIGN. The men in Engineering nodded assent when Ed Wells was chosen to head the group of designers who worked in that room, apart from the rest. When they'd see Wells slip in the door, they had the feeling he was in his right place. He was quiet and competent. A tap on the shoulder and he'd come out of deep thought with a smile, not a frown.

Every so often Claire Egtvedt would go down and lean over Ed Wells' table. This time he had a new question. Did they have enough information on turbo-superchargers to put them on the B-17?

Ed said he wasn't sure, but that he could get it.

"Oliver Echols wants to equip the static test ship for high altitudes."

"How high?"

"Twenty-five or thirty thousand feet."

"Not cabin supercharging?"

"No, just engines." But Egtvedt added, when they discussed it further, that he didn't think they could always be partial to the engines. The people in the airplane needed air as well. Something would have to be done sooner or later about supercharging the passenger cabins. A special supercharger, or air pump, could be used to put more air pressure in the cabin for high altitudes, if the cabin walls were sealed to hold it in.

Wells shuffled through some drawings and brought up a new version of the four-engine transport they'd been working on. Egtvedt scrutinized it with one eyebrow lowered, one gathered high. Wells had drawn the body cross-section as a perfect circle, giving it, from the side, the symmetry of a slenderized dirigible. The circular form would make it easier to contain the pressure of a supercharged cabin, he pointed out. Egtvedt was in agreement with the concept.

"The interesting thing," said Wells, "is that when you pressurize the cabin, you're forced into a better looking design."

"That shows it's right," Egtvedt said.

The new high-altitude transport that followed in design was named the Stratoliner. It would utilize the wings and tail surfaces of the B-17 Flying Fortress. Pan American Airways liked the idea and agreed to underwrite part of the cost of the pressurized cabin development. To them it was a chance to get up over the weather. They signed for three planes, and TWA ordered six. Then Wright Field contracted for turbo-supercharger development on the B-17. Aviation was moving upstairs.

But first there were big ships nearly ready to come to test.

The XB-15 was a 5,000-mile bomber capable of spanning a continent—a deadly weapon. But it was also a big beautiful airplane, Ed Wells thought, viewing its red and white tail stripes bright in the morning sun. To Wells the new plane was a symbol of what they were trying to do: stretch, strain, work to make the airplane something superior. It was evident that this wasn't a business you could walk in; you had to run to keep ahead. Still, you had to know what you were doing at every step, or you could be in deep trouble. As Jake Harman once put it to Wells, "You've got to be just as conservative as you can allow yourself to be while you're running ahead real fast." You were always trying to make the airplane do something that an airplane had never done before. The XB-15 was an example—trying to see how big you could make a plane, how far you could make it go.

When Wells asked himself why they were doing it, he thought of the preamble to the Constitution. "We the people of the United States, in order to . . . provide for the common defense . . . and secure the blessings of liberty to ourselves and our posterity. . . ." America wanted to preserve, not disturb. The Government even hesitated to buy this sort of airplane lest someone think it had aggressive intent. "Be sure to explain that its purpose is to defend our coasts," Washington had cautioned when the new bomber first emerged into public view.

At a distance about equal to the XB-15's range from Seattle, Adolf Hitler was pondering the source of power, too. Conquest was "not only a right but also a duty," he had written. Der Fuehrer saw not only the Third Reich, but one day the German race as "master of the world." But Wells wasn't thinking as much of Hitler as of the work to be done to make good America's trust. He had no illusions about the XB-15, now ready for flight. It was notable as a proof of what could be done with size, and how range could be stretched, but he knew it was far underpowered. The B-17 could fly circles around it.

On October 15, 1937, Eddie Allen wheeled the giant to the far end of the Boeing Field runway. Gentle, thoroughgoing Eddie Allen was now a consulting engineer and test pilot for various companies and was rated the best in the business. Major Johnny Corkille, the Air Corps representative at the plant, was with him at the controls. Satisfied, Eddie cut loose, rolled ponderously down the runway and took off. The big ship came off the ground like an airplane. The two auxiliary gasoline engines that Bill Irvine from Wright Field had proposed were working away in the back end, charging the ship's seven miles of electric wiring. Eddie found the bomber stable and airworthy, though sluggish in speed. Tests continued through November, until the plane was ready for delivery. Then it slid down to Hamilton Field, California, to widen the eyes of field crews there. Private R. F. Fowler of the 31st Bombardment Squadron sent the *Air Corps Newsletter* his impressions: "Because of the distance between motors, the most practical means of communication is radio. The crew on one engine may be enjoying perfect weather while the crew on the neighboring engine is engulfed in a blizzard. At the last landing one person got aboard unnoticed and wasn't found for days."

The first of the Pan American Clippers was approaching the zero hour for launching in late May 1938. Most of the 50,000 parts were now in it. Factory manager Fred Laudan, quick-stepping, quick-talking, was all over the plant and in and out of project engineer Ed Duff's office to see about final changes. Laudan, meticulous but pleasant about it, had lost his last spare hair about the same time the last piece of scaffolding came off the hull. Now carpenters were cutting away the whole back side of the assembly building so the hull could be dollied out to a newly built dock where high derricks could attach its wings. Out there it looked for the first time like an airplane, a tremendous flying boat. Pan American Airways had named it the *Atlantic Clipper*.

A national radio network had its microphone set up on the dock when the day came for the launching, May 31. Tide tables set an insistent deadline of 5 P.M., for the ship to hit the water so there would be ample depth to get out through the shallows and link up to a barge for the trip down the waterway, under the Spokane Street drawbridge and into the bay. Lowering it into the water would be a delicate operation. When the hour struck the ship began to move and the radio men were on the air.

"This mighty triumph of American enterprise, this great Flying Clipper ship that will span the Atlantic and the Pacific carrying the flag of the United States to world supremacy in the air, is being lowered majestically into the water here in Seattle." The announcer spotted Laudan coming by. "The vice president and factory manager of this plant, Mr. Fred P. Laudan, is directing the operation. We are going to ask him to say a few words to our nation-wide radio audience." An assistant grabbed Laudan's arm and coaxed him to the microphone. "Mr. Laudan, what does this occasion mean to you?"

The harried Laudan spared one glance from his ship. "To me? It means just one great big headache." Hurriedly, an aide summoned him away.

Newspapermen from the East arrived for the flight. Jim Piersol, *The New York Times* reporter and something of an aeronautical engineer, wore a sceptic's scowl. "The tail is too small for all that airplane," he said.

"Quit worrying," said Wellwood Beall. "It's been tested. It's based on the XB-15 and that's doing all right."

Wednesday afternoon, June 1, the ship was towed to a buoy off Duwamish Head. She rode regally past Port of Seattle piers. A Pan American tender launch and three Coast Guard picket boats followed, carrying the press and officials. The engines would be run up first, with the ship tied to the buoy, then they'd do some taxiing. Eddie Allen revved up the four 1,200-horsepower Wright Cyclones with a roar that roused the hillside and sent up great tails of spray. After a time the fourteen-foot propellers were stilled and Eddie leaned out the high window of the control cabin. His small shoulders and intent, sensitive face looked tiny above the big hull.

"Going to taxi?" someone asked from the press boat. Eddie shook his head. They had to change the fifty-six sparkplugs.

Thursday Eddie taxied easily about the bay. Cars lined the hillside streets. Afterwards the press wanted to know when he'd fly. "Just possibly tomorrow," Eddie said. "We have a thousand controls and each of them has to be adjusted two or three times before we go up."

It was 3:30 on Friday when the *Atlantic Clipper* struck out for the open water of Puget Sound. The picket boats were trailing, hawklike. The Clipper was way ahead now, pushing out past Alki Point where the first white settlers of Seattle had climbed wooded shores eighty-seven years back.

There was a fresh wind sweeping down from the Straits of Juan de Fuca and the water was choppy. Eddie seemed to be having difficulty. The ship rocked when he slowed it, as though in delicate balance. "Keep as close to him as you can," Beall coached his Coast Guard skipper. They had to allow a good deal of open water between them for safety's sake. Eddie swung around into the lee of Magnolia Bluff. He slackened speed and felt his way back toward the city before a following wind. The right wing was low. Beall said to André Priester of Pan American, "I guess they aren't quite used to it."

"Seas are tricky," Priester said, tolerantly. Eddie started to turn to starboard toward the mooring. Beall saw the right wing coming down. He stiffened; it was still coming down. The wing-tip hit the water, started sinking, the left wing pointing high to the sky.

"Get over there! Come in behind!" Beall shouted to the picket boat pilot. The wing-tip seemed to be digging in and taking the ship with it. The right outboard engine was nearly down to the water. Eddie was gunning the right engines full out and had the tail hard over. They couldn't bring the picket boat very close. Then, slowly, the wing began to come up. Now it was in the clear, the ship swinging around the other way. "It's going on over!" Beall shouted. The roll didn't stop at center; the left wing was going low.

Eddie cut the engines dead. A man crawled out of the navigator's turret on top, with life jacket. Then another and another. They were crawling up the high wing, out toward the tip. Their weight brought it down into balance against the wind. It stayed level.

Beall heaved a great sigh and got over to the Clipper. The crew threw a sea anchor out to hold it until they could get a tow. Beall turned to Priester. "I'm glad we put watertight flotation compartments in the wing-tips. They may have saved her."

By dark they got the ship back to the barge.

"Not seaworthy?" asked reporter Piersol.

The *Atlantic Clipper* had been lightly loaded and the fuel was in the wing tanks instead of in the sea wings, so the center of gravity was high. That may have made her unstable. For the next test they'd ballast. On Saturday, June 4, they put 2,600 gallons of fuel in the sea wing tanks and a ton of lead shot in the passenger compartments. Tomorrow she'd fly: 6 A.M. was cast-off time.

The bay was still as a millpond. The newsmen were aboard the picket boats with questioning gaze as the boats cut the water again on the trail of the 314. Things went better on the water, but there were no indications of flight. All day the ship taxied back and forth. Occasionally it stopped while mechanics came out to work on the engines. It grew late; Eddie headed back. Then, turning into Elliott Bay, the wing-tip went in the water again. Again they got it out.

The newsmen demanded to see Claire Egtvedt. "What *is* the trouble?" they asked.

"Remember," Egtvedt said, "no one has operated a boat like this before. The co-pilot gunned the engines on the wrong side by mistake. We may decide to lower the tips of the sea wings to make it steadier."

André Priester stepped in. "Those troubles are trivial," he told the reporters. "The real news is in the high-speed runs. The spray curls back clean, under the sea wings. This is a real airplane—not one that covers itself with spray so it can't get off well."

Tuesday the plane was loaded to 77,500 pounds, just 5,000 pounds under its maximum, and was set for flight, but a strong wind was up. At five o'clock a message came from up-Sound that the wind was slackening. It was a good omen. Eddie headed the Clipper west. With throttles open he skipped off the water past Duwamish Head and Alki Point, then taxied downwind. At the end of a long run he put about and prepared for a take-off to the north, while Beall in the leading picket boat got the other boats into position.

At 6:17 P.M. the great roar of the Cyclones sounded across the water and Eddie was moving toward the picket boats. The watchers raced full speed ahead to stay parallel. Salt spray in the face and high excitement aboard, they bounced through the waves as the big-hulled flying boat roared past them, sailing high on the step. Everything was rushing—water, wind, airplane. Ahead, the great hull skimmed the surface, lifted up, straight on up, steady into the air, up and up into the northern sky. Yells and applause broke free into the freshness of the wind. They watched the flying Clipper sail out of sight.

After a thirty-eight minute flight Eddie Allen landed on Lake Washington, where further testing was to be based. Beall caught up with him at Matthews Beach later in the evening. "We had power to spare," Eddie said, "but when I got off the water I couldn't turn. There's just not enough rudder for that big body. When we got to 2,000 feet, I used power on one side for a wide ten-mile turn."

Beall looked at Allen, painfully. "I guess we didn't know as much about control surfaces as we thought we did."

The Clipper model went back in the wind tunnel with a double, then a triple tail. The angle of the sea wings was lowered for better stability on the water.

They were expensive changes, with six of the big planes under construction. Claire Egtvedt could see plainly that the Clipper contract was going to come out with a loss. The Stratoliners would, too, unless more of them could be sold, to take advantage of the engineering and tooling that had already been paid for. The cost of research and engineering for big airplanes—though Egtvedt thought of it as an investment for the future rather than an expenditure—was tremendous. He looked at the charts. The original 299 Flying Fortress had taken 153,000 man-hours of engineering. The Clippers were taking 380,000.

Egtvedt wondered if anyone quite realized what this meant. You wanted to build something new that would provide an advancement in aviation—something that was needed. You had to guarantee what your new thing would do before it was built. You couldn't sell enough to make a good production job—yet you had to establish a price that wouldn't scare the customer away. You knew it would take three or four years to finish the job. The cost of labor and materials might go up in the meantime. You had a plant full of new people who had to learn how to do the job. Then there were changes that you hadn't figured on, and other changes the customer wanted —all costing money.

You had $14 million worth of orders to fill and only $4 million of working capital. Your capital was already spent for plant and equipment and materials and work in process. So you had to borrow from the banks to make your payroll. You could get more capital to work with if you could make a profit, but not if you were operating at a loss. And you were the man responsible. Everybody looked to you: employees, stockholders, customers. Wearied and worried Egtvedt sat at his desk and pulled out his slide rule, wishing desperately that the little white stick in the brown case could solve this as it would an engineering problem. But it could not.

Jake Harman was out from Dayton to check work on the turbo-superchargers being installed on the engines of the B-17A. Ed Wells showed him the bullet-round bodies of the first three Stratoliner transports on the assembly floor, hoping to interest him in such a pressurized cabin for the B-17. "We can get you better than three hundred miles per hour at 25,000 feet and a bomb load of 9,900 pounds," he told Harman.

Harman didn't spark. "I'm afraid I've got some bad news for you," he said finally. "The War Department has turned down General Echols' request for funds for a pressurized bomber program. They've asked us to put no four-engine bombers in our estimates for fiscal 1940-41."

Ed Wells went back to his engineering.

6

Adolf Hitler's forces had moved into Austria and der Fuehrer was shouting in Nürnberg: "The German Reich has slumbered long. The German people are now awakened and have offered themselves as wearer of its own millennial crown." His shrill voice had penetrated the White House in Washington. Calling in his military men, President Roosevelt wanted to know how much the airplane industry could expand its production, if need should come. If it was going to be war, it would be in the air, the President had concluded.

General Hap Arnold, made chief of the Air Corps when Oscar Westover was killed in an accident, was soberly ready for the question. General Westover had held that the future of aviation, both military and civil, was "indelibly linked with the success of the big airplane," and Hap Arnold agreed. But he was concerned about the Seattle plant's ability to produce Flying Fortresses in numbers. None of the B-17 Bs on order was delivered yet— only the first thirteen B-17s. Arnold asked Boeing to work out a license agreement under which Consolidated in San Diego would produce B-17s also, if needed. But Consolidated engineers were quick with an alternate plan. "The Fortress design is four years old," they said. "We can give you a new airplane that's faster and has a longer range. We could get it out in a hurry." Arnold couldn't deny

that that made sense. Consolidated got started on the
B-24.

At the hour when the warning bell was ringing in Europe and in Washington, the future of the Flying Fortress
was in doubt. Still, new things were happening. On December 31, 1938, Eddie Allen and a crew of four took the
first Stratoliner into the air. The flight went well. The
Atlantic Clipper was delivered and Clipper No. 2 set out
across the Pacific. Aboard, Wellwood Beall thought of the
time he had headed out this way before by ship. He
wished Jeannie could be with him now—Hawaii, Midway, Wake—westward across the world's widest ocean.
He thought of the people at the Cathay hotel, and his
words of wisdom: "It's just a stunt." Those people would
know better now. They'd know that he knew better.

With stops en route the trip lasted three weeks. On
March 14, Beall stepped again onto the Pan American
dock in San Francisco. The newsboys on the dock were
shouting something. News of their flight? He could hear
a little better: "Nazi troops in Czechoslovakia."

An apprehensive Congress was considering Roosevelt's
proposal for a half-billion dollar defense program, $170
million of it for airplane procurement; but Washington
was still resisting the B-17. In lieu of this, Sales Manager
Fred Collins was working hard to get more airline orders for the Stratoliner transport. Eddie Allen had finished his part of its initial testing. The pressure cabin
hadn't been tried in flight yet, though it had been pumped
tight in the plant and given a ten-man rubdown with soap-
suds to see if the air would bubble out at the seams. It
didn't.

Two representatives of the Dutch airline, KLM, were
in Seattle to fly in the Stratoliner. The visitors weren't as
interested in the supercharging as in the control problems of a four-engine plane. "What happens," asked Albert von Baumhauer, the engineer of the two, "if you have
two engines out on one side and the rudder full over for
a maximum angle of yaw"—that would have the airplane
crabbing sideways—"and then put it in a stall?"

Bob Minshall looked at Ralph Cram, the aerodynamicist.

"You have no reason to do that with a big ship like this," said Cram. Still, von Baumhauer wanted to know. He had made a study of this. It was agreed that they would try out various angles of yaw at low speeds, not stalling speed, and would get some measurements of forces with a spring scale attached to the control column. They would also do sideslips, stall tests and other stability tests.

It was a gloriously bright Saturday afternoon in March 1939. Mount Rainier was out bold. Phones rang. The sheriff's office had a report that a giant plane had crashed in the Mount Rainier foothills near Alder, Washington. Radios went on. An eyewitness said the plane had fallen out of the sky in pieces. It had four engines. The Stratoliner was to have been flying in that vicinity.

The sight in the mountain woods was heart-rending. Sheriff's deputies had taken Test Pilot Julius Barr out from the pilot's seat; von Baumhauer, the Hollander, from the co-pilot's seat; chief engineer Jack Kylstra, Ralph Cram, Earl Ferguson, five more.

The stark story was pieced together. They had been near stalling speed, at the point of starting the stability tests, or possibly the sideslip tests. The cabin supercharging had not been in operation and was not a factor in the accident. They had gone into a spinning dive. At an altitude of 3,000 to 5,000 feet, still with plenty of room but with hills looming black and imposing below, they had pulled out of the dive so suddenly that the wings and tail surfaces broke from the excessive loads.

Bob Minshall, who was in charge in Egtvedt's absence, literally held his head and wept that night. "What am I going to do? What am I going to do?"

Claire Egtvedt came home.

The President's rearmament program had been authorized and the first $50 million for airplane procurement appropriated. An initial order for Consolidated B-24s had been placed. No Flying Fortresses. Perhaps the only chance for business now would be in jumping over the competition with a superbomber design, Egtvedt had thought, calling for Ed Wells.

Months earlier Wells and Egtvedt had gone to talk with Oliver Echols about new bombers and the General had given them a long, sad look, saying that the only "requirement" he had permission to fill was for a 3,000-mile plane in the B-17 and B-24 category. "But that isn't what we need," Echols had said. "What we need is 4,000, better 5,000 miles. And we don't want to sacrifice speed and altitude to get it . . . or armament. We need better armament."

"We can put in a lot of armament and cut down the performance, or we can keep the performance up and stay out of the fighters' way," Wells had said. "Which is better?"

"Both," said Echols. "We ought to do both."

At Langley Field they had talked with Bob Olds. "Our job," said Olds, "is to defend these coasts. If there's an aircraft carrier approaching our shores, we have to be able to go out and bomb it before it gets close. Thank God we have the B-17. It's the only thing that can do it. But we're skating on thin ice. We have to bomb them by daylight, and we only have enough radius to reach the carrier on its last day. We want radius enough to work them over the second day out. But we haven't been able to get any money for that kind of airplane."

To do what Bob Olds was talking about would require a range of 5,000 miles.

Egtvedt and Wells took stock on the way back from that trip. "It's obvious the airplane they're buying and the airplane they need are two different things," Wells said. Egtvedt knew it, too, but the idea came hard. It meant more new development, more research, more expense, with the business already operating at a loss. High speed and long range, both, Echols wanted. You couldn't do it with any conventional design.

"On everything we've done so far," Egtvedt said, "we've started out with a purpose—an honest purpose.

That's what we've got to keep doing. We've got to build the airplane that we think best meets the need."

Back in Seattle, Wells got Giff Emery in Preliminary Design started on a superbomber study. "See if you can find some way to get the drag down," he said. "Way down." That was their only hope of accomplishing what Oliver Echols had asked.

They started on the nacelles housing the engines. These were the big drag items on the wings. "Let's try putting water-cooled engines inside the wings. Do away with the nacelles; just have the propeller shaft coming out." It was at least a new approach. It didn't look too promising at first. Then the engine manufacturers said they could build a flat engine that would fit better in the wings. There was a new ray of hope.

Egtvedt was anxious to learn of progress after weeks of design effort. He asked Wells to come up.

"We've got 4,500 miles range and 300 miles an hour—just what Oliver asked for," Wells said, but he paused and looked down, then looked Egtvedt in the face. "Claire, you said we should always start out with an honest purpose. If we're going to be honest about this, it isn't a good airplane. With the engine in the wings there's no good way to retract the landing gear. The structure isn't good around the engines. We can't make the wing any thicker."

Test pilot Eddie Allen was in Bob Minshall's office, his brown eyes earnest as he sat on the front edge of his chair, his heels hooked over the rungs. He leaned toward Minshall.

"We have an opportunity here that exists nowhere else, Bob. We've come to the point where we need exhaustive research. Not just on the ground but in the air—flight research. Flight and aerodynamic research."

Minshall was interested.

"Now," Eddie's finger shot up enthusiastically, "you can't do that sort of thing in small airplanes. You have to carry all kinds of instruments and equipment. Here you are with a stable full of big airplanes. You have the need. You have the future in big airplanes. You're the ones to do it."

"Just what do you have in mind, Eddie?"

"The day when you build an airplane and call in a pilot like me to test it is over. There should be a full-time, fully staffed department constantly carrying on this flight research, and the same department should carry on a constant program of wind-tunnel research. The two go hand in hand. They should both be part of the process of designing the plane, not just testing it."

"Would you be willing to head a department like that?"

"There's nothing I'd rather do," said Eddie. "But on one condition. We should be free to do our own work. We should report directly to you. Of course we'll work closely with Engineering."

Minshall talked with Egtvedt about the proposal. Egtvedt okayed it, and they made Eddie Allen director of aerodynamics and flight research. Wellwood Beall took Jack Kylstra's empty chair as chief engineer, with Ed Wells as assistant.

There was a spirit to go ahead. Eddie and N. D. Showalter, military projects chief, took the Number 2 Stratoliner into the air. They repeated the stall tests and found that the ship came out nice and straight. The cabin superchargers were tested at high altitude. They worked fine. Over-the-weather flying was here to stay.

Eddie said he wanted to work on the extreme angles of yaw—the crabwise flight that was being investigated before the accident—but he'd start first in the wind tunnel. He wanted to assure that the plane couldn't get into those extreme angles even in test flights, if that was what the pilots were doing up there the day of the crash. A new $16,000 ten-foot wind-tunnel model of the airplane was built with propellers powered by little electric motors and with remote control on its tail surfaces—something they hadn't had before.

Eddie didn't recruit a team. The men he needed gathered around him. George Schairer, an aerodynamicist who had left Consolidated, asked Eddie for a job. Eddie took him on, told him to spend most of his time with the new model in the University of Washington wind tunnel. He did and came up with a new stabilizing dorsal fin not only for the Stratoliner but for the B-17 as well. "What should be more stable than a plane you have to aim bombs from?" Eddie asked, approvingly.

Schairer at twenty-five was proving a brilliant analyst. He looked the part, with high forehead, thin-rimmed glasses. Schairer talked with Beall and Wells about the pressurized superbomber studies. The problem was how to get the drag of the airplane low enough. Wind resistance was the big obstacle at high speeds. Even when they had tried putting flat engines inside the wing, they still hadn't reached the performance goal.

"Had you thought of going at it the other way around?" Schairer asked. "The wing itself is your biggest item of drag. Instead of enlarging the wing and putting the engines in it, why not make the wing just as small as we can and then go to work to clean up the engine nacelles?"

Eddie Allen and Schairer made studies of what such a wing would do for the superbomber. They got 390 miles an hour and pushed the range up to 5,333 miles, with 2,000 pounds of bombs. They'd have to make the small wing carry forty-seven pounds of load per square foot to do it. That was stretching it a long way as compared with thirty-two pounds per square foot in the Fortress. But it would give them the performance they were looking for.

The old enthusiasm that could work out any problem was returning. Everyone felt the superbomber design was on the right track.

The President's rearmament program was going ahead, and it seemed inconceivable that the Flying Fortress would not be ordered in great numbers. Lawyer Bill Allen went to talk things over with Egtvedt. "Why don't you try to get Phil Johnson back in the company?" Allen suggested. Phil had been gone since the time of the United Aircraft Corporation breakup in 1934. "The need now is production. That's Phil's long suit."

Egtvedt talked to Johnson who had been set for retirement and was not eager. Would he come back as president? Egtvedt would become chairman. It was late August 1939.

September 1, out of false stillness, *Blitzkrieg* struck in Europe. Polish foot-soldiers ran without direction from under Hitler's screaming dive-bombers. Communist Russia attacked Poland's rear. Nazi tanks raced on as the world went into shock. *Blitzkrieg. War.*

7

Phil Johnson greeted tension with a friendly air. "This is a slightly different proposition than we had in the '20s," he said, settling into the executive chair of president to survey the new situation.

He used to know what an airplane was. Now planes were so enormous and complicated that no one man could know them. There were a dozen different kinds of engineering involved: mechanical, structural, hydraulic, electrical, aerodynamic, radio, acoustical, sanitary—he couldn't say what all. Scores of different skills and semi-skills were now used in the plant.

There was the financial situation. The company was in over its head, treasurer Bowman showing a loss of $2,600,-000 for the first nine months of 1939. They'd have to get some money somewhere quickly. England and France were crying for airplanes, but only certain kinds of airplanes; not Flying Fortresses. "Flying targets," the British aviation press called them. Johnson believed thoroughly in the Fortress, but it didn't change the fact that Douglas and Lockheed had big orders on their books from the Allies because they were building twin-engine bombers; Curtiss and some others had big orders for pursuits.

The signs were not clear, except for the one that said there was much to be done. Phil Johnson grabbed the

control column and took off. In October he went east
with Bill Allen and two Seattle bankers, to see about getting a loan from the Reconstruction Finance Corporation.
He asked Allen to start on a plan to sell new stock. He
called in Beall and Eddie Allen to talk about new designs
—the superbomber that was coming along. Wright Field
was highly interested, but still had no requirement for it.
Congress was still turning down appropriations for long-
range bombers as "aggressive"; they might get us em-
broiled in Europe's war.

But chief of staff Malin Craig had appointed an Air
Board to make a study of hemisphere defense before
his term of office expired on September 1, 1939. The day
that Hitler invaded Poland the Air Board's report hit the
desk of General George C. Marshall who was beginning
his six-year term as chief of staff. No longer were naval
forces and coastal defense batteries sufficient to protect
the U.S., the report said. Airplanes could hop from Europe
to South or North America. A threat to the western
hemisphere was a threat to the United States. The distances and the speed of air action spelled only one answer
—a flexible, long range air fleet. General Marshall was
impressed.

"This establishes, for the first time, a special mission for
the Air Corps," said the new military head on whom fell
the responsibility of facing the grave threat of war. He
appointed General Frank Andrews as G-3, Chief of Operations, on his staff, and Flying Fortress-loving Frank
Andrews became the first air officer ever to sit with the
generals who governed the Air Corps.

The impact quickly hit Wright Field. When Ed Wells
visited Dayton late in 1939, he found the place astir.
"Keep working on that big bomber," Oliver Echols said.
"We're going to have a new requirement soon. It'll take
all you've got to meet it." Jake Harman was on the Requirements Board as production bombardment chief under Major K. B. Wolfe, in charge of the production division; also Don Putt, now experimental bombardment
project officer. A piece of paper that came from Major
Putt's desk was the seal on a plan long in the making. The

official notice reached Seattle February 5, 1940. "R-40-B," it was labeled.

The circular asked that all interested companies submit proposals, within one month of receipt, for a 5,333-mile, high-altitude, high-speed bombardment airplane, with detailed data and drawings. *Urgent.* A full-scale mock-up to be built by August 5, 1940. The first airplane to be delivered by July 1, 1941, and any additional planes at the rate of one a month thereafter. The bell rang, putting Engineering on an all-out basis.

"Let's get the speed up over four hundred," Beall had kept urging. With the wing that Eddie Allen and George Schairer were developing, this now appeared within reason. High altitude would help make the speed possible. They could carry the fuel for 5,333 miles' range with more than a ton of bombs, but the gross weight would be 85,000 pounds. That would be a plane twice the weight of the B-17 Flying Fortress. The only way they could get that speed and range would be to cut down drag. With twice the weight they couldn't allow any more drag than the B-17 had. According to calculations the small low-drag wing would now have to carry sixty-four pounds per square foot, when for years it had been agreed that thirty to thirty-five pounds was the limit.

"How far do we dare go?" asked project engineer Lyle Pierce.

Eddie Allen was reassuring, "You can get away with it if you have a big enough flap." Eddie was the man who had to fly it and his confidence gave them courage. A huge landing flap on the trailing edge of the wing was planned, adding one-third to the wing lift; then it could be rolled downward and the curvature would have the effect of adding still more. Even then the landing speed would be fairly high, but Eddie said it would be within bounds.

It was war on drag. All rivets would have to be flush. Gun turrets could not protrude. Nacelles around the engine would have to be skin-tight; there'd be no room to tuck the landing gear up into them. Instead, the gear would have to fold up flat in the wing.

How to pressurize the body, when you had to open up huge doors to drop the bombs, was a problem. It was decided to pressurize the control room up front and the gunner's compartment in the back, then connect the two with a long tube over the bomb bays through which the crew could crawl. Designers measured the chunky Beall for size and built a sample tube for the mock-up. When it was finished, Beall tried it out. Twenty feet down-tube his voice came back, hornlike: "I can see light," and a moment later he wriggled out of the other end with a puff. "It's O.K., boys, I made it."

French troops were standing watch on the Maginot Line. Nazi troops were massed behind the Siegfried Line. Colonels George Kenney and Tooey Spaatz were in Europe observing for Hap Arnold. "Germany put more planes in the air in one raid over Poland than we have in our whole air force," they reported.

Egtvedt negotiated orders to build a Douglas attack bomber for the French and the British. Fred Collins in Washington learned an order would be coming through for forty-two more B-17s.

Word was still awaited on the superbomber. Beall and preliminary design chief Don Euler went to see Oliver Echols, but Echols didn't want to talk about the superbomber yet. "Figure out how to get more guns in those Forts," Echols said. "Tail guns especially. And armor plate to protect the crew."

Minshall parried from Seattle. "A tail turret will upset our whole balance in the airplane. We'll lose all our performance advantage if we load it down." Unenthusiastically, they got some studies started.

There was still no decision in the superbomber competition. Beall hung on. He learned theirs was the only entry that could make over four hundred miles an hour. Then Echols called him in. The colonel was uneasy. "No one has come up with what we need," he said. "We've got to have more armament—powered gun turrets, leakproof fuel tanks, armor plate, higher cabin supercharging, space for eight tons of bombs on short flights. We're going to extend the competition for thirty days."

"But you wanted the performance," said Beall. "If we give you all these, we'll have to cut down on the performance."

"We want these and the performance, too." There was unyielding determination in Echols' voice. Beall got the new requirements in detail, then called the plant. "Put these things in, but keep the speed over four hundred," he said. "We've always been conservative. Now is the time to stretch a point."

"We've already stretched it all we can," said Wells. "We've started out with 48,000 pounds and ended up with 85,000. If we get any heavier, it's going to ruin the airplane."

"See what you can do."

On April 9, 1940, Hitler attacked Norway and Denmark. This was it—war in Europe. France and England dug in; America shuddered.

A disarray of demanding, disturbing thoughts kept battering at Ed Wells as he viewed the dour prospect of doing what Oliver Echols asked with the superbomber. Suddenly the whole thing had become vitally important. By the time the superbomber could be built, war might be raging everywhere. Anything might happen. There were rumors that now the Air Corps regarded the B-17 as only a stopgap; that the new long-range bomber was what was needed for America's defense. It had to be successful. Wells felt that the original design would have been; it was whistle-clean and potent. But Echols' changes were murderous. Lyle Pierce, the project engineer, brought the new weight list in to him.

"It adds 26,000 pounds," Pierce said. Limply, Ed told Pierce to start on a new design. Beall rallied them over the long-distance phone. "This is going to be the most important airplane in the whole program," he said. "Douglas, Lockheed and Consolidated are in the competition with us. We'll have to give it everything we've got. The

Army is talking about ordering production quantities before the experimental plane is built."

This last news troubled Wells all the more. "Is this the plane we should be building?" he asked himself. He thought of Claire Egtvedt's counsel: honesty of purpose. Could he honestly get behind this airplane? "We're apt to end up with a white elephant on our hands," he told Minshall.

"I don't know what we can do," Minshall said. "Maybe you'd better work up an alternative." The more Wells worked on the smaller alternative, the less he liked the big one. Finally he went with Minshall to see Phil Johnson. "We don't feel right about the big airplane," Wells told the president. "Should we drop it and submit a smaller one?"

Phil Johnson knew the issue. Wells and his boys had their feet on the ground. On the other hand he knew what Wright Field wanted. "What if we should get in the war?" he thought. "The Army knows what you're up against in war." Johnson recognized Wells' quiet sincerity, but sometimes men didn't know their own strength.

"Now, Ed," he said, "if you *had* to make a good airplane out of this, could you do it?"

Wells looked at Johnson. He thought for a moment, then answered, "Yes." Johnson smiled. "Let's submit it and win the competition."

More Blitzkrieg. In dark of night, May 9, the Luftwaffe hit Belgium and Holland. On May 10, Stuka dive-bombers vaulted the Maginot Line and screamed down on France. In the stress and tension of May 11, Beall took the data on the superbomber to Oliver Echols. On May 12, King Leopold surrendered Belgium. In Washington, Dayton, Detroit, Los Angeles, Seattle, things were popping fast. Roosevelt asked Congress for $1,100,000,000 for arms.

Beall and N. D. Showalter took the new B-17 armament studies to Colonel Echols. When Showalter listed the various alternatives on the blackboard, Echols walked over to the list. "Here's what we want," he said, and put his finger on power turrets for top and bottom, twin guns in the tail, eight .50-caliber guns in all, armor plate, leak-proof tanks. "Arm it for combat.".

"That'll take a new model," said Beall.

"All right," said Echols. "Get it going. We can't wait for a superbomber now."

British troops were being driven out of Dunkirk. Britain blacked out, pounded by Hitler's bombers. The RAF went into the sky to do battle. Major K. B. Wolfe alerted eastern representative Jim Murray in Dayton. "Get set to produce the B-17E. We're going to order 250 of them."

Engineer Don Euler was waiting in Dayton on the superbomber. Major H. Z. Bogert, acting chief of the experimental engineering section, suddenly summoned him. "We're giving you a contract to cover engineering and wind-tunnel models and a wooden mock-up of your plane we're designating as the B-29. Push it. Cut the red tape. Move. We may want two hundred of them." Euler reeled from the office to phone the plant. "Two hundred!" They had never built a B-29.

On June 14, Paris fell. Echols called in Jim Murray and Euler. "We're asking Congress for money for 990 B-29s." Euler looked at Murray and swallowed hard. Echols continued without looking up, "Ten in '42, 450 in '43, 530 in '44." A new plant would have to be built in Wichita, Kansas, to produce them. Then Echols turned to the Flying Fortress. "All previous estimates are obsolete," he said. "We'll contract for 512 B-17Es. But there'll be lots more later." A Seattle plant addition already under way would have to be doubled again to handle the production.

Britain was in mortal struggle. The Luftwaffe was coming over nightly now, a thousand planes strong. There were fires everywhere. Water mains were broken and useless. Each night took another five hundred lives, injured two thousand, while RAF Spitfires fought back. It was "blood, sweat and tears," said Churchill, resolute at the helm.

When the British asked now for B-17s, the Air Corps agreed to send over twenty of the sixty it had in service. They'd be fixed up with armor plate and leak-proof tanks, but they would not have the tail guns or the new power turrets. The Flying Fortress would soon see battle.

George Schairer and his aerodynamicists were at Cal Tech wind tunnel with the new wing model for the B-29 superbomber. They had tested it first in the University of Washington tunnel, then at Massachusetts Institute of Technology. It showed signs of "compressibility burble," a mysterious new phenomenon that engineers were trying to learn more about. When a plane got going fast enough for the air over its wing surface to approach the speed of sound, strange things would happen. The air would act like a solid instead of a fluid, and would tumble away from the wing. It was a new kind of "stall," stalling not at lowest but at highest speed. No one knew what would happen if you let this go on. Probably everything would break apart.

Schairer was a precise searcher. He could see that "burble" would occur over some parts of the wing but not over others. At Cal Tech tunnel he had the latest corrections in the wing model. The wind in the tunnel lashed at it. The grotesque arms and counterarms of the balance mechanism below the tunnel wrote their mathematical hieroglyphics on the big instrument panel. Schairer and his aerodynamicists peered through the window at the effects of the wind's fury, and at the instruments, hour after hour, day after day, making changes and adjustments. They studied the recorded graphs and charts at night. The wind tunnel results on the wing shape looked hopeful, began to look better still, then finally looked right. Schairer wired Eddie Allen: "We have it. We're coming home."

But there was still the problem of control forces, an ever-changing problem that was growing more demanding as planes grew bigger and faster. Would one man have the strength to move the control surfaces of a big, fast plane like the B-29? One manufacturer had tried powered controls, but they'd proved a failure. There couldn't be any failure in the B-29.

"Do you think it can be done?" Eddie Allen asked Schairer.

"I don't know, but I have a feeling it can."

From experience they had the control tab. You could move a small tab on the end of the control surface and then let the wind on the tab help you move the rest. This was part of the answer, but not enough. They also had the balanced control, where the part ahead of the hinge swung across the wind and helped move the bigger part behind the hinge. But control surfaces were too light with the balance they were using. They'd overcontrol. It was a highly complicated matter to get them just right.

They began working on it in the wind tunnel, trying all sorts of changes in the shapes ahead of the control surface hinge line. It was well known that the only changes affecting the result were those ahead of the hinge line. No solution appeared. One day Schairer was looking over some tables of figures from the wind-tunnel experiments. On one test the results were completely out of line with all the others—much better. He called the test group. "What did you do? You haven't changed anything ahead of the hinge line."

"That's what has us stumped. We accidentally changed it behind the hinge line. That's not supposed to make any difference. We never waste our time there."

"You've got the answer," Schairer said.

The B-29 design was rounding out. The weight went up to 120,000 pounds gross, wing loading to sixty-nine pounds per square foot—extremely high. All the Air Corps was watching, wondering about the bet it had placed, worried about whether the plane could get to high altitude with such a heavily loaded wing. Oliver Echols had moved to Washington and George Kenney had Echols' spot at Wright Field. Kenney called Wellwood Beall to his office. Cryptically, he wrote on the blackboard, "Plane X—wing loading fifty-three pounds per square foot, ceiling 28,000 feet," and under it, "B-29—wing loading sixty-nine pounds per square foot, ceiling. . . ." After "ceiling" he drew a sprawling question mark and turned to Beall, arms folded, his eyes sharp and demanding under his short-cropped hair.

Beall felt cornered. "We have high wing loading, all right, but we'll get 33,000 feet ceiling."

"How do you know? This plane didn't." General Kenney pointed to his X on the board.

"You'll have to tell me what Plane X is and I'll tell you the difference."

"It's a bomber we've just bought that has high wing loading."

"They didn't have the turbo-superchargers that we have," Beall said. "We can make our ceiling."

"We're counting a lot on your word, my friend," said Kenney. "There'll come the day when you'll have to prove it. In the air."

Britain battled on. The grizzled RAF had picked off German bombers until it had sapped the Luftwaffe's strength. The twenty B-17C Flying Fortresses that had been sent to England were being readied for action. RAF crews were skeptical of the airplanes, but game for a try. They trained briefly and on July 8 took two of the Fortresses across the North Sea to bomb Wilhelmshaven from 30,000 feet. They missed the target. The "Jerries" came after them. They tried to shoot back but the guns were frozen. Through riddling machine-gun fire they got home.

On July 24, they trained their bombsight crosshairs on the German battleship *Gneisenau*, and thought they scored some hits. Again the guns froze up in combat, but again they got home.

By September 12, 1941, they had made twenty-two daylight raids and had lost eight of the twenty ships, some in combat, some in crash landings. Intelligence said all but 2,200 pounds of bombs went wide of their targets. "Mighty expensive bombing," concluded the Bomber Command.

In Seattle Eddie Allen and his flight-research crews were finding out things about high altitudes. "There are a thousand details to be worked out to make apparatus function up there," Eddie said. "It's terribly cold. Greases won't work. Propellers won't work. The fuel mixture system in the airplane doesn't work. We don't have the proper oxygen system."

They set aside a couple of B-17Cs for the exploration, and morning after morning on Boeing Field, the crews would spend a half-hour breathing pure oxygen and exercising to ward off decompression "bends," then climb into fur-lined suits and go "upstairs" to tackle the trouble items one by one.

The new B-17Es, in production in the plant, gleaned the advantage of this high-altitude research. The first of the "E" models was being flown during that September of 1941, complete with powered Sperry gun turrets on top, ball turret in the belly, tail turret, new side guns and nose gun—looking like a war plane.

A tension was developing in the Pacific that wouldn't wait for the new B-17E. Japan seemed intent on pushing its conquest of French Indo-China, despite President Roosevelt's warnings. Early in September nine B-17Ds which had been in Hawaii since May were poised at Hickam Field for a flight to the Philippines, where they'd be stationed. Major Emmett "Rosy" O'Donnell was leader of the squadron. Crew chiefs were checking out the power plants. Duffel bags and personal packages were stowed aboard. Thoughts weren't so much of impending war as of the long trip out. O'Donnell briefed the pilots: "Every ship will be on its own. You have your charts. Stay with your instruments." The Pacific heavy bomber force droned westward.

On October 16, twenty-six more B-17Cs and Ds followed to complete the 19th Bombardment Group, under Lieutenant Colonel Gene Eubank. On October 18, military extremist Hideki Tojo became dictator of Japan.

In a walled-off portion of Plant Two at Seattle, the first B-29 was beginning to take form. Construction was under way in Wichita on the sprawling plant that would produce the planes. The Government was giving consideration to having other companies join in building still

more of them, as they were joining now in building
B-17s. Basic engineering data were given out to those who
might be asked to participate. One of the companies reported back to General Arnold, after its engineers had
gone over the data, that Boeing was "way out in its figures." The plane would have forty miles per hour less
speed than proposed, 5,000 feet less ceiling, 1,000 miles
less range, according to its calculations. If it was right, the
B-29 wasn't an airplane. Hap Arnold turned pale at the
thought. Was the big program turning into a fiasco at
the moment of crisis? He had to know. He put it squarely
up to Oliver Echols, on whose word he'd bought the airplane. Echols' confidence began to waver. He took Don
Putt and a delegation to Seattle to have it out.

The meeting was in Wellwood Beall's corner office in
the four-story engineering building at Plant Two. Wells,
Showalter, Eddie Allen and George Schairer were there.
The issue was bow-string tight. "You're going to have
to put on a bigger wing," Echols said. "We can't afford
the chance."

Beall knew that would be catastrophic both to production and design. "We'll *really* lose our performance if we
do that. We won't have an airplane."

"You don't have one now, according to these figures."

"They don't match with our figures," Beall said.

"You'll have to justify your figures."

Beall turned to Eddie Allen. Eddie leaned forward. "I
don't think it is still well understood," he said, his high
voice strained and earnest, "how much difference a small
change in the contour of the wing and engine nacelles can
make. We have a much lower drag from the nacelles than
you'll get from the normal way of figuring."

"How can you be sure?"

George Schairer spoke up. "We've proved it in the
wind tunnel."

"Wind tunnels can be wrong."

"But we've been in three different tunnels with it. They
all check out."

Don Putt turned to Echols. "I think we'd better investigate this further. We may be all right here." Echols' face showed relief, as though he wanted mightily to believe Putt. The meetings continued for a week and the party returned to Wright Field. Major Bill Cragie, of the experimental engineering section, seemed confident that the 29 would be okay. So did Putt. Finally Echols told Beall, "Go ahead as you are."

8

Plant Two was a flowing tide of Flying Fortress parts and assemblies. Production was coming up: twelve Forts in October 1941, twenty-five in November. There'd be thirty-five in December. Then, December 7, came the unbelievable, electrifying newscast:

"Pearl Harbor has been attacked. Untold damage has been done to the U.S. naval base and to the city of Honolulu itself by unidentified bombing planes."

Jake Harman called. "Start building airplanes."

"How many?"

"My instructions are you just start building. Never mind the schedules. Tell us how much money and what things you need when."

Sunday night in Seattle was Monday afternoon in Mindanao, southernmost island of the Philippines, across the international dateline. Major Emmett "Rosy" O'Donnell, with his B-17s at Del Monte, their crews aboard and waiting, was trying to get headquarters at Clark Field, Manila.

"Still can't get them, sir," said the communications officer.

"Hell's fire," snapped O'Donnell, "we've got to get them."

Next morning orders came. Clark Field had been

bombed out. Major Combs' squadron at Del Monte was to hunt a Japanese raider off Legaspi. O'Donnell was to stand by.

Standing by didn't fit Irish Rosy O'Donnell. When orders came late that afternoon to proceed to Clark Field, he sprang as out of a catapult. "Let's go." Approaching Clark Field O'Donnell gasped to see the buildings torn and gutted, the field in craters that told why communications couldn't get through. All but two or three of Clark Field's nineteen Fortresses were battered and crumpled on the field. These and O'Donnell's eight and Combs' eight remained the sole U.S. bombing force against Japan. He sensed the urgent mission of those eighteen or nineteen Flying Fortresses.

O'Donnell got a radio message. "Don't land here. Go to San Marcelino." At dusk in a coastal valley off to the southwest, where no B-17 had landed before, they squashed down on tall grass. Filipino guards peppered them with bullets on the way in. The men spent the night in their planes, or in the dew under the wings. "Can we take off from here?" the crew asked.

"We got in. We can get out," said O'Donnell.

"The wind is against us."

"From now on winds don't matter."

At 4 A.M. O'Donnell said he was going into Clark Field to get orders. He took off into jet-black night, made a forty-five degree turn where he knew there was a hill, and climbed on out. When he got into Clark, he radioed his squadron to follow at dawn.

Before bomb-loading operations were completed on O'Donnell's plane and two others, there was an air-raid warning. O'Donnell looked about quickly. "Let's get out of here." A P-40 reconnaissance brought word of an invasion fleet of transports approaching Aparri, at the north tip of Luzon, and another at Vigan. Colonel Gene Eubank, commanding the 19th Bombardment Group, dispatched the three planes that were ready.

At 25,000 feet, above Vigan, Rosy O'Donnell spotted a big ship. "My God, I think it's a carrier. Let's take it."

The bombadier started his long bomb run. Over the target nothing happened. "Bomb release is struck," the bombardier shouted.

"Try again." In bursting ack-ack O'Donnell wheeled about and made another run. This time they got part of their bombs away. The vessel below was zigzagging violently. They kept at it. It took forty-five minutes to get all the bombs out; none hit the target. O'Donnell was sobered. "It's not so simple," he thought.

The raids on Clark Field drove the 19th Bombardment Group back to Del Monte. As fast as the ground crews could get things repaired, they kept delivering their punches. Out and back; out, riddled and back, the crews of the Flying Fortresses learned war in the days that followed. One of the Forts that escaped the December 8 bombing was Captain Hewett Wheless' plane. "Shortie" Wheless was flying reconnaissance in heavy weather off Formosa when the Japs hit. On December 14, in a three-plane attack on a Japanese transport, Wheless got separated from his mates in low clouds. He went on alone. He was on his bomb run at 9,500 feet, when eighteen fighters swarmed him. Four of them closed in, one on each side, two on the tail. Gunners in the Fortress poured it to them. One of the fighters went down. Wheless called back to his crew. "You're getting 'em. You're getting 'em."

Then Private Killin, the radio operator, was killed at the belly gun. Navigator Meenaugh came to take his place, shouting, "I'll pay 'em back."

The fighter on the other side dropped away in a smoke-trailing spin. More explosive bursts came through the sides of the ship. Both waist gunners were wounded and had to leave their posts. Sergeant John Gootee, with a bullet in his right wrist, grabbed one of the guns with his left hand, swung it after a fighter. The two fighters on their tail were riddling them mercilessly. With the ship holding straight on the bomb run, the side gunners couldn't reach them.

"Bombs away."

Wheless hit the rudder and swung the ship sideways to

give the gunners a chance to pick off one of the pursuits on the tail. Bombardier Schlotte came back to lend Gootee a hand at the side guns. Fifteen fighters remained, attacking in waves, in a bedlam of noise and action. The belly gun had been shot out. Gootee got another fighter, then his gun jammed. Number one engine was dead. Everything was riddled. Finally all the guns were shot out of action or jammed. They sat back and took it.

Twenty-five minutes after the running battle started, the Japanese fighters were silent, out of ammunition. Some of them came up close to look in the windows. The radio was destroyed; one fuel tank ripped wide open but not on fire; oxygen system out; tail wheel shot away; front tires shot flat; two-thirds of the control cables shattered; side walls a sieve; but they were staying in the air, droning on at low altitude.

At dusk they sighted Mindanao. Drizzling rain obscured the hills ahead. Wheless sighted a small airfield near the beach and headed his crippled ship for it. Too late he saw the field was barricaded. They smashed on through, rolled two hundred yards on flat tires, then the wheels locked. They stubbed up on the nose and settled back down again to rest. Seven shaken and injured men climbed out and patted the battered ship. "Good old gal. Wonderful gal."

Grizzled, bandaged, grease-stained, a fighting family alone before the weight of an ocean of moving warships, nursing its four-engined steeds with a brotherly affection, the 19th Bombardment Group fought on with its remnant of Forts. When the Philippine invasion forced them off Mindanao, they filled up the fuel tanks, loaded the 17s down with as many men as they could carry and staggered off for Australia.

Major General George Brett arrived in Australia to take command at the end of December. The problem of how to reinforce the Philippines grew desperate. Distances were too great for movement of pursuit forces. Japan controlled the sea, and therefore the bases. The only practical plan was to fight a holding action until air and naval strength could be built up in the South Pacific to work back.

The Japanese were already driving on Southeast Asia. The patched-up Forts and their crews went up to Java. More Forts joined them by way of India: B-17Es with tail guns and power turrets. Colonel Gene Eubank, a man who had helped make the Fortress a fighting airplane in pre-war days, when he'd come to the plant with the ideas of the operating squadrons, got them organized for businesslike raids.

There was an invasion convoy coming through Macassar Straits. The 19th took after them on January 22 and 23, and U.S. War Department communiques took prideful note: "Seven Flying Fortresses sank one enemy transport, set fire to another. Five enemy planes were shot down. All of our bombers returned to their base." "Eight Flying Fortresses sank a transport, hit a cruiser. One bomber was lost." "Another transport destroyed, another set on fire. Two fighters shot down. All five bombers returned safely."

Enemy fighters treated the new B-17Es with caution and respect. "Four-engined fighters," Radio Tokyo called them. But on February 15, 1942, Singapore fell, and Java was becoming untenable. Five remaining Forts dropped back to Australia.

The war was going badly in Europe and North Africa and plans called for most of the new Fortresses from the factory to be sent to the European theater. Some B-24s were expected in the Pacific soon, but with the intermediate bases in enemy hands, distances now were far too great for either the B-17 or the slightly longer-range Consolidated B-24. The B-29 Superfortress, still unflown, was the only hope; and even the B-29 couldn't reach Japan itself until island bases could be won, or land bases established in China. This last seemed the best possibility, if the Japanese could be held there. But the meager forces in Northern Burma weren't holding them. B-17Es that could be spared from Australia were flown to Karachi, India, in March, to help.

Talk in the streets of Karachi was gloomy. "The Japanese will be here by summer," people said. General Joe Stilwell, falling back in North Burma before the Japanese invaders, called on Air Force Commander Louis Brereton for support. Burma had only one major port: Rangoon. Japanese troop supplies would have to go up the railroad from Rangoon to Mandalay. From India the bombers began their mission against the docks of Rangoon. The pummeling continued until there were no docks left. The Japanese took the Burma Road, but India still remained as a staging base for aerial approach to Japan through China.

There was a grave new concern about the B-29, secret white hope of the U.S. Air Force. The fierce realities of aerial combat, such as the B-17s were experiencing in the Pacific and the British were experiencing in Europe, had put fire behind an unwelcome question. Would the remote-control guns in the 29 work against quick-maneuvering fighters coming at the airplane in numbers?

The power-operated turrets that had been put on the B-17E—the two-gun turret on top and the ball turret in the belly—were working fine. A man could sit there with his sights and the power would pull his gun around as fast as he could move it. But the B-29 had a pressurized body, and if you used this kind of turret, you'd lose all your pressure through it. Moreover, the streamlined body had to be kept free from things like turrets. The Air Force armament lab had solved the problem with guns controlled through periscope sights. You watched for enemy fighters in the periscope eyepiece, as from a submarine, and aimed your gun accordingly. The awkwardness of this, the narrow field of view, struck horror in the minds of Air Force operations people.

"We've got to change it," General K. B. Wolfe told Jake Harman in Dayton. "Everybody in the Air Force is on top of me about it. Go out to Seattle and get them to put on turrets. Don't listen to any backtalk. We've got to do it."

In Seattle Harman gave them the emphatic word.

"We don't like the periscope any better than you do," answered N. D. Showalter, the chief of military projects. "But what are we going to do? We can't just stick ball turrets on the airplane. It's so clean now that the landing gear, when you put it down, has as much drag as all the rest of the airplane put together. What would happen to our performance if we stuck turrets out there? We won't have any bomber left."

"This isn't a case of what we want to do. It's what we have to do," said Harman. "It isn't a bomber if you can't fight with it either."

Other engineers were called in. They wrestled for two days, skipping meals, skipping sleep. The more they tried to prove the periscope, the worse it looked. But Showalter and Wells couldn't agree to the big turrets either. Then Colonel Roger Williams from the Wright Field armament section proposed the use of an electronic remote control idea that General Electric was working on.

"It's a long shot," he said, "but it might work." The concept was that a gunner would aim a remote sight and electronic tubes would reproduce the same movement in all the guns. At least it was a break in the cloudy sky. Could electronic tubes withstand the rigors of battle? Was this just walking out of one complicated set-up into a more complicated one? If it worked, it would solve the armament dilemma and save the airplane's high performance. G.E. engineers were called. Everyone lent a hand to develop a model. It looked encouraging. It had to work.

Jake Harman called K. B. Wolfe from Phil Johnson's office. "K. B., we have a different. . . ." He didn't get any further. K. B.'s voice came back, "Did you get them to put on the turrets?"

"No, but. . . ."

"I sent you out there to do a job. I want that job done." K. B. Wolfe's burden of responsibility and the drive that had made him the dynamic center of the Air Force production program were coming through the wires and broadcasting into the room.

"But we've got something better." Jake got an opening and gave Wolfe the new plan.

"All right, then," Wolfe said. "But if it isn't any good . . . I sent you fellows out there to do a job and, so help me God, if it isn't right I'm going to break every one of you. You'll be worse than second lieutenants. You've had it . . . You'll have to call Echols in Washington and explain it to him."

The G.E. central fire-control system went in the B-29, and the big Superfortress, product of many hands, again became a secret white hope.

Tremendous planning was going on in Washington, sufficient to explain the Air Force's insistence on certainty of the B-29's design reliability. New production plans were being made and there was a mystery-shrouded program that stemmed from a note scribbled to Franklin D. Roosevelt by white-haired Albert Einstein from the Institute of Advanced Study at Princeton in 1939. Read by only a select few men, the note was now giving rise to cryptic, encouraging, top-secret reports from scientific laboratories, and was generating plans for a big desert experimental station in New Mexico.

Tall Robert Lovett, the new Assistant Secretary of War for Air, was one of those who added things up to an inevitable answer. The defeat of Germany would require tremendous blows by air; the defeat of Japan would depend even more on aerial bombardment. While the country was reaching deep for money and manpower to put out the fire in Europe, it would have to reach deeper to build the long-range attack on Japan. Nothing but the B-29s could do that job. Furthermore if the fantastic tests at Alamogordo proved out, nothing but the B-29 could carry the *atom bomb* to Japan.

General Echols asked Wellwood Beall to come to Washington as soon as possible. When Beall stepped into Echols' office the next day, a little weary from all-night flying, the General's look was grave. "The United States Government," said Echols, "is about to spend more money on one project than any other project of the whole war.

This project is the B-29. We haven't even flown the airplane. We're worried about the tremendous risk if it
doesn't pan out. Now you're the chief engineer of the
Boeing Airplane Company. We want to know, really—
the survival of the whole country may depend on this—
we want to know what you really believe in your heart,
whether that will be a good airplane or not."

Beall took a deep breath. Here and now the test of
vision was courage. It was not blind courage that was
called for, he knew, but courage of decision that might involve the lives, hopes, future of millions. This kind of
courage could only be based on a firm faith. He thought
of the step-by-step progress that had made the B-29 possible; of the men who had made it possible; their faith;
their devotion to a goal that they knew was vital. The
1,900 men in the engineering department were as one in
this airplane. These men *were* the airplane. Their work on
the first B-29 was mostly done now. It had only to be
proved.

Beall looked Echols in the eye. "Yes," he said. "It's
really going to be a good airplane. If you'll give us first
priority on test facilities and let us do all the testing we
want to do, when we want to do it—flight testing, systems testing, all kinds of testing—if you'll assign us the
airplanes to do this, I'll guarantee that we'll get you successful operating airplanes."

Echols went in to see Hap Arnold. "All right," said
Echols when he came back. "We'll do what you ask."
Then he laid out a production program that would cost
$3 billion. Four companies would build the superbomber.
The B-29 was not just an airplane now, but a giant pro-
gram and a faith.

The American people and their allies needed a strong
faith in the spring of 1942. They were forced out of the
Pacific, off the continent of Europe, into the bottom of
Asia and across the Mediterranean onto North Africa. It
would be a long, bitter struggle to gain that ground back.

But the voice of Franklin D. Roosevelt sounded encouragement to those at home at the fireside radio. He

told the heroic story of Captain Hewett T. Wheless and his Fortress fight in the Pacific. "Our planes are helping the defense of the French colonies today," said the President, "and soon American Flying Fortresses will be fighting for the liberation of Europe."

9

Brigadier General Ira Eaker got a call from Hap Arnold early in 1942: "I want you to go to Europe to study the British Bomber Command. I want you to operate a bomber command of our own as soon as we can get planes."

"But I'm a fighter man," said Eaker.

"That's what we want, the fighter spirit in bombardment."

"That's a challenge. O.K."

"When I was in England," Arnold said, "they told me our Fortress couldn't stand up against the German fighters. You and I know that if we can't bomb with this plane, we can't bomb. Tooey Spaatz is organizing the 8th Air Force to go to Europe. Tooey wants to know if we can plan on daylight bombing and hit the target. I want you to get the answer. Come back and tell me if we can do daylight bombing."

Ira Eaker landed in England with a briefcase full of 8th Bomber Command plans and a head full of questions. Why were the British so opposed to daylight bombing?

"We aren't opposed to it in principle," said Air Marshal Sir Arthur Harris, head of the RAF Bomber Command. "It's the losses. We can't stand the crew losses, and we can't manufacture airplanes that fast. We tried it, but had to give it up. The Germans tried it and had to give it up. When the target is well defended, bombers have to have protection of darkness."

Had the British really given the B-17 a fair trial? The 17 was designed for this.

"The RAF crews weren't well trained to use the Forts," said the air attaché in London. "There was a lot of pressure to get the American ships into action. They didn't have the Norden bombsight, and the crews never got on to the old Sperry sight. They didn't have the new gun turrets. Then they flew singly instead of in formation. The Jerries really hit them."

But could the 8th go in with the new Forts and survive? "This is the big league," said Brigadier General Al Lyon, air officer for Major General James Chaney, head of the U.S. Armed Forces in the British Isles. "It's incredible how much stuff the Germans can throw up. You're going to have to feel your way by stages, but it can be done. It's got to be done. That's the only way you can take out the targets."

Lyon had helped Chaney and his chief of staff, Brigadier General Joe McNarney, analyze the Battle of Britain. Goering hadn't put enough bombers in the air and hadn't pinpointed targets. What Goering had failed to do in Britain, the Allies must do in Germany, Chaney had concluded. The measure of effectiveness was bombs on target versus bombers and crews lost. If you had small losses but got few hits, you were just prolonging the agony. You had to concentrate on hits and find the means to keep your losses down. U.S. bomber crews had been trained for daylight precision bombing.

Eaker summed it up: "It's a gamble, but we've got to place our bets. If we can't make a go of it, we can still go over to night bombing. But, let's face it, we couldn't use the Forts at night without a major modification of the airplanes. The flame of those turbos on the bottom of the nacelles would be a dead giveaway." To extend the exhaust stacks and obscure the glow from the turbo superchargers would cut down their performance. There was no question. The theory of daylight precision bombing would have to come to a test. "Yes," Eaker told Arnold and Spaatz. "We should go ahead as planned."

In late June the crews of the first group of Flying Fortresses followed 8th Air Force commander Tooey Spaatz to Goose Bay, Labrador; to Bluie West, Greenland; to Reykjavik, Iceland; to Prestwick, Scotland, and down through the overcast to the flat green table of England. Three Forts were left behind, forced down off-course in Greenland. More squadrons followed. "Little Americas" began springing up all over the English countryside. "Let's get going," was the word.

English experts frowned at the B-17E armament and the "tiny cramped quarters" for the tail gunner and ball-turret gunner, yet the British had a warm welcome for the Americans. "The spirit of these lads is refreshing," said reporter Ronald Walker in the London *News Chronicle*.

There was long training before the first mission. More questions. How tight a formation could they hold? The tighter the formation, the greater the mass of gunfire to ward off fighters. How fast could they go without burning out engines? How high? The more altitude, the greater the safety, but the higher they went, the less bombing accuracy. How much armor plate could they afford to carry? Too little and the crews would get it. Too much and the weight would slow them down. They practiced evasive maneuvers. It all took time. The Germans dropped notes on the airdromes. "Where are the American bombers?"

By August 16, eighteen crews of the 97th Bombardment Group were ready. Tomorrow, they'd attack railroad yards at Rouen, where Joan of Arc, half a millennium before, had died for the liberation of France. They got their preliminary briefing. This was it. They tried to remember every little thing they had cram-learned, tried to put out of mind the question, "What will it be like?" and the unwelcome fear.

At 1526 hours, August 17, 1942, Ira Eaker was in the Fortress *Yankee Doodle* as Colonel Frank Armstrong lifted the leading plane over the trees. At 1539, the

twelfth plane was in the air. They pulled up into formation and rendezvoused with their RAF fighter cover.
They climbed to 23,000 feet, droning eastward over the
green, unwarlike countryside, across the Channel, wondering, rehearsing. Only minutes now and they'd know.

A river, a city, the long strands of the marshaling
yards—their target—loomed ahead and far below. They
entered their bomb run. Black puffs of ack-ack began
reaching up for them, jolted them, but all rode on.
"Bombs away." The pepper-fast burst of smoke punched
out a pattern on the ground, encompassing the yards.
They could see fighter planes taking off below, pulling
up now, chasing them back. Only a few RAF fighters
took them on. Was it over?

At Grafton-Underwood, Tooey Spaatz, staff aides and
mechanics were waiting. The returning specks appeared
in the gathering dusk. Four-engined. Three planes; six.
They were letting down; nine, ten, eleven, twelve. All
back. All whole. The men swarmed the field. "You made
it. How was it? How'd we do?"

"Milk run."

Ira Eaker returned to 8th Bomber Command headquarters to find a note from Air Chief Marshal Sir
Arthur Harris on his desk: "*Yankee Doodle* certainly
went to town."

Eaker didn't disclose his joy. "We won't get cocky.
One swallow doesn't make a summer," he told his men.

The raids continued. They hit Abbéville, then Dieppe
and Amiens, without losses. Then, August 21, on the
way to attack a target in the Low Countries, the RAF
Spits were delayed in making their rendezvous. Two
dozen Jerries took on the unescorted bombers during
the bomb run and after. The nine Forts in formation poured out their battering fire. Two of the pursuits
dropped in flames. One Fortress, with engine crippled,
dropped behind. Five FW-109s swarmed on it. A
twenty-millimeter shell smashed in, injuring pilot and co-
pilot, but they flew on. The tail gunner got a Focke-
Wulf. The ball-turret gunner, revolving crazily in the
Fort's underbelly, knocked down two. Number Three

and Number Four engines were hit but kept going. The shattered B-17E limped home, trailing the formation.

Word spread quickly. "The Forts can take it and get you back."

The first B-29 Superfortress was wheeled out for ground tests of systems and equipment in September 1942. Eddie Allen's men packed it with measuring and recording instruments while Eddie fended off questions about the date of flight. "There are many items of new equipment," he said. "Getting them all to work at once is like throwing up a handful of coins and getting them all to come down heads." With a crew of seven, Eddie taxied, tried the brakes, the elevators, the ailerons. He lifted a foot or two off the ground, came back; lifted ten feet, came back; lifted fifteen feet, came back. Finally, on September 21, the plane was ready.

The four Cyclones sent back a comfortable, reassuring rumble. One at a time, then all together, Eddie revved them up. Next moment he was slithering down-runway, a symphony of motion and irrepressible power; thunder going by. The wheels came off the runway. Eddie held the airplane low downfield for a moment of security and acceleration, then climbed on up—the great new thing, the hope in many minds, the question mark in many others, disappeared in the sky down the valley. Eddie came back with an eloquent smile. "She flies," he announced.

Ed Wells was pleased but cautious. The war, the Air Force, the $3 billion program were pushing them—pushing them too fast, Ed felt. More tests brought out troubles with equipment and power plants, but the basic aerodynamics were sound. The plane was stable; stalls were smooth. The big control surfaces, once an enigma, were light and responsive. Eddie Allen paid tribute to the work that had been done in the wind tunnel. He had sold Phil Johnson on construction of a modern tunnel at the plant.

"Every step we take from now on is going to require more and more wind-tunnel time," he said.

Eddie Allen was a scientist at heart. He loved the search for a fundamental principle; not so much with his hands as with thought; not so much with his own findings as with the findings of his group. "For me to sit here and make design decisions would be the worst kind of folly," he would say. "This is a group effort. We have experts, younger men who have made a study of these things." When one of these men came up with a discovery, Eddie was on his feet with delight. "Is that true? Tell me how you found out."

Allen let his men go at it on their own and for the most part they were dedicated just as Eddie was. One noon at the hangar, some of the flight-test group were talking. "It's odd," said pilot Marvin Michael. "Did it ever occur to you that the men around Eddie Allen are all somehow the same? Don't smoke. Hardly take a drink. Earnest, clean fellows."

"It's a fact. I wonder if he picked them that way, or if it just happened?"

"I don't know," said Michael. But it brought back to him his first contact with Allen—how, when he was still in engineering school and working part time at the Stearman plant in Wichita, he had written to the famous pilot asking for advice. He'd really never expected an answer, but he got a long one. He would never forget the way Eddie began it: "Your letter interests me very much because it well expresses the grand struggle against big odds towards an achievement." What they were doing now was a struggle, but a grand struggle for achievement, Marvin Michael reflected. Their hearts were in it. It wasn't just for themselves, but something for others in time of need.

The present need was plain. The crews of the Flying Fortresses and Liberators were struggling now, under the command of General George Kenney, to help Mac-Arthur win his way back to the Philippines. Eisenhower's forces were in North Africa. Spaatz's 8th Air Force, Eaker's 8th Bomber Command, were hammering away. It was not the kind of achievement men liked, but desperately necessary. The war wasn't of their making. The job was to finish it, get free of its clutches.

Michael and many others of Eddie Allen's flight-test men were carrying on their own struggle and were enjoying it, but for one thing which the men at the hangar discussed guardedly. A strained relationship was developing in flight test. Administrative people in Eddie's office were usurping authority, playing discords in the symphony, raising tempers. Eddie didn't see or wouldn't use a reprimand. Michael pondered this problem and was concerned. At one point, when tension was highest, he talked to Eddie about it.

"I know," said Eddie, "but I'd rather let it go. I hate to hurt anyone's feelings." As the tests went on there was a growing tension over power-plant difficulties; an unspoken tension over the unsolved personnel problem; tension over the war. Frail, conscientious Eddie Allen absorbed and kept to himself the nagging pull of all three.

As flight tests continued there were more and more power-plant troubles. Aerodynamically the airplane was proving out well, but in the first twenty-six hours of flying, engines had to be changed sixteen times; carburetors were changed twenty-two times; the exhaust system had to be revised; four of the leak-proof fuel cells had developed leaks. Trouble had also developed with the controls that feathered the propeller blades into line with the wind, to stop them from windmilling in case of engine failure.

On December 30, Eddie and his crew took the second B-29 for its first flight. They were testing the propeller feathering when the alarm came. "Fire in Number Four engine!" It was the rear blister observer on the interphone. There was a shrill whine that meant the propeller was running away. Eddie turned quickly to the flight engineer. "Feather Number Four." It wouldn't feather. "Fire extinguisher." Smoke and sparks were streaking from the exhaust stack. Gears in the propeller gave way and slowed the wild windmilling, but the fire was getting worse, gouts of burning oil streaming through the cowl flaps. "Give it another CO_2 bottle."

The extinguisher had no effect. Smoke began pouring into the cockpit through the bomb bay. Crew members were coughing and choking, their eyes smarting. Flames were trailing in long fingers from the nacelle access door. It was raining; visibility was poor and clouds were lowering. When they were half a mile from the field, the last CO_2 bottle was fired into the nacelle. This one seemed to smother the fire, but smoke and carbon dioxide fumes grew denser in the cabin. The landing would have to be accurate, no chance for a go-around.

Eddie skimmed over high-tension wires, felt for the end of the 5,000-foot runway, downwind. They were on the ground. Number Four engine flared up again in full fury as they rolled to a stop. A standby fire truck was there in a minute and put it out. The crew jumped from exits.

Everyone knew they were skating on thin ice with the tests after that. Eddie Allen asked himself again and again, "Should I call off the flying?" Then he would read the week's casualty lists in the war, think of how the men were crying for new equipment, how America needed the B-29. There were stacks of requests on his desk for data critically needed by engineering and the shops, by plants all over the nation. Eddie had told the Army the required two hundred hours of flying could probably be completed in four or five months. Three months were gone now and they were barely started. The testing went on.

Ira Eaker's 8th Bomber Command, by winter of 1942, was a hardened, scrappy core of combat crews. In the fall the two groups of B-17Es had been joined by a third equipped with Consolidated B-24 Liberators. These three groups and their fighter escort, on twenty-three short-range missions, claimed 104 enemy planes shot down, 108 more probably destroyed and 117 damaged. But they had learned grief, too. They had lost eighteen bombers, thirteen of them shot down by enemy fighters, five by anti-aircraft. The losses of equipment and men were not being replaced, because new forces were going to help Major General Jimmy Doolittle in the big North African campaign. In England, the cold, wet winter with its mud at the airdromes, its fog, its nightly backout bore and the silent, empty seats at the breakfast table after yesterday's raid, weighed heavily.

Ira Eaker was wearying of small hits at nearby targets along the Channel. "If we can get the equipment, we can knock Germany out of the war from the air," he said. "By destroying Hitler's factories we can put an end to his air force. By destroying his munitions plants and communications we can stop his armies." But every week Hitler was building stronger defenses. Now was the time to mount a gigantic air offensive, Eaker felt.

"You haven't yet tested the defenses over Germany itself," British officers cautioned. "Those targets are impregnable by daylight." The old issue. The crisis came at Casablanca where the Allied High Command was gathered in January 1943. Hap Arnold summoned Eaker there. "I'm sorry to have to tell you this," Arnold said, "but the President has agreed to give Churchill our bombers for night bombing."

It hit Eaker like a Messerschmitt head-on. For a fraction of a second he reeled, then caught fire. It was wrong, dead wrong. The Forts weren't designed for night bombing. They *could* do the job by day. Eaker knew military discipline, but he'd have to fight this decision, even if it cost him his job. "Our planes aren't night bombers," he said. "Our crews aren't trained for night bombing. The losses will be much higher. It's a tragic decision and I won't be a party to it. And I reserve the right to tell the American people at the appropriate time why I quit."

"If you feel that strongly about it," said Arnold, "I'll arrange for you to talk to the Prime Minister."

Eaker had the feeling that Hap Arnold was glad he'd spoken out as he did. He received a message: "The Prime Minister will be waiting for you at his villa." Eaker had come to know Churchill in England. He went promptly.

"General Arnold tells me it has been decided to turn our bombers over to night bombing," Eaker told the Prime Minister. "I think this is a great mistake. I've been in England long enough to know that you would want to hear both sides."

Churchill smiled. "Sit down." Eaker handed the Prime Minister a single sheet of paper on which he had written the case for daylight bombing. Churchill read it. Near the bottom Eaker heard him mumble audibly, "Around the clock." It was the place where he'd said that with the British bombing by night, and the Americans by day, they'd give the Germans no rest, bomb them around the clock. Churchill looked up. "I took this action because I have a strong feeling against your losing your young men," he said. "Your losses are greater than ours. You haven't convinced me, but you have convinced me that you should have an opportunity to prove that you can do this. When I see the President at lunch, I'll recommend that we do this."

In the House of Parliament, Winston Churchill stood up to deliver his report on Casablanca. Eaker had been sent a ticket to the balcony. There was an ovation for the great British leader. He began stating the decisions that had been reached. Then he announced that the Americans would continue their daylight bombing. "The British will bomb at night and the Americans by day," said the Prime Minister, glancing up at the balcony. "We shall bomb these devils around the clock."

It was a grey day in Seattle. The twenty or so department heads and officers who constituted the Boeing executive staff were gathered on February 18, 1943, in the board room for the weekly meeting. Phil Johnson sat at the end of the table. Executive vice president Oliver West was reporting on production. One hundred seventy-six Fortresses would be delivered this month; in May the rate would reach two hundred. The telephone rang in the anteroom. Ed Wells slipped out to answer it. He reappeared at the door, face ashen. "The tower just got a message from Eddie. They're coming in with a wing on fire."

The meeting broke up. Sirens were wailing on the field. No airplane coming in. Then, to the north, a great column of black smoke. There was the dash for cars, the traffic jam, the police guard, the firemen shooting water at the blazing four-story Frye meat-packing plant.

"The plane's in there."

Out of the tragic confusion came the news: Eddie and all eleven of the crew lost, and nineteen Frye employees.

Piecing the story together was like fitting the parts of an eggshell. It was already empty. An engine had caught fire south of the field. They had put it out with CO_2 on the way in. Eddie had elected to swing around for a safe landing from the north. Then a second fire broke out. A magnesium part burned and dropped, burning holes in the lower skin, and this ventilated the fire to the fuel tanks just when Eddie must have thought it was controlled. They were too low to jump. They didn't quite make the north end of the field.

Eddie Allen's "grand struggle" ended, but not his achievement. A memorial went up just south of Plant Two. It was something that had been dear to Eddie's heart, something important to the future— "The Edmund T. Allen Wind Tunnel and Aeronautical Research Laboratories."

10

While all Boeing was trying to recover from its loss of Eddie Allen, his crew and the B-29, all the Air Force was likewise mightily concerned. A new program of installing fire stops was laid down, and K. B. Wolfe talked sternly to the power-plant manufacturers, who protested that they, too, had been developing their product under war pressure. Everyone knew it was a crisis for the B-29 program. There could be only one solution because commitments had gone too far. Jake Harman went to General Wolfe. "How about a special department to take over all aspects of the 29 program, production, experimental, test flying, training, combat? Get the ships into action at the earliest date. You'd be the man to lead it."

"If you'll work with me on it. . . . Let's go and talk to Washington about it," said K. B.

With a directive that would require Hap Arnold's signature, they headed for Washington. The idea seemed to make more sense every mile of the way. It would revive the morale in the B-29 effort: a red streak program to get the 29 ready for combat; a special B-29 Air Force, under the direction of Hap Arnold himself, that could be dispatched on long-range missions anywhere in the world; an independent, self-sufficient force that would operate from secret advance bases. From China. . . .

Oliver Echols said he'd approve it. Wolfe and Harman

went down the hall to Hap Arnold's office. K. B. laid the paper on Arnold's desk and waited. Arnold read it and slapped his desk. "Fine. Why doesn't somebody else do something for me once in a while?"

"You like it, General?" Harman asked.

"I've got to see about this. Where are you staying? I'll call you."

That night they got a call at the hotel. "Someone wants to talk with you. Be careful what you say." Then Hap Arnold came on. "Project approved. Go back home and prepare a presentation. Bring it back as soon as you can. Plan it for you-know-where."

"You-know-where" was China. Arnold had seen General Marshall. The days ahead were maps, training bases, operating bases, logistics. The President would make arrangements with Great Britain and India, make a deal with Chiang Kai-shek to build secret B-29 bases in China. Meanwhile, the airplanes. . . .

K. B. Wolfe and Jake Harman went to Seattle, armed with a superseding authority, bursting with plans known only to themselves, Hap Arnold and a few others. The fixes had been made on the second B-29, fire stops and all. Harman would be the test pilot. Check lists and counter check lists were drawn. "Don't even think of the possibility of losing this one. That would end all."

May 29, 1943, ground testing was under way: brakes, acceleration, propeller governing. The last pre-flight item was to get off the ground far enough to check flight controls, see that they were adjusted right, then everything would be set for a flight the next day. K. B. Wolfe, Phil Johnson and Beall were in Johnson's corner office. Harman came down the field in the B-29.

"He's going to go this time," Beall said.

The engines had that positive roar. K. B. and Johnson were at the windows. Everyone else in the Administration building was at the windows by now. The wheels came up. Then—what? The right wing was going down. They were banking steeply. They had no altitude. The plane staggered crazily down the fence line, behind a building row, out of sight. A cloud of dust. The three men tore out of the room white-faced.

Not till they got down the highway could they see that the airplane was there on the runway, safe and sound. The Jake Harman who climbed out of it was a man shaken and puzzled.

"What in the world happened?" asked K. B. Wolfe.

"I don't know. I gave it the antidote . . . cut the left engines, gave full power on the right engines, both of them. Flaps were half down. It just kind of righted up and I chopped everything and there we were. Damn quick, boy."

"You're sure the aileron controls are right?"

"I don't know."

They looked. The aileron control cables were reversed over the pulley. Harman saw Phil Johnson's eyes snap.

"For God's sake, don't fire anybody," Harman said. "Because it was really my fault. It was written right there in front of me to check."

There was an investigation for sabotage, but it was inconclusive. Harman flew the plane. It was made ready to be taken to Wichita, where a Kansas prairie was now transformed into a war plant teeming with twenty-five thousand employees, already completing their first B-29.

The lesson of the reversed aileron cables dug sharply into the subconsciousness of every inspector, every assembly mechanic, every one of the 33,000 employees in the Seattle and Renton plants.

Plant Two at Seattle had become an amazing 1,500,000 square feet of B-17 production density. There were row upon row of chopped-off sections of bodies and wings, each alive with riveters and installation mechanics, some men, but mostly women in slacks. Aisles between the body and wing jigs were streets of clattering commerce, with stop-and-go intersections preventing a traffic tangle of the fork trucks, the flat beds, the long trains of carts carrying parts. Overhead, the little orange cabs of the railway of cranes were constantly bringing down sub-assemblies from the balcony behind, and leapfrogging Fortress body sections over each other to the final assembly area.

Two years ago no one would have believed that that space now would be turning out two hundred Flying Fortresses a month. Or that it would be turning out two hundred a month with fewer employees than there were a year before when the company was proud of its one hundred a month. Or that Executive Vice President Oliver West could sit with his charts and predict three hundred a month a year from then, still with the same number of employees. The "learning curve" on that chart showed convincingly that they were learning how to mass-produce.

Most any of the women wearing the little Army-Navy "E" for Excellence pins would say there was a reason they were learning so fast, a reason close to their heart. He was somewhere on the sands of North Africa, or maybe hitting the beach of Sicily, or in one of Ira Eaker's bombers over Germany.

On Pacific isles, sands of Africa, siren-ruled streets of Europe, war was searing the globe. Epicenter of the storm and fire was Adolf Hitler's *Festung Europa*—Fortress Europe. Hitler hadn't envisioned it just this way. His eye had been grim-set on victory. Superiority, surprise, victory. Hitler had taken inspiration from the past—the days of conquest, empires of Charlemagne and Frederick the Great. When he planned his war he and his generals had raised their sights high enough to see the air force as a preface to swift ground attack, until he had met the unexpected in the Battle of Britain. The RAF had destroyed his bomber force.

Again Hitler looked back. If he couldn't destroy England by air, no one could destroy his *Festung Europa* by air. He could raise, in air defense, twenty or thirty times the strength of the RAF that saved England. Let the Allies come with their bombers. He'd destroy them in the air. He wouldn't waste effort building any more bombers to hit England. The scientists were developing pilotless rockets that could do that later. For now he'd build only fighters—three thousand a month by the end of 1944. When he had destroyed the attacking air force, he would be safe from land invasion.

American leaders looked at what must be done. The issue was drawn at Casablanca: the attacking Allied air forces versus the German defending air force. The British would be going in nightly to area-bomb cities. But there was only one way to destroy the German air force: engage it in combat and destroy the factories that were producing it. The German air industry and its supporting elements became the first priority target in the spring of 1943. Everyone knew what that meant.

Ira Eaker looked at his equipment for the job. A few hundred heavy bombers—Flying Fortresses and Liberators. The Forts had the better high-altitude performance. Those tedious months of work in Seattle with the first turbo-superchargers and Eddie Allen's high-altitude research were important now. Anti-aircraft lost fifty per cent of its accuracy with each 5,000 feet above 15,000. The Forts had the better pilot visibility and stability for close-formation flying, and the tighter the formation, the better the defense against fighters. Those months of wind-tunnel and flight-test research that gave the B-17 a dorsal fin and a whole new tail-surface design were important now.

The Liberator, on the other hand, had the longer range. It was better suited for the long runs in from bases in North Africa. Each plane for the job it best fitted. It would be the B-17 for the main assault. Flying Fortress against Fortress Europe.

The stern work began. In June 1943, 257 Forts hit a synthetic rubber plant at Huls in the Ruhr Valley. Twenty Forts were lost, but forty-seven German fighters were knocked down. Other strikes followed. The last week in July was the big test—sixteen targets to be bombed, among them the Focke-Wulf fighter plants at Warnemünde and Oschersleben. In the fierce battles of that week eighty-four Flying Fortresses were lost, but

296 enemy fighters were claimed shot down. In August Ira Eaker, now commanding the 8th Air Force, laid the next mission problem before Brigadier General Fred Anderson, heading the 8th Bomber Command. "We've got to get at the Messerschmitt plants. Are you ready for it?"

Anderson looked at the targets file. Messerschmitt fighters were built in three big industrial complexes at Leipzig and Regensburg, deep in Germany, and Wiener-Neustadt in Austria. On the way to Regenburg was the big ball-bearing words at Schweinfurt, another key target. "I have 380 B-17s operative," said Anderson. "Less than half of them have wing-tip tanks. We could send LeMay's 3rd Division to Regensburg and on to North Africa, and send the 1st Division to Schweinfurt the same day. I think that's our best chance. Give them all the strength we've got. It'll be a battle all the way in and out."

On a deep penetration like this the range of fighter aircraft would permit escort only part of the way. They'd be mostly on their own. But the Regensburg plant produced thirty percent of all the Messerschmitt fighters, and the Schweinfurt plant half of Germany's ball-bearings. To put them out commission was worth a tremendous effort. Germany knew that also, and had located anti-aircraft and fighter strips all along the 450-mile path. "We'll give 'em a birthday present. August 17 is the anniversary of our first raid on Rouen," said Anderson.

The thousand-sided project of planning a mission began—this one the biggest, the most critical yet attempted. Weather was the big "if": weather over English airdromes, over the target, over landing strips in North Africa. On August 16 the weather officer said conditions over the continent and over the Mediterranean the next day would be the best they'd had in two weeks. It wasn't clearing up much over England, but he thought they could get off.

"We'd better take it while we can," said Eaker. Teletype operators began clicking out the yard-long orders to the divisions. Divisions began translating it into instructions for groups.

At an airdrome in East Anglia a teletype machine was beginning its authoritative chatter. "We're takin' a long ride tomorrow," said the major, watching it. "Tell the men to pack toothbrushes and a change of underwear." The bustle in headquarters, the ground-crew chores around the airplanes, the speculation among the combat crews began. "Where to this time?" "How's *Portia*'s Number Three engine?" "Better get some shut-eye." No one voiced the thought that was deepest in his mind.

At 0015 hours a jeep starting out from the motor pool broke the night stillness of the station. Its thin blue headlights came down the perimeter road, up to a Nissen hut where the Intelligence officer was sleeping. "You're wanted at headquarters."

There was that damp, low overcast in the air, that familiar acrid smell of coal smoke, the sound of a patrol plane overhead. Through the double blackout doors at headquarters, the brightness of the light was blinding at first. The duty officer was at the big wall map. He turned to the Intelligence officer. "I've pulled out the target files for you. Regensburg." Across Germany, up the Danube River, off in a valley, an oblong group of factory building: Regensburg.

Motor pool was coming alive now, cooks getting up. The Old Man was at headquarters, staring long at the map. At 0300 combat crews were reaching for their gear, climbing into it. Not much talk. The truck for the mess hall was outside. At 0400 they were filling out the benches of the briefing room, pulses quickening. Up front the Old Man stood: Colonel Archie Old, Jr., thirty-six years old, commander of the 96th Group. "We're hitting the Messerschmitt plant at Regensburg today. Anyone here who doesn't like ME-109s staring him in the face, let's get rid of the place that builds them. We land in Algeria." There were hums and low whistles.

The Intelligence officer spelled out the target information. The weather officer took the stand. The flak officer pointed out anti-aircraft batteries along the way: "Stick close to your course and you'll be out of range of most of it." They got the assembly point for circling into combat formation, the IP—the Initial Point of the target bomb run, route details. Daylight was approaching.

The flying control officer: "Let's check watches. Ten seconds before 0517 . . . five seconds . . . four . . . three . . . two . . . one . . . hack."

The chaplain: "God be with you."

Colonel Old would lead off the 3rd Division unless Colonel LeMay, the commander, elected to go along. Back in division headquarters thirty-seven-year-old Curtis LeMay, a man whose thought, action and being could be summarized in the one word "duty," was biting a cigar. Weather was still marginal, worse than marginal at 1st Division bases where the mission to Schweinfurt was scheduled to follow them by ten minutes, and at Fighter Command bases. Bomber Command phoned that they might have to hold. LeMay's eyes were set under his unwrinkled forehead and thick black hair. He knew his men could get up through the stuff for the division assembly. He had been drilling them on instrument take-offs. Things didn't get done by putting them off. He called General Anderson at Bomber Command. "We'll get in the air and hold over Lowestoft. We'll have to depart there by 0930, to make North Africa before dark. Give us the code word by radio, if it's all right to go."

At the 96th Group base the mist of morning was a multi-motored rumble. The first shadowy form of a Fortress moved out from its dispersal point, then another and another, nose to tail around the perimeter track. They queued up with propellers flailing the air. Seconds and minutes ticked off on the sweep hand of the control-tower clock and on wristwatches of bundled, squat crews in the planes. Minus five minutes, minus four, three. "Guess LeMay isn't coming," said Colonel Archie Old. "Are we all set?" Minus two.

A staff car drove up. The stocky LeMay stepped out. "Hello, Archie. You take Number Two plane. I'll go in Number One." LeMay climbed aboard. In the cockpit pilot and co-pilot snapped to attention, started to get up.

"Stay where you are," said LeMay. "I'll stand right here between you."

Number One plane moved down the runway, into the air, Old in Number Two, thirty seconds behind it. Another thirty seconds and Number Three was airborne. Precisionlike, the chain continued, one plane lifting from the runway end while the next was midway down it and another was starting. LeMay trailed smoke candles out of the lead plane, first time they'd tried that, to help assemble the formation in bad weather.

Grouping together 96th Group assembled with 94th Group from its station. The 100th came up from another direction, 390th, 95th, 385th, 388th—a great circling chain, adjusting, falling into places—the planes in each squadron arranging themselves into the three-dimensional wedge that offered a crisscross of gunfire; the squadrons arranging themselves into lead, high and low positions; groups arranging themselves into lead, high and low groups for a combat wing, a great wall of fire power; three combat wings lining up six miles behind each in a thirteen-mile chain, 126 planes in all. The groups were using a tightened formation that LeMay had perfected earlier, when the Germans had found they couldn't stand the rearward fire of the Forts and had begun concentrating on the difficult head-on attack.

"Flying Fortress" took on a new meaning, not an airplane now but a tremendous flying force, half a mile high, half a mile wide. A Flying Fortress with a thousand gun turrets winging to attack Fortress Europe.

It was 0930 at Bomber Command, the zero hour for decision. First Division, which was supposed to leave for Schweinfurt ten minutes after the departure of Third, to divide enemy strength, couldn't get off maybe for an hour, maybe two, because of weather. Escort fighters couldn't get off. Third Division, in the air, couldn't be delayed and still make Africa before dark. The question was as heavy as the 315-ton load of bombs now ranging overhead. Send LeMay's planes on alone or abort the whole mission? All the preparation; the critical impor-

tance of the target; the climax of a year's buildup. . . .
Eyes shut tight; it was a decision that hurt. This was war.

Over Lowestoft, England, 0935 hours, Curtis LeMay
got the green light from Fred Anderson. The circling
mass unwound behind the spear point, headed straight
over the Channel, LeMay standing motionless between
pilot and co-pilot, eyes dead ahead.

Barely inside Holland two Focke-Wulf 190s started
climbing up, noses high, strictly for business. They bored
straight through the second group, nicking the wings of
two Forts, then half rolled and dived under the third
group, guns blazing, threading through the tracers of
Fortress machine guns. The fighters were hard to get, in
this rolled-over position, because their undersides were
heavily armored. The damaged Forts held their places.
Interphones were busy. "Give 'em shorter bursts . . .
there'll be plenty more coming . . . lead your target."
Gunners breathed hard, the rubber bladders of their
oxygen masks filling and emptying with tense rhythm
under their chins.

More fighters were rising ahead, all over. From LeMay's
lead plane it was like a hawk scaring up sparrows. Reports
crackled in the interphone. "FW-190s at ten o'clock,
level."; "A whole squadron, twelve o'clock high . . .
Hold your fire till they're in range." The top turret
blasted behind LeMay's head. The whole ship was quaking with the recoil. The air was pungent with the smell
of powder. "Watch 'em. Coming up all around the clock."
Two Forts in the low squadron fell out of formation on
fire, crews bailing out. Fighters were falling from the sky.
Into it and through it, the armada moved on, straight on.

Archie Old in Number Two ship pulled out of formation with a runaway prop, fought a running battle with
eleven fighters back to the Channel. A Fortress, *My
Prayer*, went into a dive, on fire. Seven men bailed out;
the top-turret gunner, injured, parachute damaged, stayed
on and beat out the flames while the pilot got the ship out
of the dive and the co-pilot manned the guns against chasing fighters. At housetop-level they made it back to the
Channel.

LeMay stood silent at the spear point, coolly measuring the skill of German pilots in maneuvers he had been drilling his groups to combat. The triple threat: three fighters pulling ahead and then burning in head-on at eleven o'clock, twelve o'clock and one o'clock, high, breaking away at eight hundred, five hundred and three hundred yards in wing-ups and belly-up dives. The scissors movement from ten o'clock, high, one plane pulling up fast over the top of the formation, the other diving to the right from four hundred yards. The sneak attack, coming out of the sun. The swooper diving attack from six to twelve o'clock, high. The double cue coming in head-on from long lines on both sides. Roller coaster, long 3,000 yard dive from twelve o'clock, high, swooping up to a stall under the chin of the lead squadron, cannons firing, then falling off in a steep dive.

Fighters were everywhere, pulled from fields in all directions and evidently refuelling and coming back up. The battle was unceasing. An hour, two hours, moving always onward in roaring sky, punctured by falling airplanes, screaming dives, blossoming yellow parachutes.

From the Third Combat Wing at the rear of the column, the scene ahead was an inferno. White tracer streaks crisscrossing the sky. Flak puffs hanging everywhere. Racing fighters with cannon belching from their wings. Parts and pieces in the air. Shattering noise. A door coming by in the air. A man hurtling past, doubled up in a rolling ball. Fighters lobbing in rockets. The Germans were throwing in everything they had.

Still on, entering the third hour, Curtis LeMay stood motionless, twentieth-century gladiator at the forward post of his bucking chariot, churning on through flak and fighters, leading his thirteen-mile battle fleet relentlessly to its objective, Regensburg.

"We're over our IP," called the navigator. "Bombardier taking over." They locked into Automatic Flight Control's iron groove for the approach. "Bombs away." The bombs fell true in the target rectangle. A quick right-angle turn to the south, with less enemy fighters following now—the Germans weren't expecting bombers this far inland—and the new course was set toward the majestic peaks of the Alps. North of Brenner Pass LeMay circled for stragglers, trued up the formations. No attacking fighters now, only speculation over remaining fuel supply. One ship, definitely running short, headed off for a crash landing in Spain. Another, *Pregnant Portia*, engines failing, got its silent, praying crew as far as the Mediterranean where all ten men hung tight on a five-man raft through the night, finally to be sighted by a B-26 and taken ashore by British Air-Sea Rescue. The airmen from the missing *Portia* occupied ten seats in a North African church the next Sunday.

The 1st Division had been three and a half hours late getting off on its mission the same day for Schweinfurt and had to battle all the way in and out. Out of the 376 planes dispatched on the two August 17 missions, sixty were lost to enemy action. "Sure, we had losses," said LeMay. "But the Germans had losses, too." The Germans lost 288 fighters in the combat, crews claimed, as well as a Messerschmitt factory which had been producing 250 ME-109s a month—30 percent of German fighter production—and a good part of the nation's ball-bearing production.

It was grim. Up to now U.S. losses had averaged five percent of planes dispatched. At that rate five raids a month would wipe out the bomber force in four months, without replacements. This day's loss was sixteen percent. Five more days like it would wipe them out. Washington was alarmed. But there was no doubt that the bombing was effective. Germany was desperate. "Keep hitting them," was the order of the day at Bomber Command. "The faster we come back at them, the faster we'll get the job done."

It took time to patch up the planes and reorganize the combat crews. More planes were arriving from the States. Through September they flew simpler missions. By October they were ready for a big week's offensive. A record 399 planes went out October 8, hit Bremen and other targets. Thirty were lost. Next day a force of 357 planes hit targets as far east as Danzig and ninety-six of them—Le-May's men—bombed Marienburg, two hundred miles east of Berlin. Unexpected this far east they hit Marienburg from 11,000 feet, destroying the Focke-Wulf plant without touching the adjacent prison camp. Climax of the week was a second raid on Schweinfurt, on October 14, by 291 planes of the 1st and 3rd Divisions. Colonel Archie Old, who didn't get to bomb Regensburg, led the 3rd Division.

It was another battle like the last one. After the fighter escort left them at Aachen, Germany, it was combat all the way, against a force totalling seven hundred enemy fighters. On the target approach the flak and the fighter onslaught were appalling. Old, in the right-hand seat of the lead plane, could see thirteen fighters converging on his plane. There was an incredible wall of flak ahead. They couldn't deviate with the ship now on the automatic flight-control equipment.

"You mean we've got to fly *through* it?" asked the top gunner. Forward in the plexiglas nose, some of the flak hit Bombardier Latham in the stomach. He doubled and fell. Navigator Hodson picked him up, set him back in place over the bombsight. "Hit that target."

Latham did. "Bombs away," he whispered. They banked and turned to the right. Fifteen or twenty fighters shot toward them, got the two inboard engines. Both engines started burning. Old signalled Number Two plane to take the lead. Five or six enemy fighters took after the crippled plane as Old went into a sixty-degree dive from 22,000 feet to broken clouds at 4,000. He levelled off and feathered the two burning engines. Number Three wouldn't feather completely. The fighters kept attacking. They got Hodson, the navigator. Lieutenant Jones took Hodson's place. Then he was wounded.

For two hours there were three to twelve fighters pumping shells at them in relays as they skipped through low clouds. A lot of those fighters didn't get back. Bombardier Lathan was wounded again. Losing altitude badly Old unfeathered Number Two engine and got it started. It started burning again. He tried Number Three till it, too, began to burn, then went back to Number Two. Alternating between the two damaged engines, they stayed in the air. Old called crew stations on the interphone: "Tail gunner, are you O.K.?"

"I'm O.K."

"Waist gunners?" Every other man was wounded. Old had a 20-mm. shell fragment lodged in one hand.

The clouds got worse—no visibility at all. They were losing altitude. "Throw out everything," Old ordered. Even then they could barely maintain flight on two engines. There was nothing now but thick soup, struggling Fortress, and fervent prayer.

Fuel was running out when they broke free into sunshine and sight of the English coast. They made it to an RAF field at Gravesend. Fire started in the wing when they let down the landing gear. Everything was shot up, gaping holes from cannon shells all over the ship, between them the sieve that was left where flak pieces had gone through. The brakes were useless. Fire trucks overtook them while they were still rolling, pouring on foamite. They stopped twenty feet from the fence. Archie Old, weak and dripping, thumped the control column with his one good hand. "Baby, you wouldn't let us down."

At stations throughout England, the night of October 14, 1943, Intelligence officers debriefed weary men. They claimed 186 enemy fighters shot down in the sky battle. The target was hit squarely. On the other side of the ledger sixty more B-17s and crews were lost, 138 ships damaged—even worse than the anniversary raids of August 17. Twenty percent of the planes dispatched were gone.

A shocked Washington cried out. "Were the British right? Is the cost of daylight bombing prohibitive?" Congressmen descended on Hap Arnold with demands for an explanation. Arnold countered: "We finished off Schweinfurt, half of Germany's vital ball-bearing industry." But Arnold, too, was alarmed.

11

Everything was being done that anyone could think of to give the B-17 more protection. More engineers were on the Flying Fortress now than there had ever been in the eight-year history of the series. Changes were being pumped into the production lines and into finished planes at modification centers as fast as those engineers, the company's field service engineers with the combat forces and the Air Matériel Command at Wright Field could work up new ideas to meet the changing pattern of war. So many guns had been stuck in the nose that gunners were getting in each other's way. In the next model, the B-17G, a powered forward turret was being added under the nose.

Hap Arnold knew all this, but Wellwood Beall, summoned to Arnold's office, reminded him. "We have the chin turret coming along."

"It ought to be coming faster."

"If there's anything we can do, we want to do it."

"After Schweinfurt everyone on the Hill has been jumping on me," said Arnold. "We've got to cut down our losses. Go over there yourself and get a first-hand picture. I'll get you a priority."

Two weeks later Beall's cab took him to 8th Air Force headquarters. Ira Eaker was glad to see him, gave him the picture in a hurry. They had found out two things. If

they had enough B-17s en masse, they could get through
to any target and they could hit the target. But they were
going to have to cut down on the deepest penetrations
until they could get longer-range fighters for escort.
"The old dogma that you can't have a fighter with the
range of a bomber is out," said Eaker. "Long-range fighters are what we need right now." Beall recalled that Ira
Eaker was once a fighter man. Monk Hunter, head of the
8th Air Force Fighter Command, was adding tanks to his
P-47s and P-38s and would soon be getting the long-
range P-51s. It took teamwork to win a war.

Beall asked the general: "What can we do to make
these buggies do a better job for you?" Eaker told him to
talk to the men at the bomber stations, so Beall made the
rounds with his service engineers who were close to the
operating crews. On his way to his hotel through the
blacked-out streets of London, Beall saw a huge flash.
There was a rocking explosion a block away. He hurried
toward it. A two-story brick building was laid open, the
middle of it a heap of timbers with men and women
stumbling out, others crying, "Help," and moaning in the
darkness. A fire was breaking out next door. Beall
helped an elderly lady to a first-aid post. "Oh," she was
saying, "there are dozens of people buried under there."
Home Guard rescue squads came into the chaos to form
human chains over the debris, bearing out on stretchers
those who were alive.

One lone dive-bomber had done it. "What are our
fleets of bombers doing to Germany?" Beall thought, and
shuddered. *If we have enough B-17s we can get through
to any target,* Ira Eaker had said. What would they do to
Germany with the thousands of new Forts now in production, long-range fighters for protection, thousands of
tons of TNT to drop with precision? War was frightful.
In war you had better have the best equipment.

America had learned that when caught in war you'll
ride to success or defeat in the equipment already developed, not something new and too late. The Flying Fortress was seven years old when the nation entered war,

but it was the framework on which America depended, through eight successive models, for its aerial offense against Hitler in Europe.

The B-29 Superfortress, designed two years before Pearl Harbor, was too late for the war in Europe, and only by putting it in production before testing of a prototype, only by forcing it at every turn, was it possible to make it ready for war in the Pacific. The strategic bombardment in Europe had shown what could be done, but the timetable in the Pacific right now looked much slower than the one in Europe. There were the tremendous distances, the ground and water, to be won back.

The heroic assault on Guadalcanal was at once a preview of the grief ahead and the promise of its success, but no one would predict how many years it might take. How long could a nation stand all-out war? The B-29 Superfortress, subject of ever-mounting pressure, still having its trouble with engines and equipment, was still the white hope and the great need.

In November 1943, at Cairo, Chiang Kai-shek told President Roosevelt he would have B-29 bases ready in South China by April 1944. The President said the U.S. Army Air Force would be there to use them. In December Hap Arnold sent K. B. Wolfe to India to begin setting the stage for the B-29 strikes at Japan. K. B. left Brigadier General Blondie Saunders behind, with Colonel Harman and Colonel Tommy Chapman as wing commanders, to organize the crews that would take the Superforts into action.

Boeing-Wichita, with 29,000 farm hands, housewives and shopkeepers turned airplane builders, had gotten its first Superfortress in the air in June 1943. Arnold had set 175 B-29s as the starting minimum for the 20th Bomber Command. Equipment makers and parts builders throughout the country were involved in the production blitz, many of them, too, producing ahead of full test of their equipment. Engine deliveries were slow. There was a shortage of steel.

Hap Arnold came out to the Wichita plant to see how his 175th Superfortress was coming along. He found its body section just entering final assembly. "This is the plane I want," said Hap. "I want it before the first of March."

The 175th Superfortress—*General Arnold Special*—was rolled out of the Wichita plant on February 28 and rushed to a modification center. At the Kansas bases few of the planes were in flying condition. Crates of parts were coming in from all over with new combat equipment ordered to go into the ships. Flight training was lagging for want of airplanes. Saunders and Harman were trying to organize combat crews. Most of them were men with B-17 experience in England. The B-29 was a big, strange airplane compared to the 17. The pilots didn't like the windshield. Gunners were trying to get onto the centralized fire control. The radar bombing system was baffling. Everything was so technical a crew man had to have seven experts to consult. The men were uneasy.

So was Hap Arnold who had promised the planes would leave for China and India on March 10, 1944. On March 9, Arnold flew to Salina air base. "How many planes are ready to go?" he asked.

"None," said the base. "We can't get the parts."

"What? I want to know where every missing part is by tomorrow morning," blazed the chief. A barrage of telegrams went out. A week later still no planes were ready. The critical need was for technicians. General Orval Cook, production division head, flew to Wichita on March 17 and called Earl Schaefer, the general manager. "I'm at the airport. Come over right away. I want you to go up to Salina with me. We've got to find some way to cut these 29s loose."

Half an hour later they stepped into the cold blast of the wind at Salina and climbed into a B-29 where mechanics were working.

"Here's what I've still got to do," said a distraught crew chief, looking at his list. "Change the flap switch link, fix the emergency relief tank, change the flux gate compass transmitter, the side sighting dome, recalibrate the fuel gauges, fix the rudder tail rib, tail skid actuators, tail turret stops." Another ship was the same story. Another.

"Can you give us a storm crew of five or six hundred mechanics to help push this through?" General Cook asked Schaefer.

"How soon?"

"Today. Hap Arnold says come hell or high water the last plane has got to leave by April 15." Schaefer knew what this would do to his production. But he knew, too, what it would mean to send faulty equipment into battle. "You have the transportaion ready and we'll have the men in four hours," he said. Next day the six hundred were climbing stepladders around the planes in driving sleet and snow, wearing 20th Bomber Command high-altitude flying suits for protection, pitching into the Battle of Kansas.

Beall came out from Seattle and caught it from Colonel Bill Irvine, who was in charge. "What's the matter with your wiring diagrams for these planes?" Irvine asked. "Nothing works. You push a radio switch and the bomb doors come open."

"Let's have a look." Beall found the wiring had been changed at two different modification centers. "No one knows what they've got in the ship now," said the electrical foreman. "We just have to trace it through."

For four weeks the Battle of Kansas went on. Gradually order came out of chaos. Combat crews were piling their duffels and equipment aboard while the mechanics were still working. Earl Schaefer watched one day. There seemed no end to material going aboard. "How heavy are you loading these?" he asked.

"A hundred thirty-five thousand."

"A hundred and thirty-five thousand? Do you know the maximum gross is 120,000?"

"Yeah, we know. Your maximum on the B-17 was 48,-000. We flew at 60,000 all the time in England." This was war. The planes were loaded to 135,000, then to 140,000 pounds.

At one o'clock on a morning late in March Colonel Jake Harman emerged from the operations building at Pratt in flying togs and parachute harness. There was snap in his step. He hoisted himself into a B-29 and took off into the night. The first Superfortress was India-bound. During the next two weeks a secret fleet followed his path to Morocco, to Cairo, to Kharagpur, where K. B. Wolfe, commanding general of the 20th Bomber Command, was waiting.

The continent was strange, the people were strange. Short runways and the 120-degree temperatures of India brought new problems. Engines were overheated and overtaxed. There were spare-parts shortages. Then there was the long haul over the Himalayas. Every bomb, every gallon of fuel that they would need in China had to be hauled over that Hump. "Butch" Blanchard, Saunders' deputy, flew the first plane over. The temperatures of all four engines went up to 290 degrees.

"Let's just hope they hold together," said his worried flight engineer. They got away with it. In the weeks that the B-29s were tankers and freighters, the 20th Bomber Command learned more about how to operate the engines and the cowl flaps for better cooling. But the men weren't learning gunnery, formation flying, radar bombing.

June 5 was the date for the first shakedown mission, to bomb railroad yards at Bangkok. They would fly in loose formation and use radar bomb-sighting. They'd take off from the India bases.

Jake Harman led off at 0545. Ninety-eight planes followed from fields in the Kharagpur area. One crashed on takeoff. Fourteen turned back with equipment difficulties. The rest winged out over the Bay of Bengal at 5,000 feet, and five hours after takeoff were climbing in four-plane elements to 25,000 feet for the bomb run over the Gulf of Thailand to a cloud-covered target. Some of the elements didn't get together, due to the clouds. There wasn't much enemy opposition—moderate flak, but inaccurate. The crews had to make repeated runs to get their bombs away, coming in from all angles at miscellaneous altitudes before they were through.

Then came the long flight back. Fuel was running low over the Bay of Bengal when they sighted something ahead that the weather forecasters hadn't given them—a vertical cloud bank that was black as night. Typhoon. Some of the crews headed into it, guessing it would be short and intense. They took a terrific shaking and came out the other side. Others tried to go under. Dirt and debris and the roofs of huts were in the air at 4,000 feet. Two planes ditched in the bay.

All that night and the next day K. B. Wolfe was rounding up his pack from fields all over India. The crews that ditched were rescued. They'd learned that the B-29 ditched well. That news, at least, was a comfort to the men.

Wolfe got an urgent message from Hap Arnold on June 6. The Joint Chiefs of Staff wanted an attack on Japan to relieve pressure on an "important operation" in the Pacific. Wolfe suspected that the "important operation" was the naval assault on Saipan. Washington picked the steel works at Yawata as the target and ordered a night mission with planes navigating individually, believing the 3,200-mile round trip from the China bases would take too much fuel to allow formation flying.

The mission was set for the night of June 15, 1944. Jake Harman, who was to lead the flight, was having trouble with his engines. "Better take another plane," K. B. advised him.

"I've been flying this one all along. I feel at home in it. It'll be O.K."

On the morning of June 15, the men were briefed. "Tonight we begin the organized destruction of the Japanese industrial empire," K. B. Wolfe told them. K. B. was set to go along in the lead plane with Jake. Then an order came that commanding generals should no longer go on missions.

At 1616, sixty-eight Superfortresses began taking off from hand-made runways near Chengtu for the big test. The flight started out comfortably enough. A well-soundproofed airplane, pressurized, slipping along at 230 miles an hour—the speed for best range. Jake Harman thought of all the effort that had gone to make this possible. He thought back to the days of the old Keystone

bombers, the first B-9 monoplane bomber, the revolutionary Model 299 Flying Fortress, and now he was in
the Superfortress, the weapon built for victory. They
were really on their way. He wondered if the enemy
knew it.

All the crews were wondering about this, too, and
other things. There were hours of mounting tension in
the darkness that spelled uncertainty. Three of the planes
had trouble and had to turn back. A thousand miles out
one of Harman's engines sputtered and quit. Jake looked
at the flight engineer who shook his head. Jake coaxed
the throttle. This couldn't happen to him now. This was
the big event he had lived for, planned and worked for.
He was leaning forward in the pilot's seat, coaxing the
big plane. Then another engine began to falter and lose
power. He fussed frantically with the controls. His fist
came down across his lap.

"We'll have to go back," said the flight engineer.

At Chengtu airbase, K. B. Wolfe, pacing the tiny operations building, passed one hand over the top of his head
in an unconscious echo of the days when he had hair
there to smooth down. He wished mightily that he could
be up there over the Yellow Sea with those B-29s. Instead,
he waited—waited for just one code word: "Betty"
would mean a successful mission. Six hours, seven hours.
"They should be getting close." Seven hours, five minutes; eight minutes.

Colonel Blanchard burst in from the radio room. "It's
Betty over the target!"

K. B. let out a great long breath.

The wait for the returning planes was as bad as the
wait during the outbound trip. Jake Harman got back
first, long-faced. Wolfe gave him the good news. Harman grunted. He just went around shaking his head and
hitting his fist on everything he came to.

The rest of the planes began to come in. The men were
tired but happy. "We saw sixteen fighters, but most of
them never got a shot. There were a million searchlights.
A lot of flak came up, but it went behind us. They never

got our speed." A few of the planes were damaged by the flak, but none was shot down. Navigating back over China with no radio aid, however, had been a strain and a trial. Three of the ships got lost and crash-landed, or ran into mountains. Still, in military terms, the losses were light.

Recon photos showed the bombing accuracy on the Yawata mission was only fair. Radar was still a tricky thing. But the men knew now what they could do. That was the big thing. Later missions stirred up greater enemy opposition. But most of the Nipponese pilots were wary of the Superforts' guns and stayed out of range.

In July Hap Arnold cabled K. B. that he was needed back home to ride herd on the soaring B-29 production program. Blondie Saunders assumed command. On August 29, Major General Curtis LeMay arrived in China to head the 20th Bomber Command. LeMay protested against the order that had kept Wolfe and Saunders from flying on missions. "I've got to go along or I'll never know what I'm up against," he insisted. Hap Arnold finally consented. LeMay came home from a raid on Anshan, September 8, to announce: "We're going to learn how to put more bombs on the target. We'll do it by daylight. They won't stop us."

America in the summer of 1944 had gone through two and a half years of war. The "arsenal of democracy" had poured forth a torrent of production, feeding a furious new assault by Ira Eaker's bombers on the strategic targets of Germany, sending soldiers in lashing waves upon embattled Italy and now across France in Dwight D. Eisenhower's tidal wave of invasion.

There was a spirit for victory, a will to bore in, though bitter the cost, and get it over with. The 8th Air Force, in late February, sent out 1,000 bombers a day to break the back of the Luftwaffe. Prepared to take losses as high as 200 bombers a day, they had gotten by with 137 lost in six days. That was still a mighty cost in lives and equipment, but the percentage of losses was going down. The weight of numbers and the improved fighter cover made the armada a fearful one for the Germans to encounter.

The 15th Air Force made coordinated attacks with B-24s from bases in Italy, and the RAF Bomber Command pelted into the same target areas through the dark hours. Fifteen hundred German fighters fell out of the air in February. Factories that accounted for ninety percent of Germany's remaining aircraft production suffered sudden havoc. In March the hub city of Berlin flinched under a rain of bombs from 660 Forts.

England was a giant flat-top loaded with new aircraft. Through summer and fall the sky over Germany was a many-fingered path of white vapor trails. The ground below was blackened wherever a pin on Bomber Command's big wall map showed another target picked off. Aircraft plants, oil industry, transportation points; there were scarcely any strategic targets left. The Germans were coming at the Flying Forts with new jet-propelled fighters, but they had already lost the best of their fighter pilots and the massed U.S. bombers and Mustang long-range fighters now accompanying them were overpowering.

On September 14, 1944, Phil Johnson suddenly died of a stroke, while visiting Wichita. Machines and work stopped in silent tribute in two hundred acres of Boeing plants. It was said of Johnson, "He has shortened the war." A saddened Claire Egtvedt, in the office of chairman, resumed active management while seeking a new president. The war went on.

In the Pacific the Marianas had been taken—Saipan, Tinian and Guam. Bulldozers had carved great airstrips for the B-29 Superforts of the 21st Bomber Command, a new unit of the 20th Air Force. Brigadier General Haywood "Possum" Hansell, who had been planning B-29 operations from Washington, landed the first Superfort on Saipan on October 12, 1944, and eight days later Brigadier General O'Donnell arrived to lead Hansell's first Wing. Vastly different, thought Rosy O'Donnell, from the little 19th Bombardment Group in which he had withdrawn from the Philippines less than three years before.

On November 24, Rosy O'Donnell, in the Superfortress *Dauntless Dotty*, spearheaded a daylight formation of 111 B-29s over Tokyo. At 445 miles an hour ground speed, before a 120-knot wind, they swept through fighters and flak and dropped 277 tons of bombs by radar through an overcast. They lost two B-29s over the target and shot down seven enemy fighters. O'Donnell and Hansell were disappointed with their accuracy, but the main attack on Japan was irrevocably under way.

The drive for victory in the Pacific had reached a relentless pace by early 1945. General Curtis LeMay had been moved to the Marianas to assume command. Washington wanted to try fire-bomb raids on Japanese production centers. General Hansell had tried a couple of raids with incendiaries, inconclusively. LeMay had tried one from China, with fair results, but the aim wasn't good from high altitudes with the strong winds. It would take a lot of bombs, too, to start a conflagration. "What would you think of going over Tokyo at low altitude—five or six thousand feet—at night, with a good heavy load of incendiaries?" LeMay asked his staff. "Navigate singly, not in formation. Put the fuel you save into more bomb load."

It would be a huge gamble. There was controversy. They'd be flying right down in the flak. For years the Air Force had been learning and practicing high-altitude precision bombing of strategic targets, and high-stacked formations for mutual defense up where flak was less accurate. This would be a complete reversal.

But today's problem wasn't the same as yesterday's. In Europe factories were concentrated. In Japan they were scattered all through the cities, cities built largely of wood and susceptible to fire. In Europe the bombers were up against the skilled Luftwaffe. LeMay had found that Japanese pilots couldn't match them. Only one-fourth of the B-29's bomb capacity was being used on the

missions to Japan, because of the big fuel load. The long
climb and formation flying used up the fuel. Then there
were the high winds. If you bucked them, your target
run took forever; if you went downwind, the target
zipped out of the sights; if you went crosswind, the
bomb-sight wouldn't take it.

More important to LeMay was the time factor. He felt
that in Europe the air battle would have been decisive
without a land invasion, though the ground forces would
never agree with that. Plans were moving ahead now for
invasion of Japan against Japanese land armies that were
still practically untouched. He was sure that the 21st
Bomber Command could bring the enemy to its knees.
But if this were to be done, the air attack would have to
be stepped up and finished off in short order, ahead of the
timetable for invasion. LeMay sat staring into space.
Then he gave his verdict.

"If this works the way I think it's going to, we will
shorten the war."

On March 9, bomber crews at briefings in Saipan,
Guam and Tinian listened in shocked silence. Maximum-
effort night incendiary attacks were to be made on major
Japanese industrial cities. Bombing altitudes would be
from 5,000 to 9,000 feet. No armament or ammunition
would be carried. Gunners would be left home. Bomb
loads would be stepped up from five tons per airplane to
seven and eight tons. They would attack individually,
not in close formation. Tokyo, most heavily defended,
would be the first target.

"Is the Old Man crazy?" the stunned pilots asked.

They went, General Tom Power in the lead. They
came back next day a changed air force, sobered, matured. "You'd never believe it," they said. "Tokyo caught
fire like a forest of pine trees." The experience had been
rugged. Mountains of smoke built up over the target.
Following planes had to go into it to bomb. Great up-
drafts of heat hit them like a stone wall. Two of the planes
flipped over on their backs. Downdraughts broke seat
fastenings and sent crewmen crashing against the ceiling,
all in blinding smoke and heat, with flak in the air, white

searchlights flashing up, and bewildered Japanese pilots bursting through. "If ever an airplane went through a test, that was it," they said.

Out of 302 planes over the target, fourteen were lost, all to anti-aircraft fire. Photo reconnaissance showed sixteen square miles of the city destroyed. Eighty-five percent of the planned target area was wiped out. Two days later they did it to Nagoya, then Osaka, then Kobe. Japanese defenders couldn't cope with the onslaught. B-29 losses grew less. Crew spirit was up. They were going to town. Japan couldn't stand much of this. The war would be over.

Like Tokyo, Berlin was crumbling and burning beneath 1,000-plane raids of Fortresses and Liberators. Its defending air force was gone. Eisenhower's forces, after von Rundstedt's army was broken at the critical Battle of the Bulge, had been moving faster and faster. The Russians were closing in from the east.

Germany surrendered, what was left of it, on May 7, 1945. "Where there is no vision, the people perish."

On the other side of the globe LeMay's fire raids were methodically blanking out the Japanese war economy. Rosy O'Donnell led a second raid on smoking Tokyo, the biggest, this time at medium altitude. It was awesome, terrible. Through the brilliance of the searchlights, the black bursts of flak and the night fighters flashing by, the incendiary bombs were falling from 303 planes, in bright flashes of flame and billowing smoke. Rising shafts of heat shot some of the planes hundreds of feet in the air, then dropped them back down. A piece of sheet-metal roofing came up and struck one of them at 16,000 feet. The plane flew on with the piece lodged in its wing.

O'Donnell circled off to the side to watch. Tokyo was a seething cauldron, aflame from 3,000 tons of napalm and oil incendiary bombs. The fire covered eighteen square miles of city. It seemed like a nightmare. A few militaristic aggressors had started the thing, and this was the retribution on Japanese millions—the terrible boomerang of war.

The campaign went on into summer. Yokohama, Kawasaki, sixty-seven other target cities. What was there left of Japan to wipe out? One or two targets. Hiroshima.

The mysterious party of Colonel Paul Tibbets that had been poking about the B-29 *Enola Gay* down on Tinian took off at 0245 on August 6, winged across the 1,600 miles of water, over the still city of Hiroshima, and at 0915 dropped a bomb. A crew put on green goggles, watched with suspense for fifty seconds as the bomb dropped toward the center of a sprawling city. There was the single, multi-sunpower flash, the weirdly glowing ball of fire, the shock, and then the mighty ascending column of smoke, mushrooming up and up to 50,000 feet.

America and all the world gasped at a power too revolutionary, a destruction too shocking to contemplate.

President Truman had asked Japan to accept the Potsdam surrender terms. Still defiant in defeat the Japanese military government said the terms were unacceptable.

Then Nagasaki. A second atomized city and 35,000 more people dead after Hiroshima's 75,000. Japan surrendered.

12

Peace meant rest, relief and opportunity regained, but also for airplane men, the urgent problem: what to sell? What new military airplanes would be needed to insure the peace?—a question Ed Wells had to ask. He concluded that speed was the big need, if there was to be a postwar bomber to replace the B-29. This had become evident before the end of the war. To be effective against new jet fighters that were coming into use, the bomber would have to have jet speed also. Wells had watched tests of the experimental Bell jet pursuit at Muroc Dry Lake, California, in September 1943. That was two years after Hap Arnold obtained drawings of one of Frank Whittle's jet engines from England and asked General Electric to make a copy of it. Inspired at Muroc, Wells had had preliminary design chief Bob Jewett work up a design of a jet bomber, with the wings shaved down to nothing, to try to get maximum speed. They'd have to sacrifice range and they'd have to sacrifice armament.

Wells and Jewett had taken the design data to Wright Field and on to Washington in March 1944.

"Would you take speed as a substitute for guns?" Wells asked Oliver Echols.

"Maybe so," said Echols. "If it's fast enough you might get by with just a stinger turret in the tail, and flak protection under the engines."

But they weren't able to get the calculated speed up much over 400 miles an hour. Even then the air would be passing across parts of the wing so fast that it would be approaching troubles with the mysterious "compressibility burble." When it approached the speed of sound, which was called Mach Number One, for Professor Ernest Mach, drag would go up and stability and control would encounter unknown dangers.

Still, in the engineering meetings that followed in Seattle, it had become more and more clear that the success of the jet bomber would depend on one thing: speed. George Schairer and his aerodynamicists had been giving the subject considerable study. The whole principle was different. With jet power you were putting all your fuel energy into pushing a jet stream out the back. The nearer you could get your airplane to the speed of that jet coming out the back, the more efficient your engine. "If you go only four hundred miles an hour," said Schairer, "you're just pushing air and burning up your fuel. You won't get any range."

But the "compressibility" problem was in the way. "We'll just have to beat it out in the wind tunnel," Schairer had concluded. He ordered construction of seventeen different high-speed airfoil models, thin wing sections of various shapes.

The testing had gone slowly. The Air Force, conscious of the country's late start on jet planes, began pressing the aircraft industry for proposals on quick construction of some experimental planes. Ed Wells' position was that they should not propose an airplane until they learned how to make a successful one. The wind-tunnel tests that showed most promise were of a long, narrow wing, straight out and tapered like the B-29, only razor-thin. But much of the speed advantage of the slim wing was cancelled by the drag of the big double-jet nacelles on the wings. A new design put all the engines in the body. That increased the speed so they were really up against troubles with compressibility burble, better known as "high Mach Number" effects.

It all looked too uncertain. Wright Field drew a contract, not for an airplane, but for a wind-tunnel program to prove the practicability and safety of the design.

Should they have gone ahead with something more conventional—simply hang jet engines on a plane like the B-29, instead of trying to go after maximum speed? But that wouldn't be honesty of purpose, Wells felt, when they had already concluded that a jet airplane should be designed to take full advantage of jet power. You had to throw away the past and start anew. That was why it was taking so much time.

The extra time they were taking was forcing its own answer to the question. The Air Force had gone ahead on contracts with North American, Consolidated and Martin for medium jet bombers of conventional design. Boeing was behind in the race. Now they'd have to come up with something better.

In May of 1945, aerodynamics chief George Schairer was at the Pentagon preparing to go on a special mission into Germany. He was serving as a member of the Scientific Advisory Board of the Army Air Force, headed by Dr. Theodore von Karman of California Institute of Technology.

It was the noon hour. Schairer was walking with the Chinese professor, Dr. H. S. Tsien, another member of the Advisory Board, down one of the mazelike corridors toward a lunchroom.

"What do you think about Bob Jones' theories down at NACA on high-speed wings?" Dr. Tsien asked Schairer.

"What does he say? I haven't talked to Bob lately."

"He thinks that if you make a narrow wing and set it at an angle to the body, it will have entirely different characteristics in the vicinity of the speed of sound than the ordinary straight wing."

Schairer was interested. "Has he run tests on this?"

"It's mostly a theoretical conclusion. There's a lot of debate going on about it down there. He's starting some experiments. He thinks he can prove it."

On the flight to Paris Schairer sat alongside Tsien to continue the discussion. Was Jones' theory right or wasn't it? They both got out slide rules and pads of chart paper, and began figuring. There were some fundamental calculations they could apply: the increased effective width of the wing if it were swept back at an angle, the changed angle of the air striking the wing and flowing back over it. It would be more like a sideslip than straight flight. What would this mean? They had always taken it for granted that the wing had to go straight out. Had they been going along like sheep, without examining all the possibilities?

Schairer and Tsien pored over their figures. There wasn't much conversation, mostly thought. There was time for thought through the night, with miles of black water going by below them. Other lights were out, just the tiny shafts from two reading lights over the two engineers, tuning in to the laws of mathematics and flight. By morning Schairer was in firm possession of a new viewpoint. It certainly looked interesting, he was acknowledging. If you swept back the wings, it seemed to make a big difference in the drag. It looked like a way to get the speed up so they could really use the power of the jet engine. He wondered if it was too good to be true. Was there a catch?

"I can see no reason it shouldn't work," he said to Dr. Tsien. "Can you find any?"

"No, I can't."

The morning Germany surrendered to General Eisenhower at the schoolhouse in Rheims, the von Karman scientific party arrived at Reichsmarshal Goering's Aeronautical Research Institute at Brunswick. Colonel Don Putt had arrived ahead of them and had taken command of the German research center. U.S. military guards were outside. Putt had arranged to have the offices and files unlocked. Schairer was with Dr. Hugh Dryden of the NACA on the first evening when they started their search. They went into several rooms, trying to get the lay of the place. "These look like the wind-tunnel files," said Hugh Dryden. "Do you read German?"

"No," Schairer said. "But numbers are pretty much the same in any language."

Peering into the scientific mind of the enemy, left here on paper, seemed a strange business. Dryden was over in one corner of the room, reading at a table. Schairer went through some file drawers. He spotted the names of some of the men he knew who had once studied under von Karman. He came to some drawings. "Hey!" he called to Dryden. There was a drawing of a model with *sweptback* wings. Some charts, columns of figures, yes, wind-tunnel results. Schairer scanned them, astounded. There were fragments of the same formulas he was working with on the plane with Tsien. He searched to see how they had come out. More papers went down the same track—a solid track.

Next day von Karman, too, was excited about this and other finds. They called Dr. Adolf Busemann, one of the Institute's top theoretical aerodynamicists. "What about this?" von Karman asked him. "Where did all this sweepback business come from?"

"Don't you remember? Rome? Volta Scientific Conference in 1935?" von Karman tried to recall. "You remember my paper on supersonic aerodynamics? It told how sweepback would reduce the drag at supersonic speeds."

Von Karman sat up. "Of course I remember. When did you find out it would work?"

Dr. Busemann shrugged. "No one paid any attention. Finally Messerschmitt ran some tests and everybody got excited. The ME-262 is under construction now with forty-five degrees sweepback."

Next day Schairer encountered a fellow-engineer, George Martin who was in Germany with another Air Force group, and told him the story. Martin listened intently. "You mean this idea's been lying around for ten years?"

"You know, I was familiar with Busemann's paper myself," Schairer admitted. "You just don't see a thing until

you want to see it. Then you find the answer you need
has been there all the time."

Seven men sat at the long board room table on September 5, 1945, Claire Egtvedt presiding. With the surrender of Japan, B-29 production was being reduced from
155 planes in August to 122 in September, then it would
go down to twenty per month. The necessary reduction in personnel was going along in orderly fashion.
Egtvedt moved to the main item of business on the
agenda: the election of a new president. The selection
committee made its report. William M. Allen, the company lawyer, was the unanimous choice. Handshakes and
congratulations were being extended to Allen when Miss
Lind, Egtvedt's secretary, appeared at the door. She
handed a note to Egtvedt, which he read, then looked up
uncomfortably.

It was a note from Bob Neale, the operations manager.
They had just received word that the Air Force was cutting the B-29 schedule to fifty for the current month,
then to ten a month until February. Neale said most of
that number were completed already. He proposed a
plant shutdown announcement before the four o'clock
shift change. Egtvedt glanced at his watch. It was three-
thirty.

The payroll was running at half-a-million dollars per
day. There was no choice. He looked at Bill Allen who
nodded gravely. Egtvedt turned to his secretary: "Tell
Bob O.K."

The Bill Allen who inherited the postwar problem in
September 1945, was thin, balding. There was a down-
turn to the corners of his mouth in a "let's face the facts"
manner, but his brown eyes kindled with sincerity and
his whole face lay ready to radiate a love of good humor. To news reporters that evening, he said, "I haven't
figured out yet whether my election caused the contract
reduction, or they gave me the job because they knew it
was coming."

But when he hit the pillow that night there was another night, weeks earlier, surging in his thoughts. It was the night after Dietrich Schmitz of the Board's selection committee had taken him to lunch and pressed him for an answer on the presidency. Allen had sparred for time. He was a widower, with two daughters, ten and five years old. "Heaven knows I have little enough time for them now," he had told himself again and again. "They need the time I give them, and more too." If he were to step into this job, his time wouldn't be his own.

There was no great salary incentive. His earnings in the law practice were already about equal to the president's salary. He knew there were troubles ahead— readjustment, financing, the competition for new business when every company would be struggling for life. He'd be stepping right into the middle of it. He was happy in what he was doing. All his training had been in the legal profession and by now he felt a certain mastery of it. The Boeing presidency, on the other hand. . . . "I just don't have the qualifications for it," he had told a family friend and neighbor, Mary Ellen Agen, someone he felt he could talk to.

"But, Bill, if they've decided you're the one for the job, who are you to say no?" she had said.

Dietrich Schmitz was waiting for that answer.

"My convictions are unchanged," Allen told Schmitz finally at the lunch table. "I don't feel that I'm qualified for the job. From the personal angle there's every reason to remain where I am. However, the problem has to be solved. If I can arrange some replacements in the law firm, then . . . I'll accept."

That night Allen had made a long list of things he'd have to do if the job were given him:

Must keep temper—always—never get mad.
Be considerate of my associate's views.
Don't talk too much—let others talk.
Don't be afraid to admit that you don't know.
Don't get immersed in detail—concentrate on the big objectives.

Make contacts with other people in industry—and keep them!

Make a sincere effort to understand labor's viewpoint.

Be definite; don't vacillate.

Act—get things done—move forward.

Develop a postwar future for Boeing.

Try hard, but don't let obstacles get you down. Take things in stride.

Above all else be human—keep your sense of humor —learn to relax.

Be just; straightforward; invite criticism and learn to take it.

Be confident. Having once made the move, make the most of it.

Bring to task great enthusiasm, unlimited energy.

Make Boeing even greater than it is. . . .

It was a stern discipline and self-challenge. Suddenly it had become tremendously important.

When Allen came to work on September 6, the big corner office looked as empty as he knew the plant was at the moment. The forty-foot expanse of windows suggested the whole world was looking in: the city of Seattle, employees and their families, the Government, the airlines. But he knew those windows were meant for him to look out of, to see again the bustle of activity. Acutely aware that this result was now up to him, he asked his executives to come in.

There were orders for a few B-50s, the improved version of the B-29 and for C-97s, a military transport with wings like the B-29s. Egtvedt had just testified before the Mead Committee of Congress on how imperative it was to keep up enough aircraft development and production to retain skills and facilities. It took large orders to maintain a plant like this, and it took a big plant to build a modern military bomber.

Allen's first question was: could they get more orders for B-50s? Ed Wells affirmed that the 50 was a good airplane, with a wing now 650 pounds lighter and 16 per-

cent stronger than that of the B-29. Almost everything had been redesigned. "The trouble is," he said, "it
still looks like a B-29." The Air Force had bought 3,898
B-29s. It was well stocked.

Wells spoke of the jet bomber study that was coming
along; "I'd like to talk with you about it as soon as there's
time," he said to Allen.

"Let's take first things first. We need something we
can build now." Allen knew there'd be 29,000 employees
lined up in the cafeteria yard the next day for their pay-
checks: $3 million. The demanding question was: "How
many of them could be put back to work?" These were
the people who knew how to build Boeing airplanes.

Commercial transports? Negotiations were under way
for a big ship called the Stratocruiser, a commercial version of the C-97. But there had been no sales. The difficulty was that Douglas and Lockheed had started
earlier on new transports while Boeing was still working
all-out on B-29s. It was hard to meet their price and delivery dates. The Stratocruisers should fit the airliners'
needs: 340 miles an hour; 3,500-mile range; big enough
for long-range travel comfort; pressurized cabin; room
to move around and relax; two decks; lounge and snack
bar below; circular staircase; big dressingrooms. Yet if
they didn't get orders soon they'd be too far behind to
ever quote competitive deliveries. They would have to
produce at least fifty to get the price down to the million
and a quarter that Fred Collins, the sales manager, said
was the limit. Could they price the plane that low? You
could go out of business operating at a loss just as much
as you could if you didn't have orders, Allen knew.

When the discussions were over, Allen sat long looking
out of his new-view windows. He watched a maintenance man walk across the huge apron. He thought
again of the people who were Boeing. Could he take the
risk of starting the Stratocruiser without firm orders?
The money would begin going out fast when a force
of men started working on the project. Which was the
greater risk, do something or nothing? He got Beall on
the phone in New York, talked to Bowman, the treas-

urer; to the other members of the board. It was time for the weekly staff meeting. Everyone looked to him.

"We're going to start fifty Stratocruisers," Bill Allen announced at the meeting. *Act. Get things done*, he reminded himself. "The Number One task for all of us now is to see that we sell them."

The next week there were lines at the state unemployment benefits windows. Money wasn't coming into the downtown stores. An alarmed community had called a mass meeting at the Chamber of Commerce. Bill Allen addressed the meeting. "I can assure you we will use diligent and aggressive effort to put our plants to use on a full-time basis," he told the concerned audience. The state manpower director said the real shock hadn't been felt yet. People started having their say from the floor.

"I tell you folks, the best thing you can do is go back to Iowa," said one man. He turned and shook his finger at Allen, seated on the stage. "I know these people aren't going back to work at Boeing, and you know it." Another man jumped to his feet with a resolution that the Government be asked to take over the plant. Somebody seconded it. Allen caught himself. *Never get mad.* Then someone else got up and said, "That's a silly idea. It's the the Government cancelling the orders that's caused all the trouble in the first place." The crowd laughed.

Ed Wells and George Schairer had a great hope that the radical new jet bomber with sweptback wings would prove out. But it was coming hard. Wright Field reaction ranged from fascinated interest to practical doubt. Sweeping back the wings would decrease the wing span, and the range of an airplane was roughly in proportion to its span. The plane would gain speed only at a sacrifice of range. And practically no one in the Air Force liked putting the jet engines in the body, which the aerodynamicists argued was mandatory in order to have a clean, high-speed wing.

But in Seattle the new idea had taken deep root. It offered too sensational an advance in performance to be passed by, Ed Wells thought. Bill Allen gave him the green light. "If that's what you're for, let's go after it."

Wells named a whole new project group, headed by George Martin. Schairer started a comprehensive new wind-tunnel program. On September 13, 1945, a formal proposal went to Wright Field: a sweptback airplane with four jets blasting back over the top of the body and two more from the tail. Improved fire walls would offset the objection to engines in the body.

Colonel Pete Warden, a serious-minded young engineer who was now the bombardment project officer, took the proposal to a staff meeting.

"Why should the Air Force finance some wild idea George Schairer has?" asked one colonel. "Let's cut out this foolishness." The armament laboratory brought in results of some gunfire tests made in a twenty-foot wind-tunnel. Fifty-caliber bullets had been fired into the burner section of a roaring F-80 jet engine. The result was an uncontrollable blowtorch out of the side of the engine. "That settles it," they said. "Put six of those engines in the body of a bomber? No."

"I don't think we should scuttle the project," said Colonel Warden. "There may be ways of working around these problems."

Ed Wells and preliminary design chief Bob Jewett arrived in Dayton to get the disconcerting news. It was hard to take. "This place is a gloom dispensary," said the pensive Bob Jewett. For two years he had been putting most of his effort on this project. So had a lot of other people. They'd thought they really had something. Now this.

Back at the hotel the two engineers kicked the problem around, tried to bring order out of confusion and frustration. Again the question arose: should they go back to a conventional design? But they'd found they could get the speed up by using a thin wing. That was progress. They'd found also that they could get rid of much of the drag by sweeping it back. That, too, was progress. Certainly it had raised problems to put the engines in the body, Wells admitted. He had never felt completely happy about that. But where else was there to put them? You couldn't do away with engines. The thought occurred, "out, away from the wing. Why not?" Ed remembered some wind-tunnel data that George Schairer had brought from Germany, on experiments with engines out on the struts. It hadn't looked very good. Still, it could be a way out.

"It might work," Bob Jewett acknowledged, "if we could get them far enough away so they wouldn't disturb the airflow over the wing." Wells drew a sketch—things always seemed more plausible on paper—and sent it back to Seattle for consideration.

The aerodynamics staff took a dim view. "We have a clean wing. Let's not go back and muddy it all up again."

"Why not give it a try?" Schairer asked. A new series of tunnel tests was begun, the "broomstick tests." A model engine "pod" was stuck out on the end of a "broomstick" and tried out in every position they could think of: below and behind the wing; straight below the wing; above and behind; above and in front; below and in front. That last position was the best. It looked odd, but it seemed to work.

"This isn't going to be so bad," aerodynamicist Ben Cohn confessed when the figures began to come in. The trick was to thrust the pods far enough forward. Then the drag was no greater than when the engines were in the body. The body could be more slender. By putting four of the engines in twin pods slung under the wings and the other two out on the tips of the wings, the structural weight of the airplane could actually be decreased, because of better distribution of weight. That added to the range.

There was a surge of new enthusiasm, this time on a basis that Wright Field could share. Wind-tunnel test results looked good. The top speed was going to be more than six hundred miles per hour and they still could control the airplane at low speeds for landing. But there was no quantity market for the plane.

Airlines had by now ordered forty-two Stratocruisers, with more in prospect, and the Air Force was going to take on more B-50s. The jets still seemed a long way off. Curtis LeMay, now head of Research and Development in Washington, kept pointing out that not one jet under development had range enough to do a global bombing job. He was more interested in the heavy-bomber design competition—a long-range airplane with propellers driven by gas-turbine engines that Boeing and other companies had been studying for a year. This was coming even slower than the medium-range jet. No one had devised anything that would meet the range requirement.

The medium jet bomber—Stratojet they were calling it—was in wooden mock-up form by April 1946. An Air Force mock-up board headed by Colonel Ed Nabell and Lieutenant Ken Holtby came out to go over it. Some things they didn't like. One was the arrangement for retracting the landing gear. The tricycle gear had been rigged to fold back into big openings in the side of the body. "It's a Rube Goldberg affair," said Colonel Nabell. "Look at all that gimcrackery." There was a brief and not too spirited defense from the Seattle group.

"If this is the best we can get, maybe we'd better reconsider whether we want the plane at all," said Nabell.

It was decided to try a bicycle gear with wheels in tandem. Pete Warden had been advocating that, but the problems loomed large. Then they worked one out, adding a small outrigger wheel to keep the wing-tips off the ground. When they added up the estimated weight, it was 1,500 pounds less than before—a bonus that could go into more range.

Every mile of range they could gain was golden. At best it was far short of what the Air Force wanted. They could increase it somewhat and the altitude, too, by adding to the wing span, but this was hard to do and still preserve the narrow, thin wing, because there was an engine stuck out on each wing-tip. But by dropping the wing-tip engines down in pods like the others and running the wings on out beyond them, they could do it. The span was increased from one hundred to 116 feet.

That was the final touch. Now everybody liked the airplane. It looked right. An artist's drawing of the finished design fairly leaped with speed and slender symmetry.

When they looked back over the long series of drawings that showed the metamorphosis of the design, they were struck that each change made it look better. The progress might have stopped on any one of them, but the drawing kept talking back, "Don't stop there—keep going. Bend my wings back so I can go faster. Bend back the tail surfaces, too. Right. Too heavy in the middle, though. Get rid of those body engines, get the weight out along the wings. Better. Now a little more here. Tuck in the landing gear. Good. Now add on to the wing-tips. Now let me see. . . . Wow! Is that me?"

Yet it wasn't the picture that did the talking, it was the numbers that came out of wind-tunnel tests, out of design calculations, out of what Wright Field wanted to do. Oddly, it seemed, every time the numbers insisted on a change, the picture, too, looked better. It was the visible sign. Finally, the equation balanced perfectly, and the picture said so: a long, tapered body, trailing off into the parting flare of swept-back fin and stabilizers; wings that were slender as a fine steel blade, sweeping out and back and gently down, relaxed and poised for beauty of flight; jet engines leaping forward from those wings with open mouths that seemed to say, "Give us sky to eat."

Ed Wells put down the drawing with quiet joy. He and George Martin, the project engineer, both knew the B-47 Stratojet had jelled. So did Wright Field shortly after. It approved the purchase of two experimental models.

While Fred Laudan, vice president for experimental manufacturing, was organizing a crew to rush out the two Stratojets to compete with the North American, Martin and Consolidated jets, word came in June 1946, that the Boeing long-range bomber study had won the design competition in the heavy bomber class. The design was for a 360,000-pound airplane, twice the weight of the Stratojet, powered by turbine-propeller engines. There'd be a contract for further engineering work on it—a big job reminiscent of Project A back in the thirties. This one would be called the B-52.

13

The business was going jet. The old reciprocating engine, marvel of ingenuity with its myriad working parts, now seemed the hard way, compared with the jet. When Frank Whittle, inventor of the English jet engine, visited Seattle, George Schairer asked him: "How did you come to invent the jet? How much did you know about what was going on in Germany, Italy, France and this country?"

Whittle replied that he didn't know anything about what the rest were doing. "But I wasn't exactly the inventor. It was just time for someone to develop the jet engine and I was the one who did it."

"You're too modest," Schairer told him. But Schairer, too, had seen like evidence that the "new idea" wasn't really new. Rather, it was often lying around, waiting for someone to see it, as had been the sweptback wing.

But the revolution in jet power was still tentative. Its application to fighter planes was taken for granted; for larger airplanes it would have to be proved. The jet's huge appetite for fuel loomed as a tremendous handicap, particularly for commercial transport use.

Yet the question of ultimate commercial application was one that intrigued every engineer. In Bob Jewett's Preliminary Design unit Elliot Mock had made a rough study of jet transport possibility before the end of the war and it had looked interesting. Later, Jewett was reviewing the subject with Ed Wells.

"We entered the war with one kind of power, the reciprocating engine," Jewett said. "We came out with four new kinds: jet, turboprop, ramjet and rocket." He wondered how long it would be before they could start applying some of these to transports. Wells agreed that they should get started on a comparative study of the jet and turboprop to find out.

In Preliminary Design, Jewett had a new man, Bob Hage, a keen young engineer who had been aerodynamics chief at Wright Field during the war. Jewett laid three possible assignments before him. The future transport study was one of them.

"You mean I have a choice?" Hage asked.

"I'd rather have you work on the thing you're most interested in."

Hage's face brightened. "This one," and his finger went down on the jet transport study. His reasons were deep rooted.

He had left M.I.T. with a master's degree, ready to devote himself to the engineer's intuitive love of order and progress toward perfection. He had stepped out, instead, into what seemed to him the grotesque disorder of war. When he went to Wright Field to offer his services, the war experience was stimulating but not satisfying. He got first word of the development of jet engines and helped plan for their use. He also got a first look at the fiercely accelerating pace of development of weapons of destruction. At night he would sit in his room and think about how the peace could be kept once it was won and what could he do that would help. He'd keep coming back to one thing. People had to learn to know and understand each other better. Better transportation and communication were the big needs. Now the problem and opportunity were on his lap.

Jewett asked him to give it a good analytical study, taking all the time it required, comparing safety factors, comfort, Civil Aeronautics regulations, costs especially.

"Everyone says a jet transport isn't economically feasible. Let's find out." Hage dug in with vigor.

Operations were being carried on at a loss. Postwar costs were high, orders low. Men like General George Kenney, trying to build up a postwar Strategic Air Command, were protesting bitterly against the production slump.

"America must make up its mind whether it wants the best Air Force or none at all," said Kenney. "It's like in poker; the second-best hand wins you nothing and costs you dough."

When President Truman named Thomas Finletter chairman of an Air Policy Commission in July 1947, Bill Allen with other industry presidents tried to show the importance of continued progress in the air. A growing uneasiness over Soviet Russia gave force to the inquiry, and also to the demand of Curtis LeMay and others that the country's new strategic bombers be ships with inter-continental range. The six-engine Consolidated B-36 was the nearest approach, but it was slow and there was concern over its vulnerability. The range of the proposed turbo-prop B-52 was being stretched by every device to try to make it meet LeMay's objectives, but it would not.

The smaller Stratojet, though spectacular in speed, would be woefully short of range, LeMay contended. To get the speed, you lost out on range. That was the dilemma of jets. There even was talk in the Air Force about switching the B-47 Stratojet to turbo-prop power.

But the Stratojet was nearing completion, a gleaming piece of metal artistry. Experimental manager Al Jacobson and superintendent Bud Hurst wouldn't let a workman on it except in stocking feet. Even a shoe scuff would cut down its top speed several miles an hour, the engineers kept emphasizing. Bob Robbins, the pilot who had been selected to test-fly it, had already "flown" a full-size set of the airplane's control surfaces in the wind tunnel at Moffet Field, California, and now was practicing his role in the cockpit. It was a ship almost the size of the B-29, yet with a cockpit like that of a fighter, with a crew of three instead of twelve because jet engines required less controls and instruments, and because its six-hundred-mile speed, helping it to escape interception, was substituting for gunners.

When the Stratojet rolled out of its walled-off, secret place onto the Plant Two apron for system checks in September 1947, it seemed to its builders a thing eager for flight, too beautiful to have its integrity questioned. Cliff Roberts, engineering representative recently stationed in Washington, went to tell General LeMay about it. The General was interested but unenthusiastic. He said they had no requirements for production of the airplane. "You have to get some range in it." Even the turbo-prop B-52 wasn't getting the range LeMay wanted, though the design had grown fat with fuel tanks and was getting out of reason in both size and cost.

Roberts brought out engineering curves showing the range-stretching efforts on both projects, but LeMay was silent. It wasn't that he didn't want jets, Roberts knew. The General had been enthusiastic about jet speeds. It was simply the matter of range. LeMay was sticking to his guns, and there was no way of arguing the point. Searching for something to break the impasse, Roberts thought of refueling. He remembered the refueling demonstrations Tooey Spaatz and Ira Eaker had made in the 1920's, a test refueling at Wright Field during the war, the work the British were doing in refueling development. Could refueling be done at turbo-prop and jet speeds?

"We could get you any kind of range you want if we'd take hold of this refueling deal," he suggested.

LeMay didn't answer. The session ended.

Back at the office Roberts talked it over with Washington Representative Jim Murray.

"Do you think the suggestion registered?" Murray asked.

"Well, he didn't throw me out."

Test pilot Bob Robbins and his co-pilot, Scott Osler, were waiting only on the weather. To insure a safe landing the plan was to take the Stratojet off from Boeing Field and land on the long runway of Moses Lake air base, across the Cascade mountains in central Washington. It had to be clear at both fields and over the mountain range. This was a lot to ask of the Seattle weather bureau in winter.

On the morning of December 17, 1947, Robbins started for the plant under a grey sky. The forecaster saw hope that the cumulus cover would break up. When someone discovered it was the forty-fourth anniversary of the Wright brothers' first flight, the hope grew to a conviction that this was the day.

Ben Werner, the flight engineer who had gone ahead to Moses Lake, reported an eighth of an inch of ice on the runways there and a local overcast that he thought would burn off by noon. Robbins headed for the airplane to check his equipment.

An inevitable tension was building up. Newsreel cameramen were scurrying about watching for position. Radio broadcasters were setting up their gear. There had been no public announcement, but cars came to the streets of Beacon Hill overlooking the field—first seven, then seventy-seven—one hundred and seventy in a miracle of multiplication. Key engineers started coming across the street toward Flight Test. Chief aerodynamicist Ben Cohn was under double pressure, his wife expecting a child, and this. She had tried him with the question, "If they both happen at once, where will you go?"

"Look," said Ben, "I love my family. But this baby down at the field, I've been working on it for four years."

Project engineer George Martin, deeply conscious that a big swept-wing airplane like this had never before been flown, racked his mind for last instructions, something that might have been overlooked.

Bob Robbins was in the cockpit. He'd rather wait in his pilot's seat than in the office. There was no commotion here, no one at his elbow. It was his own private place where he could think. Again and again he went over the charts showing the curve of take-off acceleration, the last point of refusal on the runway. He looked at his instruments and controls, the things he had watched go into the ship one by one in the year he'd been preparing for this day. Now they were all his.

Robbins felt at home with the neat rows of dials, yet he had to remind himself that they were only tokens of things highly important, that every turn of an indicator would mean a lightning-fast change in his situation, that every touch on these controls was a command call on a parcel of power such as had never before been unleashed in the air. These were six jets with 4,000 pounds thrust each, plus eighteen JATO rockets in the sides of the ship if he needed them, each with 1,000 pounds thrust for fourteen seconds. Without counting the JATO's he'd have at his fingertips three times the power of the B-29.

The morning was advancing: ten-fifteen, ten-thirty. The clock on the instrument panel was irrevocably turning toward climax—the months of experiment and study all crowded into now. Robbins looked out of the cockpit canopy. There were five hundred people watching him on Beacon Hill and, he thought, a million more. The world. Scott Osler came up the ladder and through the bottom hatch. "Ben says the ice has melted at Moses, but a patch of clouds has moved in at 2,000 feet. It doesn't look too good."

Bob climbed out. "We'd better take an early lunch." At 12:15 Ben Werner called that Moses Lake was clear. But the weather station at Ephrata, twenty miles north of there, reported a two hundred-foot ceiling. There was the possibility that the stuff would move on over the Moses Lake airfield. Seattle was still overcast, but some holes seemed to be developing. Two o'clock had been set as the deadline for take-off, to allow time for the test and a landing before dark.

Robbins and Scott Osler got on their gear, thick padded crash-helmets painted gold to reflect the sun's heat, oxygen mask and tubes hanging to the side. They climbed into the ship.

There was new word from Werner. He could see the cloud bank over Ephrata but it was just hanging there. Still the situation was too precarious, Robbins thought.

A little wind could bring the clouds over Moses Lake while they were en route. The hands on the clock kept turning. At 12:15 Captain James Fitzgerald, who was standing by with a P-80 jet fighter to take official flight pictures, poked his head in. "What say I run over there and see how it is? I can be back in half an hour."

"Good idea. Thanks. We'll wait."

In a one-jet roar, Fitzgerald's P-80 rocketed off the end of the runway and disappeared toward the mountains. After its bird-hound getaway, Robbins had a feeling the spell was broken.

The taxi strip was lined with people now. The sky was still overcast, but there was a big hole up toward the mountains. At 1:27 the P-80 raced back. It hit the south end of the runway, then came to a stop downfield. It had caught its gear on a runway light. A field car brought Fitzgerald on up and he talked to Robbins on the ground crew's interphone. "Looks good enough to me. I'd try it."

Bob Robbins breathed a prayer. He turned to Osler. "All set?" He pushed Number One starter. The turbine wound up to its super-siren screech. Fuel on. The sudden bellow of the jet was a voice of surging power. All six engines roaring now. Brakes off. They taxied to the end of the runway, paused for a quick check. Robbins called the tower: "Tell us when our wheels clear the ground." He flicked on the intercom. "Scott, we'll release brakes at counter number 2260." The counter clocked the seconds for test recording. "Fifty-seven, fifty-eight, fifty-nine, sixty." They were rolling, jets raging and yet so slow. That was the way with jet power; seemed forever getting moving, but once they really got rolling. . . .

The air-speed indicator was coming up now, runway going under faster. Seventy, eighty, ninety miles per hour. A red light came on the fire-warning panel. Number Two engine. Robbins cut the power and hit the brakes.

"It was a false alarm, Bob," Osler said in a minute. The

millivolt reader showed the trouble was in the instrument only. The decision loomed—should they go back to the hangar and check the brakes? The linings would be pretty warm after that stop. But it would mean using up time and fuel. They'd have to spend more time refueling. It was now nearly two o'clock, and it might mean losing the chance for the day. "Boeing tower, we'll taxi and try again," Robbins said. "Think we'll make it this time."

They released brakes at 2:02 P.M. Rolling . . . faster . . . faster still. The air-speed indicator, the field distance, the charts showing last point of refusal—all were superimposed on Robbins' mind. Number Two fire-warning light again. It was a false alarm again. They were racing now. This was it. One hundred and thirty-five miles per hour. The last 2,000 feet of runway were approaching fast; Robbins lifted the guard off the JATO switch, ready to fire six bottles if necessary.

"You're airborne!" shouted the tower. Before Robbins knew it they were sixty feet in the air, the ground dropping away fast. The controls felt good. Stable. Air speed was going up.

Robbins was scanning his panel, glancing outside. "Gear up, Scott." The air-speed indicator jumped. One hundred and eighty, ninety, ninety-five. Good altitude now. "Ease up on the flaps." He waited for another boost in speed, but felt none.

"They aren't going up, according to my indicator," said Osler.

"Light on Number Five." Robbins spotted another fire warning. Osler checked it. There was no time for flaps now. "O.K. on Five. She's about ten millivolts. False indication."

"Roger. Is Two still O.K.?"

"I'll follow it up . . . it's O.K. . . . I can't get the flaps up on normal, I'm going to try using emergency."

"Better leave them where they are." The deck of clouds was right over them now and Robbins didn't want to go through it on instruments. They were cutting the air and climbing fast. He eased up on the power till they came under a hole. "Try to bring the flaps up in steps now, Scott. I've slowed the airplane a little."

". . . It's all right. They're coming up," said Osler.

"Good. I'm going to get on my climbing speed now." Robbins turned the airplane sharply to the east, nosed up toward the hole, going up like an elevator. "Sure feels good."

"Roger." They were really moving.

Eyes of ground observers were glued to the swept-wing speck in the sky, the thin trails of dark kerosene smoke pouring from its six engines. When Robbins changed his heading and started his authoritative climb, it looked suddenly as if he were going straight up, and nothing was going to stop him. Up, up, vaulting the Cascades. It appeared so easy. In minutes he was gone; there was a race for the waiting airplane that would follow on to Moses Lake.

Bob Robbins was adjusting his seat cushions. Now the months of preparation, the hundreds of people lining Beacon Hill seemed unreal. This was real, the smooth feel of jet power. The throttles were only part way open. He felt wonderful, looked around. "It's sure nice to see our wings out straight."

"Sure is," said Osler. The ground droop was gone. Tips of the swept wings—they had to look way back to see them—were riding high with an easy spring that cushioned the air. This was the way they were meant to be.

Robbins played with the controls, trying some S-turns. It felt just like a pursuit plane—responsive. The controls were light. "Let's try lowering the landing gear."

"O.K. Coming down."

They could feel it hit bottom. "That wasn't bad," said Robbins. Then the whole airplane began to tremble.

"Wonder what that roughness is? Feel it?"

"Definitely."

"Hey, that's quite rough." Things were really shaking. Robbins called for flaps to slow the airplane. It was O.K. at lower speed. Probably the landing-gear doors would have to be stiffened, Robbins thought.

They were sailing high in the sky now. The big test item to get out of the way was slowing down to the point of stall, to confirm their predicted landing speed. Robbins called out the item on the flight plan. "Condition 86. It's begun at counter number 3690." The ship slowed . . . "Counter number is 3725, speed about 142. Still feels very good . . . 140, 139. How does it look? All right?" Seemed they were standing still, but the plane was riding on even keel. It wouldn't fall off on a wing. That was good.

"I have 133 miles an hour now at counter number 3780 . . . I felt just a little buffeting . . . 132 . . . there, that's pretty good stall warning." They felt the vigorous buffeting that designers want to occur well before full stall, so a pilot can't get into a stall without knowing it. "I'm going to slow it down to 125."

The ship approached stall. Still it was steady and straight. Robbins felt relieved. This was an *airplane*, he thought. It was behaving wonderfully. "We've got about seven miles per hour stall warning at least. No tendency for the airplane to fall off." He tried it again. Confirmation.

Robbins turned off the power boost that operated the controls, found he could manage them if necessary at these speeds without the boost. He shut off Number One engine with Number Six on full power. There was no stability problem should an engine go dead. All good. He tried a make-believe landing in the air, condition eleven on the flight plan. He liked the way it felt. The airplane was smooth. No tricks.

Robbins circled and began a descent toward Moses Lake. He came down fast. This was a swept-wing jet airplane; things happened fast. He lined up with the runway, began the letdown. "Are gear and flaps checked down?"

"Roger. My red lights are all off. Green lights are on. Flaps full down."

"Hydraulic pressure is O.K. Gear and flaps down. We should be O.K."

"All the generators are working fine."

"O.K. Thanks. We are at about 158 now with 52 percent rpm. We're going to do it all right, I think . . . It's 135 now." They were over the runway. Ten feet in the air. Robbins could see there was no use doing a practice go-round. He chopped four engines. They were on the ground, rolling fast. There was a shimmy in the right-hand outrigger wheel. It shook the airplane quite a little, but now they were slowing down. An item for the mechanics to fix. Here they were, Moses Lake. It was all over. Robbins taxied over to where a group was waiting.

"Are you clear on the canopy, Scott?"

"O.K."

"O.K. Canopy coming open." Robbins looked out and grinned at test engineer Ben Werner. The grin opened into a huge smile when he saw the joy of the men on the ground and realized what it meant. It was a smile he couldn't turn off the rest of the day, through the round of hearty handshakes, through the post-flight conference, the radio speeches, the press interviews. Bob Robbins was sure it was a new brand of airplane that would put an end to the old. "You just have to fly it to appreciate it," he said. "It's wonderful."

Thomas Finletter, chairman of the President's Air Policy Commission, noted the news report that a new type of Air Force bomber had been flown on the forty-fourth anniversary of the Wright brothers' flight. His reaction was that it was none too soon. Poland, Rumania, Bulgaria, Hungary, Yugoslavia, Albania and parts of Austria and Germany had become satellites of Soviet Russia. Czechoslovakia, Greece and Turkey were threatened. In Asia, the Communist forces of Mao Tse-tung were bent on conquest of China. In Berlin the American, British, and French sectors were an outpost a hundred miles inside Soviet-occupied territory. General Lucius Clay, the U.S. Military Governor in Germany, warned that the Russians might at any time choke off rail supplies to the two million people in the western part of the city.

It was Cold War. "As ruthless and determined a drive

to achieve world domination as a hot war," said the Harriman Committee, which was working to help European nations under the terms of the Economic Cooperation Act.

Thomas Finletter and his commission wrote in their report that the oceans were no longer enough to safeguard America. National security could be assured only by elimination of war itself. America must work for world order, but since its attainment was hampered by lack of free travel, free communications, free press, the country "must seek the next best thing . . . relative security under the protection of its own arms."

The Finletter report, and the report of the Congressional Air Policy Board that followed it, answered the question of the aviation industry. There would have to be air power in being. The U.S. Air Force took equal place with the Army and the Navy in Secretary Forrestal's new unified Department of Defense.

Global air power demanded airplanes with global range. The B-52 design had been built up to a tremendous 480,000 pounds in the attempt to give it the fuel capacity that would provide this needed range. It was sinking of its own weight.

"We've got to cut it down to 300,000," Wright Field insisted. Grave doubts were expressed as to whether the project could succeed, and alternatives were suggested, such as the Flying Wing—all wing and no body. But Wells and Schairer maintained that the Flying Wing was no answer.

Wright Field was pursuing the aerial refueling idea, encouraged by what was being done in England. But connecting high-speed jet bombers with a hose to a flying tanker was not easy. Cliff Leisy and a team of engineers in Wichita had an idea that they could link the planes with a collapsible pipeline, a flying "boom" that would lower from the tanker to the nose of the fuel-thirsty receiver. Experimentation went on.

World tensions were building. Communists took over the government in Czechoslovakia. There were reports that Russia already had the secret of the atom bomb.

Congress appropriated funds for a seventy-group Air Force and Marshall Plan aid to Europe. Then it happened in Berlin, June 18, 1948: what Lucius Clay had feared. The signal flag plain that Soviet intentions were not friendly. The railway corridor to the city was cut off. The U.S. Air Force grimly moved an aerial supply line to the rescue.

The developments put urgency behind the B-52 intercontinental bomber. When the bomber's weight had been trimmed to 300,000 pounds, with refueling in prospect, Wright Field had concluded the design would be acceptable. Turbo-prop power plants would give maximum range. But Ed Wells was concerned mightily about the engines. Two years ago the turboprop was to have been available in two years. More recently, Schairer and Colonel Pete Warden learned it would be another four years. They could end up with an airplane and no engines, Wells feared. Nonetheless, the contract was about to be awarded for two experimental models with the turbo-props.

The Westinghouse Company revealed plans for a big new jet engine. Jets were looking better and better, turboprops worse and worse. Wells went to Bill Allen. He said he didn't think they should go further with the turboprop. "We've come to the conclusion that the airplane should be jet-powered."

Allen was startled. It would throw the program back, might bring a cancellation. "Isn't this pretty late to be proposing a change like that?"

"I know, Bill, but it just isn't the airplane we should be building."

14

Ed Wells and George Schairer went to Wright Field to talk with bombardment project officer Pete Warden about putting jet engines on the B-52. They found Warden as worried as they were about the turboprops. He was 100 percent sold on jet speed, and proud of the performance of the B-47 Stratojet which had been his baby in the project office. Warden knew also that the Bell X-1 research plane, a pointed capsule of rocket power hauled into the air under the belly of a B-29 and cut loose, was even then breaking through the speed-of-sound barrier that engineers once said was the limit. The speed race was on. "Go ahead and work up a new design with jets," the Colonel said. "But we'll have to keep on with the turbo-prop airplane until we see what can be done."

In July 1948 the contract came through to build two experimental B-52s with *turbo-prop* engines. Wings would be swept back just twenty degrees. The slower speed of the turboprops didn't call for as much sweepback as in the B-47 and they could get a better range with the wings out straighter. The project was real, and the effort to change to jets seemed superficial. Neither were performance predictions for the jet version encouraging, because the overall design had been geared to turboprops and the Westinghouse jet was short of the power they needed.

Meanwhile the seventy-group Air Force program called for more B-50 Superforts. The Berlin airlift, an incredible chain of airplanes carrying supplies of coal and food, was a potent reminder of the thin thread between cold and hot war. K. B. Wolfe and General Joe McNarney, commanding general of Air Materiel Command, came to Seattle to talk about current B-50 production.

Bill Allen wanted to talk instead about the B-47. It was seven months since the Stratojet had first flown, and there were no orders for it. Everyone had agreed it was a fine experimental plane, but there was no real requirement for it in numbers, the Air Force kept saying. Allen thought they didn't realize what it could do. "On your way back," he said, "we'd like you to go by Moses Lake and see the 47."

"Thanks, but we've got to get back," K. B. said. "We're only interested in production airplanes."

"I know, but you should see it. We can fly you over in a B-50 so you won't lose any time." The visitors were traveling in a slower B-17. "We can bring your plane over while you're on the ground."

"O.K., if we can make it quick."

The Air Force was testing the 47 at Moses Lake. Major Guy Townsend, the test pilot, felt the way Bob Robbins did. The plane had won him over. Pete Warden, who had been asking K. B. Wolfe to watch the 47 perform, was at Moses Lake also. Warden and Townsend met the arriving party on the flight apron where the Stratojet was standing. K. B. walked over and patted it. "We'd like to see a fly-by."

"It's all yours, General," said Warden, waving a hand towards the cockpit.

"Oh, we won't have time to take a flight."

"Make it long or short as you like."

K. B. had never been in a jet bomber. Major Townsend persuaded him politely: "Really like to have you come along, General."

"Well, all right. A short one." K. B. climbed in behind Townsend. McNarney went with Allen, Beall, George

Martin and Colonel Warden to the tower to watch. It was a gusty day. There was a broken overcast at 8,000 feet with a little blue showing through. Ben Werner in the tower tuned the radio to bring in the conversation in the plane.

"General Wolfe, if you want to ask any questions," Guy Townsend was saying, "just tap Captain Ridley and he'll take his headset off so he can hear you. We plan to taxi out, take off, climb to 10,000 feet and let you fly the airplane, if you want to, sir. Then we'll come in, make a pass across the runway and land. Then we'd like to make a JATO take-off for you."

The group in the tower watched the B-47 cut loose, watched it consume the runway with thunderous grace and shoot up toward the overcast. Townsend's Mississippi drawl was drifting in the tower radio, as comfortable as the line of an automobile salesman demonstrating a new car. "If you will notice, sir," he was saying at 6,000 feet and 470 miles per hour, "it takes no effort at all to roll the airplane at this speed. The boosted controls do all the work for you. You don't have to do a thing but fly it."

"Yes, that is very good."

"I'm pulling the power back now, sir, so we can make a turn without getting in the clouds."

"O.K.," said K. B., "when you get it turned around and leveled out, let me take it a little to see if I can hold it."

"Yes, sir. There is nothing to holding it. All you have to do is to think about it. The boost does all the holding for you. I'll get away from this thunderstorm and go down away from these clouds and you can have it there. . . . Now, General, you noticed I cut it back to 80 percent rpm before I started that turn. That's way back for jet engines. You would never cruise it back this far, but that was to keep from running through the thunderstorm. You notice that the air speed is still four hundred miles per hour even though I made a 180-degree turn. That will show you what low drag the airplane has."

On the ground Bill Allen turned to McNarney, bubbling over. "That Townsend won't bring him down till he agrees to buy it."

McNarney was smiling. "Certainly sounds that way."

Townsend's voice: "All right, you have it now, sir."

"O.K."

"How do you like those aileron forces, sir?" After a while Wolfe said: "O.K. You take it."

"All right, sir," said Townsend, "we'll go in now and make a low pass over the field. . . . O.K., Ben Werner, we are turning on our downwind leg for a pass over the ramp. Do you have us in sight?"

Ben Werner called, "That is Roger. We have you in sight."

The Stratojet whipped down, buzzed the field, not more than fifty feet off the runway, burned past the tower in a sky-shattering roar, then pulled up hard, steep, nose to the clouds, an arrow shooting straight to the overcast. Wellwood Beall brushed his forehead. "Whew!"

The radio: "O.K., we're down to four hundred miles per hour now . . . O.K., we're down to three hundred. Everything O.K, General?"

"O.K. here."

Then they came down. Townsend was saying: "We have 170 miles per hour, and it seems like we're slow enough to get out and walk, doesn't it?"

"Are you sure you won't stall here?"

"Yes, sir, they built some qualities into this airplane that won't let it stall at this speed."

"It's going to be difficult now to get in that B-17 and go home. You've got me spoiled."

They landed, taxied up. "I enjoyed that," said K. B., climbing out. "Wish we had a little more time to play around. Thanks very much."

"Pleasure was all mine, General."

The group watched Townsend make his JATO take-off, the hissing white tail of eighteen rockets pushing the arrowhead Stratojet up on a broadening, heightening pillar of smoke—speed and sound and sight all bursting in a cry of shocking beauty and power. K. B. was dancing from one foot to the other. When the show was over the General checked his watch. Allen walked over to him. "Leave it to Boeing to really turn out the flying machines, eh, K. B.."

Wolfe grinned. "You go t'hell, Bill Allen." He looked around. "Where's our B-17?"

When the generals had left, George Martin asked Townsend: "That pullout of yours . . . how many Gs did you pull?"

"The limit," said the Major. "I figured the country needs this airplane."

Back in Dayton K. B. Wolfe asked Colonel Warden to his office. "Is the 47 really ready for production? Is it in a practical state?"

"We're convinced of it, General."

Wolfe looked at Warden. "Well, what are we waiting for? Let's get it going." Then he went after it hard. Somewhere he had to dig up the money. He went with the Wright Field group, before the Air Council, Vandenberg, Symington. They were for it. Forrestal, Congress. They got together enough funds to buy ten. $30 million.

On September 3, 1948, a contract was drawn to follow the ten with a program of full production at Wichita. The Wichita plant, which had gone down to 1,100 people after the war, would face another massive buildup—new tooling, re-employment, new techniques, another major manufacturing effort.

The prospect of building the experimental B-52s with slow turboprops seemed lusterless now that the jet-swift B-47 was lined up for production. Yet the 52 work was going ahead fast, under a contract, with a schedule to meet. Once you had a big job like that under contract you weren't likely to let it go, even though the outlook for turboprops was becoming gloomier and the jet prospects brighter, with a new one promised by Pratt and

Whitney, which would turn out 10,000 pounds thrust and would use less fuel per mile, they said, than any previous jet.

Engineers at Seattle worked hard on a proposal to substitute the new jets for the turboprops without disruptive changes that would jeopardize the contract. They found they could get almost as much range, plus better speed, without changing the wing or the twenty degrees sweepback. The jets brought the speed up to five hundred miles per hour. The plane would still be within the 300,000-pound gross weight target. They wrapped up the proposal and took it to Dayton in October 1948, to see if they could sell it.

"The Pratt and Whitneys look good in the 52," said Wells, pulling the presentation out of his briefcase. "We think the Air Force should seriously consider the change."

Colonel Pete Warden looked over the data. Finally he said: "I don't think you've gone far enough." He paused, thumbing the three-view drawings. Wells and Schairer looked at each other.

"I think you ought to have a faster wing," said Warden. "More sweepback, like the B-47. We've been going all this time trying to get maximum range in order to minimize the need for refueling, and we're losing out on combat performance. I think we ought to be going at it the other way around. Maximize the combat performance, the thing that's important. That's what we've got to do, so help me. We've already compromised on range, with refueling. Let's not compromise any more on speed." Warden looked around the room; there was a surprised silence. "This is one of my foolish consistencies," he continued as though in self-justification. "We've always got to go after more speed."

"Let us see what we can do to get you some more," Wells said. He looked at his watch. It was nearing noon on a Friday. "We'll be back Monday morning."

"Kind of swept us off our feet," said Schairer as they filed out.

Back at the hotel suite Ed Wells held council. Bob

Withington and Vaughn Blumenthal from Aerodynamics, project engineer Art Carlsen and Maynard Pennell of Preliminary Design, were with them. All the major branches of engineering were represented. They had with them all the data on the B-52 with both turboprops and jets; also wind-tunnel data on a new jet medium bomber proposal they had hoped to present. Wells unrolled the drawings of the B-52. The twenty degree sweepback looked conservative now. "I think we'd better put this away and start again," he said. They looked at the drawings of the proposed medium bomber; thirty-five degrees sweepback, their latest thinking in jets.

"Double this in size and you just about have it," said Schairer, resourcefully. Wells spread out drawing paper on the top of the bureau and began making a three-view sketch of the scale-up. Art Carlsen and Maynard Pennell worked up a weight breakdown. Withington and Blumenthal calculated the estimated performance. Schairer laid out the lines of the new swept-back wing. By late that night they realized they had created an airplane. It had the range. Weight up only a little, to 330,000 pounds. Thirty-five degrees sweepback, 185 feet span, eight engines. The speed went up to more than six hundred miles an hour—Stratojet performance in an intercontinental bomber.

It had happened so quickly that it seemed like a rabbit out of a hat, but it wasn't that. The answer had been there all the time in their briefcases, in data they had been working on for months. The magic was the realization. Saturday morning, before the stores closed, Schairer rounded up some balsa wood, glue and carving tools, and set to work on a model. Wells organized the engineering data, lined up a public stenographer to put it in document form. By Sunday night it was a clean, thirty-three page report, bound, tilted D-10,000 (they jumped to the nearest round number that wouldn't overlap some document that might be under way in Seattle) and with scale model attached. They all agreed Schairer had outdone himself on the model—handsome, clean, eight-engined, authoritative, sweeping with speed.

Pete Warden was the one who was beaming on Monday morning. "Now we have an airplane," he said. "This is the B-52."

Stratofortress, the new B-52 design was named. As it took form in a huge wooden mock-up at the close of 1948 it held awesome promise—three hundred and thirty thousand pounds of jet airplane, with wings and tail fiercely swept back for near-sonic speed. Its eight jet engines would one day pour out 80,000 pounds of fiery thrust. Translated into horsepower at six hundred miles an hour, that would be ten times the power of a B-29. The plane would go to even higher altitude than the B-47 Stratojet. It was a new airplane in the Flying Fortress tradition, all felt—if only it wasn't too fabulously expensive. The first two experimental models were going to cost an estimated $32 million. How much production quantities would cost was still undetermined.

But this was what airplanes were coming to. Bill Allen was one who realized that only a huge and well-ordered organization could develop and produce a thing like this. It took artisans of a thousand trades to put the parts together, and men with the engineering vision to see how those parts could be united to a single purpose. It would take new investment in research facilities. No unknowns could be left to trial and error.

There was no hope of succeeding in a role such as this, Allen knew, unless you could lay away some money to work with. The year 1948 was the first since the war that would end with a profit, even if a small one. He was encouraged with this, but he assured the staff there was yet a long way to go.

It was becoming irrevocably clear that military airpower would go all-jet. Where the military airplane went, air transportation was never slow to follow. Young Bob Hage and a staff were still working in their corner of Preliminary Design to prove the jet transport practical. Maynard Pennell, new chief of Preliminary Design, a lanky engineer, casual and wistful, quickly caught the contagion of Hage's enthusiasm. The jet appeared to offer all kinds of advantages. It would provide a better ride for the passenger, smoother, faster. Apparent high operating costs came down when you figured how much more work a jet plane could do in a day. It would use lots of fuel, but it would cover the ground twice as fast with that fuel. It could haul twice as many people. Further, Maynard Pennell acknowledged that he liked working on the jet transport. "I guess most of us feel we'd like to work at least a part of our lives on commercial airplanes," he said.

Out of Hage's studies in 1947 and 1948 they now had three proposed transport designs, small, medium and large, all with swept-back wings, the wings in a high position as they were in the B-47 and B-52. Pennell went over the designs with Ed Wells and Wellwood Beall. Both were enthusiastic. Beall talked with Pan American Airways. But the cost of a jet transport development—$15 million or $20 million for the first prototype airplane—was something no airline could afford. Nor could any of the manufacturers. Even if they could there were no Civil Aeronautics Authority regulations to cover jet operations, and no manufacturer could start without knowing the conditions that had to be met. The CAA, for its part, could not be expected to have regulations worked out yet; not enough was known about jet transports. None was flying.

In England, however, the government was fostering an industry program to develop the jet transport in a bold bid to capture world air markets. Beall talked to Bill Allen about this threatened competition. "Shall we go after our own Government? We're stopped dead in our tracks. We'll never get a jet transport unless the Government will finance a prototype."

Allen met the question with a frown. He didn't see any other way around it, but the proposition had a ring he didn't like. "If the Government pays for it, you'll lose control over it, won't you?"

"I don't like it either," Beall said, "but what else can we do? Our own airlines will be buying from the British."

Other manufacturers were puzzling over the dilemma. In Congress a prototype bill was proposed to provide Government financing. But there was no agreement on its provisions. The Civil Aeronautics Board threw up its hands. "How can we get behind a prototype bill if the industry itself can't agree on it?" the Board asked.

In September 1949 Ed Wells went to England for a look at what the British were doing. The de Havilland Company had its jet Comet flying and had a production contract for ten from the Government-owned airline, British Overseas Airways. Sixteen other types were under development with Government assistance. The airlines of other European countries, dollar-poor, were leaning heavily toward the British.

Wells reported on his return that it would take an early start on a prototype to compete. "It will have to be a superior airplane to sell in Europe. Their dollar credits are very limited."

Though there was no answer to the financing problem, Wells and the others couldn't get the jet transport out of their minds. Wells and Schairer and aerodynamicist Johnny Alexander were in Dayton in late October, going over wind-tunnel results on an improved B-52 wing that turned out to be faster than the B-47 wing. There was a weekend to kill. The engineers went over to the Dayton office, sat around talking jet-transport design. "Mostly what we've done is hang a transport body on the B-47," Schairer said. "Maybe we ought to take a fresh look."

The 47 and 52 were high-wing airplanes. That didn't work out too well for a transport. The big wing structure had to go through the top of the cabin and passengers would have to duck. If the plane were ever used for cargo, that would be worse. You'd want to put your big cargo up forward, but you couldn't get it under the wing center structure. Moreover, the floor would be crowded down low in the circular body, where it would be too narrow. A low wing would be much better. The wing structure would go under the floor, to leave a clear cabin and room for passenger baggage underneath.

The landing gear was the problem. It would have to be high enough to keep the jet pods off the ground. Wells thought it ought to be a tricycle gear, not the bicycle gear on the bomber. They sketched a low-wing transport with a tricycle gear folding into the body, four engines in separate pods under the sweptback wings.

"Not bad," was Schairer's verdict.

But the B-52 program itself was becoming an issue as mammoth as the airplane, now grown on paper to 390,000 pounds gross. The Administration in Washington, caught between threats to national security and the threat of inflation at home, had been putting on an economy drive. The giant B-52 would be anything but economical. Then President Truman announced that Russia had exploded an atom bomb; the Capitol grew tense over the question of America's own atom-carrying planes. There was a hurry-up call for cost and delivery estimates on production quantities of B-52s. The figures went to Dayton in January. When Dayton passed them to Washington, there was general alarm. Fifteen million dollars each for thirteen airplanes was the estimate. The big propeller-driven Consolidated B-36 was now in full production, and many thought the Air Force should stick with it. Others felt the B-47 Stratojet, much less costly than the B-52, would be sufficient, though Curtis LeMay, heading the Strategic Air Command, was still calling for more range.

A consulting organization was commissioned by the Government to study the whole military and economic problem. It concluded that planes larger than 150,000 pounds, faster than four hundred nautical miles an hour, were too costly to be included in the military program. Problems of maintenance and handling would be too great, it said. The responsibility would be more than the average flight crew could stand. The country's economy couldn't support such planes.

Bill Allen protested. "But the 52 is the plane the Air Force needs."

15

The last Stratocruiser was delivered to British Overseas Airways Corporations in May 1950. Beall went along. He came back to report that the British jet Comet had been making a hit. If Boeing wanted to bring out a new transport to follow the Stratocruiser, it would have to be a jet. But the bill in Congress to finance an American jet prototype was dead. Beall wondered if Bill Allen would ever agree to put up the $15 million it would cost to build one on their own. That would be four times their total profit in the four years since the war. He stepped through the side door that connected his office with Allen's.

"Bill," he said, "we've got to get you over to England to see what's going on in jet transports."

Bill Allen wasn't swept away. He was concerned over their efforts to sell B-52s and some flying tankers to the Air Force. But he agreed to go to England in the fall.

Then, on June 25, 1950, the strained line between Communism and containment broke at the 38th Parallel in Korea. The United Nations Security Council voted to oppose the aggression of North Korea. Less than five years out of war, America was at war again. Not a whole war; it seemed local. But to those who'd have to go there and fight, it would seem as big as any. And there was the possibility of a bigger conflict, which fired new debate in Washington over the B-52. Curtis LeMay was now insistent. "We've got to have it," he contended. Thomas Finletter, the new Secretary of the Air Force, and Under-Secretary John McCone were strong for Strategic Air Command, but the first need, they said, was for tactical equipment for the Korean campaign. Further, the prototype of the B-52 had not yet been built and flown.

No decision had been made by the Government when it came time for Allen's European trip. Allen had married recently and his wife, the former Mary Ellen Agen, would go with him. Accompanied by preliminary design chief Maynard Pennell, Allen planned to meet Kenneth Luplow, whom Beall had stationed in Europe, and visit the various European airlines. On the way he wanted to stop in Wichita to check on B-47 production progress and get a flight in a B-47. He hadn't yet flown in one of them.

The hour was growing late when the Wichita plant business was finished and Earl Schaefer took Allen out to the flight line. The Stratojet's engines were already going. Allen's senses were a mixture of sound and emotion as he got into coveralls and parachute harness. He climbed up the rungs of the aluminum ladder, through the bottom hatch into the narrow aisleway below the tandem positions of pilot and co-pilot. Pilot Doug Heimburger was in the forward seat, in his parachute and headgear, just about filling the gadget-packed space that was allowed for him, his head up in the slender sky canopy. Somehow Heimburger looked like part of the airplane, the final part to put it in business.

Co-pilot Ed Hartz showed Allen to his place, the navigator's position right out in the bullet nose. Hartz explained the bail-out levers; how to use his parachute; how to connect his oxygen mask to the ship's supply; how to connect it to his bail-out bottle in case of emergency; how to plug the cord from his helmet into the interphone; how to push the button on the cord if he wanted to talk. Allen's head was swimming. There were decals with printed instructions all around him, emergency

procedures. He fastened his heavy seat belt. "Go ahead
and fly it. I'll be O.K."

"Would you like us to do some test maneuvers?"

"No, just a plain flight. I want to see what jet transportation would be like."

Hartz nodded, went back to his place.

The roar of the jets was increasing. But it blanked out
when Allen put on his headgear. He fussed with his oxygen mask, hoping to get it right before they took off. Its
soft rubber edges were like a hand gripping his nose
and mouth and cheeks. He watched the white lines of
the flow meter beside him come on and off as he took a
breath and felt clean, cool oxygen going down. Sharp
voices were coming through the ear pads of his helmet.
"Ready, Ed?"

"Roger."

"Mr. Allen, are you ready for take-off?"

Allen fumbled for the button, heard the strange voice
of himself in his headgear, "All set." It was clipped short,
like the others. His eyes swept the instruments that encased him. He felt himself irrevocably connected to a
tight new world of gross unfamiliarity. He had seen it
often before, but it had suddenly become real—an almost
grotesque mechanical assembly of controlled power
about to be unleashed with him inside.

The cement runway was moving beneath his nose
windows, wheeling around, stopping. There was chatter in his helmet—conversation with the tower about
clearance. The roar that had seemed distant suddenly
swelled.

"Power stabilized let's go," cracked the voice of Heimburger, all in one short breath, and they were moving
down the runway for take-off. Without a quiver they
were off the ground and the nose was pointed high. Allen
felt a great, smooth feeling such as he had not felt before.
They were going up, wind-swift. It seemed so easy, as
if no power were required, merely a hand on some lever
that gradually switched off gravity. Power had always
been synonymous with vibration, motion and noise. All
these seemed absent.

Allen looked at the navigator's bank of instruments. The big hand on the altimeter was turning around like the hand of a clock being set. He looked up through the overhead window, saw cloud fleece slipping by; looked out the side and back; the tips of the swept wings were far behind. Everything was still, no propellers turning, just the ground moving farther and farther away.

They levelled off at 20,000 feet. A firm, authoritative pull indicated they were going into a turn. Allen had his first real sense of the force of this power and speed. It wasn't so much a turning; it could better be described as a change in heading, as the Stratojet cut a great arc and straightened on a new course. Allen adjusted himself in his seat, settled back against his bulky parachute, began to feel comfortable. He was enjoying it.

When the Stratojet headed down again it was an unexpectedly steep, bottomless down. Heimburger was calling for clearance to enter "the pattern" and instructions for best approach to the field. They were gently leveling. The runway came up to meet them, touched under them, raced on by, then came to a stop. Allen untied himself and walked back through the narrow corridor to thank Heimburger and Hartz. "I had no idea it could be so smooth," he told them. He climbed down through the hatch with heavy gear and light heart, met Earl Schaefer's waiting smile. Bill Allen was delighted and proud.

The ride to Chicago, New York and out over the Atlantic in propeller-driven transports seemed slow and prosaic after the whip-quick flight of the Stratojet, but afforded Allen a chance to do some summing up. The question of future business was all mixed with the question of war and peace. In his lifetime there had been two great wars; and now a third? The notion that people could be free to live their own lives, in free competition and cooperation—why was it always being assaulted, first by emperor, then by dictator, now by Communism —state socialism?

Allen pondered the situation of socialism, an insidious

thing, he felt strongly. He thought of England, moving in this direction. Could not free economic activity bring forward a costly development like a jet transport? He wondered. Could such projects only be accomplished by the arm of government, until government controlled all? He had a feeling he might one day have to answer those questions.

In England the big annual air show of the Society of British Aircraft Constructors at Farnborough was on. C. F. Uwins, managing director of the aircraft division of the Bristol Airplane Company, called for Allen at the Hotel Connaught the morning he was to go to Farnborough.

"It's quite a remarkable show this year," the British executive said, "Comet and all."

The field at Farnborough was surrounded by grassy slopes where thousands of spectators were watching the different planes pass low in review. When the de Havilland Comet was announced, a low murmur rose from the crowd. "This aircraft," said the announcer, "has an unrivalled cruising speed of 490 miles per hour at 35,000 to 42,000 feet. An aircraft with extraordinary commerical capabilities."

The Comet was approaching, a low-wing monoplane attractively painted with silver on the underside, white on top and a dividing flash line of blue. Its wings, just slightly swept back, bulged with four buried jet engines. The plane passed low over the field at full jet speed, then pulled gracefully up. "A magnificent combination of speed and beauty," said the announcer. "Note the aircraft's docile handling characteristics."

Allen was impressed. "Appears to be a fine airplane," he told Uwins.

That night Allen joined Mrs. Allen, Maynard Pennell and sales engineer Ken Luplow at a late dinner. Pennell and Luplow had also seen the show.

"How did you like the Comet?" Allen asked.

"It's a very good airplane," said Pennell.

"Do you think we could build one as good?"

"Oh, better. Much better." Pennell's voice sprang out as though from months of waiting for the opportunity. But the business of ordering the meal interrupted them.

"What would you have different from the Comet?" Allen asked somewhat later.

"We think pods are much better than buried engines," Pennell said. "And we could provide a much better landing flap. We'd probably give it more sweepback."

"Everyone over here is anxious to know if Boeing is going to build a commercial jet airplane, Mr. Allen," Luplow said.

Allen didn't respond, and Luplow tried again. "We should have a tremendous advantage with all the engineering and wind-tunnel testing that's gone into the B-47 and B-52."

"Do you fellows think a jet transport would be a reasonable project for us to undertake, in view of our heavy commitments on the B-47 and B-52?" Allen asked.

"I do," said Pennell. Luplow vigorously concurred.

"Why?"

"I think we're in much better shape than we were when we took on the B-29 on top of our B-17 commitments," Pennell said. "We were pretty successful on the 29."

The discussion went on. Pennell and Luplow couldn't tell just how Allen was reacting, except that he kept bringing up the tremendous cost.

Later, while Luplow drove the Allens about the continent to visit heads of airlines, he kept up a discreet offensive, but Allen held his silence. Airline presidents put the question directly. "Does Boeing plan to bring out a jet transport?"

"We're reviewing it," Allen said.

When Bill Allen got back to Seattle, facing up to an accumulated deskload of paper, new orders for KC-97 tankers, and the hard facts of present and future, the romantic view of a jet transport seemed unreal. U.S. airlines weren't crying for the jet. The Air Force wasn't interested. To start such a project without big orders seemed unthinkable. It might mean pouring millions of dollars down the drain. There were no millions to be spared.

In November 1950, the siren of world emergency was screaming again as Communist China entered the Korean war. There was concern that the nations might be heading down the path to World War III, unthinkable as that seemed. The United States had embarked on development of the hydrogen bomb, with Secretary Finletter convinced that Russia was at work on it also. The consideration of aircraft to carry the bomb grew more urgent. B-47s would be available soon, but only the B-52 and the slower B-36 had the range Curtis LeMay was demanding. The experimental B-52 was yet unflown. Visiting in Seattle, Secretary Finletter declared it "of utmost importance" that the XB-52 be brought forward as rapidly as possible. "Do everything you can to expedite it," he told Allen.

Finletter and General Vandenberg were thinking seriously now about putting the big bomber in production even before flight of the prototype, to gain time in the international race, though budget officers still stood aghast at the cost figures. The first two airplanes, originally estimated to cost $32 million, had turned out to cost $53 million. There were those who said the country couldn't possibly afford a B-52 production program.

Robert Lovett, deputy secretary of defense, who was behind the B-29 program before World War II, countered: "It's absurd to say we can't afford to survive."

His counsel prevailed. A starting production of thirteen B-52s was authorized, but Secretary Finletter cautioned that future orders would be determined in competition with a new version of the Consolidated B-36, to be called B-60. The Air Force had given Consolidated approval to bend back the wings of the 36 and install eight jet engines in four dual pods to provide an intercontinental jet at less cost than for a whole new plane. It would be flying before the end of the year, a close race with the B-52 flight date.

"That's all right," Bill Allen said at a staff meeting. "We

William E. Boeing

Phil Johnson

Claire Egtvedt

Pioneering Model 40 mail-passenger plane and (below) "luxury"
Model 80 trimotor used by Boeing Air Transport in late 1920's.

Test pilot Eddie Allen, who established big-airplane flight research; later killed in wartime testing of experimental B-29.

The 247, first of the streamlined, all-metal, twin-engine monoplane transports, introduced by United Air Lines in 1933.

Pan American Airways' 72-passenger "Atlantic Clipper," 1939, inaugurates first large-scale commercial service over both oceans.

Vapor trails trace Flying Fortress mass assault on Hitler's "Fortress Europa" in World War II.

B-29 Superforts, with remote-control gun turrets and pressurized cabins for high altitudes, span the long distance to Japan.

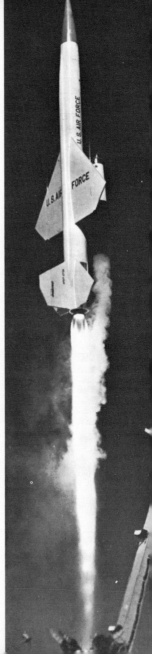

(Above) Spectacular B-47 Stratojet in jet-assisted take-off; first of swept-winged bombers.

(Right) A Bomarc pilotless interceptor is rocket-launched. This U.S. area-defense missile cruises on ramjet power.

(Left) President William M. Allen, about to make flight in B-47 Stratojet.
(Below) Giant B-52 eight-engine intercontinental bomber is refueled by KC-135.
(Bottom) 707 jet prototype rolls from Renton, Washington, plant in May 1954, forerunner of long line of commercial jet transports.

(Upper left) Twin-rotored Chinook helicopter puts combat troops in field at Bong Son, Vietnam.

(Lower left) 727 short-to-medium range trijet transport, shown in steep climbout from Boeing Field, Seattle, brings jet service to small airports.

(Upper right) Minuteman intercontinental ballistic missile, principal U.S. strategic weapon, is launched from underground silo.

(Lower right) Wind tunnel model of supersonic transport with variable-sweep wings.

The 3,600-ton Apollo-Saturn V as it will lift from Cape Kennedy on 7,500,000-pound thrust of five rocket engines; destination: Moon.

have the opportunity of proving our airplane is the best. That's all we ask. If the competition can beat us, we have no complaint. But we'd better make sure it doesn't."

Should they win the competition for a B-52 production order, it seemed reasonable to expect that the plane would need a new matching jet tanker. The propeller-driven KC-97 tanker was in production to refuel the medium-range Stratojet bombers. Now the thought arose of making a *jet* tanker-transport out of the KC-97 later along in its production. The plan looked good all around, an easy change to meet an Air Force need, and a practical road at last to a jet transport. A design was drawn up.

Allen had the drawings and data in his briefcase on a trip East in May. After a meeting in Wichita, he took off with Under-Secretary for Air John McCone in an Air Force transport bound for Washington. A B-47 was taking off about the same time. "Ask him to fly by," McCone told his pilot. The Stratojet darted past. McCone whistled. It made the transport seem to be backing up. The Stratojet cut across in front, circled and overtook them again. Then again. Its crew was enjoying the spree.

"Why don't you build a commercial airplane so we can go like that, instead of riding around in this covered wagon?" McCone asked.

Allen unzipped his briefcase. "Mr. Under-Secretary, I'm glad you brought that up." He pulled out a folder on the jet-powered advanced KC-97 military transport.

"Have you shown this to the Air Force?"

"Sure. But we're not having any success."

In August 1951 that proposal to turn the KC-97 line into a jet tanker-transport line was up for decision in the Air Force. There were objections. "The money is needed for bombers." "B-47s could be made into tankers at less cost." On August 17 came the verdict: negative. The hope of a military jet transport faded.

But salesmen Fred Collins and Ralph Bell reported that airline interest in jets was growing and they felt the Air Force would eventually come around. "Can't we build a prototype model on speculation?" Collins asked Allen. "If we had one flying we could sell it."

Bill Allen cut him down:

"Whose money are you spending?"

Allen felt the military decision against the advanced KC-97 couldn't be allowed to stand. "We've got to keep pushing it," he insisted. "It's too good an airplane for them not to buy."

Two months of pushing and there was no sign of the Air Force's yielding. Allen made the rounds of Washington himself in October. No sale.

When Beall called a meeting of his top engineers, the faces were long. "We've lost this skirmish," Beall admitted. "We've got to fall back and regroup. Let's start again, and see if we can come up with a new design that will be saleable, either to the military or the airlines." Ed Wells thought it should be a faster airplane with a full thirty-five degrees sweepback. Maynard Pennell wanted to abandon the C-97 body entirely and dust off the development work that had been done before the big effort to make the C-97 into a jet. Chief project engineer George Martin agreed the plane "could be slicked up a lot."

Collins and Ralph Bell canvassed the airlines, Military Air Transport Service, Strategic Air Command, to get their ideas, and Engineering went to work on them. The air was clearer now, with no "built-in headwinds" of old designs to be carried along. There was only the question, "What will make the best airplane?"

A design labeled "Model 707" gradually took form. It made the Advanced KC-97 seem out of date. Surprisingly, it looked almost like the design that had been sketched in the Dayton office back in 1949, when Wells and Schairer and the others were killing a Sunday afternoon.

A transport design on paper was a long way from an airplane going together in the shops, just as a B-52 started in initial production was a long way from assurance of continued quantity production, and a big plant and big personnel a long way from assurance that they would be kept busy. The stakes were large. War, near-war, technical advance, jet power had built a business that couldn't rest. Its only security was in progress, just as the airplane's only flight stability was in moving ahead, up to speed. It took a great collection of abilities to make the business go, and it had to keep going to keep the abilities. It couldn't be allowed to stall.

Nor would the business fly on dreams. Vision wasn't dreaming, but seeing through to the accomplishment. Facing this test Bill Allen recognized that much depended on himself. Once again he thought of the check list he had made when he first took the presidency. Was he being the kind of leader that the need demanded, as alive as the business? He knew that to inspire others, he had to have the inspiration himself. But that wasn't hard, he thought when he looked on the B-52 coming along in the shops. He loved to walk out to Final Assembly and gaze at its massiveness. It moved him to think that this was the work of many good men. He wanted to see that those men had a chance to keep going the way they were going.

When vice president-controller John Yeasting balanced the figures for 1951, Allen began to feel a substance behind his hopes for the future. Net earnings, though only two percent of sales, totalled $7 million. "They should be double that in 1952, with deliveries coming up fast," Yeasting said. When Beall and Wells came in with a $14 million program for new engineering research and test facilities, Allen bought it, and sold it to the Board. "The best way I know to get Air Force business is to qualify for it," he said.

There was a spirit to move ahead. Ed Wells brought in the new 707 jet transport design and Allen could tell by the look on Ed's face that he was sold on it, wanted to build it in the worst way.

Allen had been watching the B-52. He felt sure there'd be bigger production orders for it when it got in the air for a demonstration. Once the Air Force got these jet bombers there would surely be a need for jet tankers. It didn't make sense any other way. He felt sure, too, that jet airplanes would sooner or later be used on the airlines. His company was equipped with the experience and the facilities to build those airplanes. But the Government wasn't buying any. The airlines weren't making a move. Time was going by. Other companies would be getting busy, and the British would have the Comet in airline operation very soon.

Act, get things done, move forward. Now was the hour of decision. If they wanted to be in the transport business, now was the time. It was up to him. Could he risk it? He rang for his secretary.

"I'd like you to call a meeting in my office. Call Beall, Ed Wells, John Yeasting, Fred Laudan, Collins. Make it for eleven o'clock." It was a few minutes to eleven now. Miss Hiser nodded, stepped out.

Everything added up. This was the thing to do, Allen was telling himself, with quick, high notes playing in the organ of his mind. It would be a gamble. But wasn't it a good gamble? It would be a good one, if they made it succeed. The board of directors? The stockholders, whose money they'd be spending? The whole prospect would have to be investigated very thoroughly to make sure they weren't being carried away by enthusiasm. He called Miss Hiser again.

"I'd like to dictate a memo. Have six copies for the meeting. This will be a questionnaire." He dictated a string of questions about the practicability of building a jet prototype; cost, facilities, the purpose it would serve, the organization required.

The men were arriving. He told them what was on his mind, and Miss Hiser brought in the questionnaire while the meeting was in progress. Allen looked around the room when all had read it. "I want you to take plenty of time to study out the answers," he said. "We don't want to make a mistake."

In the following weeks, one by one, the answers were coming out "Yes." Emphatically. A rumor went around that something big was about to break. The spring was full of promise. In the midst of it Beall announced the B-52 was ready for flight.

April 15, 1952. Tall, rangy "Tex" Johnston, who'd worn his Texas boots on every important flight since he won the Thompson trophy race in 1946, would pilot the intercontinental giant. Colonel Guy Townsend, B-47 enthusiast, would be co-pilot. The day was bright. General Mark Bradley, Air Force director of procurement and production, was at the plant. Bill Allen and Beall went with him over to the field. The product of an effort now seven years old, its eight jet engines sweeping forward out of swept-back wings, its sharklike tail fin jutting four stories high, was going to reveal in minutes whether it would qualify as America's deterrent to enemy aggression. It was poised at the north end of the 10,000-foot runway.

People were crowding office windows, the ramp, the roof, waiting in suspense. The roar of jet thrust filled eardrums and hearts. The airplane began to move slowly, like a ship under sail, at first. How could it be so slow, wondered Allen, standing on the ramp. He leaned forward, urging it. Tex was lumbering toward them, gaining momentum, thundering with power.

"Pour it!" Allen shouted, his fist following after the ship in a haymaker sweep as Tex roared past them. "Pour her on!" The Stratofortress was accelerating rapidly now, as a jet does once its own speed adds power to its power, and was lifting easily, even lightly into the air.

Tex went on up, circled and raced back over the field, saying with a sky-cracking roar that the airplane was O.K., doing great.

"It's marvelous," said General Mark Bradley, shaking his head. Two hours, fifty-one minutes in the air proved basic flying qualities sound. More flights disclosed less drag and even more speed than expected. The Air Force left little doubt that the B-52 production program would go ahead.

Just six days after the Stratofort's first flight, the meeting to answer Allen's questions on a jet transport convened. Jim Barton of cost accounting said the prototype could be built for $15 million. Maynard Pennell said the plane would meet the range requirements of a military tanker and would have three times the work capacity of the C-97. As a commercial airplane its seat-mile operating cost would be competitive. Schairer said the same prototype could be used to demonstrate both a military and a commercial transport and could provide the performance data needed for production airplanes. Chief engineer Lysle Wood said engineering manpower was available. Experimental manager Al Jacobson said manufacturing manpower and floor space would be available. Beall said Pratt & Whitney would have engines. John Yeasting said the prototype would provide the cost figures needed for pricing production models.

Allen sent the answers to the board of directors and called a board meeting for April 22. Ralph Bell, Pennell, Schairer, Lysle Wood put charts up on easels, the case for the 707, then retired to an anteroom to await the decision. There was discussion in the meeting, but no controversy. Allen recommended the project be undertaken. A motion was made and seconded, unanimously passed. America would have a jet transport.

The organization of the job of building the prototype jet transport followed the April 22, 1952 board meeting lightning-fast. The prototype would be a 190,000-pound low-wing monoplane, 128 feet long, with swept-back wings. It would be built with a cargo body for demonstration to the military, but airline passenger arrangements would carry eighty to 130 passengers. Four jet engines would give a speed of 600 miles an hour. Senior project engineer Maynard Pennell and his staff began getting drawings to the shops. Airlines were weekly visitors to the walled-off area where the ship was being put together. But no airline was ready to buy, nor could firm prices or delivery commitments be given them until Air Force plans for the tanker-transport version were known. Allen and Beall campaigned for a military order, but without result.

Air Force interest warmed in the spring of 1954. Strategic Air Command said it needed a jet tanker. Air

Secretary Harold Talbott was impressed with the ship. To hold good an October 1956 delivery date they had offered, Allen authorized the start of engineering and tooling work on the production airplane at company expense while the Government decision was awaited. The chips on the poker table were stacking high, win all or lose all. There still were advocates for turbo-prop tankers in the Air Force, still those who wanted to use converted B-36s or B-47s as tankers. The Air Council met in Washington to resolve the differences. No word of a decision.

The prototype 707 was ready to roll out of the Renton plant on May 15, 1954. At the four o'clock shift change the big doors started climbing, folding into canopy position overhead. A band played. Out of the shadow the ship moved into the sun, gleaming in fresh paint, rich yellow on top, with copper-brown trim. Employees gave it a champion's applause. Guest William E. Boeing, seventy-two, watched with moist eyes.

On May 21, late afternoon, Tex Johnston was taxiing and testing brakes. He felt the side of the airplane going down, then a jolt. George Martin and Maynard Pennell rushed out to see the 707 crippled on the ground, its left landing-gear collapsed.

Bill Allen got the news in Wichita, wondered if it would delay the Air Force decision. When he got back Ed Wells came in to acknowledge that the trouble was due to a fault in design and a poor piece of steel. That hurt, but Allen couldn't manage a reprimand. Instead, he felt the need was for encouragement. "We don't like mistakes," he said, "but the important thing is to profit by them."

The repairs would take six weeks. While they were being made the Air Force announced it had decided it wanted jet tankers, not turboprops, and asked for competitive production proposals by August. The way was open. If only the flight test went well.

On July 14 the jet 707 was ready for flight: tomorrow at 7:00 A.M., weather permitting. In the morning, news cameramen and mechanics were on hand at five, watch-

ing a moist grey sky. It didn't look good. Flight was postponed to 2:00 P.M. At noon a big blue hole opened over
the Renton airport and the sun blazed down. A truck
towed the sleek giant three-quarters of a mile to the airport apron. Superintendent Joe Donnelly wore a smile
with the two deep furrows that were in his forehead.
"She's in good shape," he told Allen.

Tex Johnston and his co-pilot Dix Loesch got out of a
car and walked toward the plane, bundled in heavy jack-
ets, life vests and parachute packs. They paused for pictures. Allen stepped over to Tex, gripped his arm firmly.
"How do you feel?"

"Never better."

"She's in your hands, boys. Good luck."

The rest came quickly. White-overalled ground crews
moved the crowd back. Two minutes to two, Number
One engine whined up to high key and its jet blast
roared. The other three engines were started. Tex taxied
out to the runway end, wheeled around, held his power
with the brakes a few seconds—no long run-ups with jet
planes—and began to roll. Speed and noise increased. The
nose came up and 2,000 feet down the runway the 707
was off the ground, then climbing radically up.

Gleaming with color the swept-winged 707 made
a regal descent on Boeing Field a little past 3:30. Tex
wheeled over toward the flight-test hangar. It was a
happy day. Chief engineer George Martin stood in shirt
sleeves, hands in pockets, wreathed with delight. A field
car drove up behind Bill Allen and someone pulled him
out of its path.

"If it had hit me now I wouldn't have felt it," Allen
said.

16

Against the exhilaration of an American jet transport flying in 1954 stood an ominous threat, awesome almost beyond comprehension. The U.S. had exploded a hydrogen bomb; then in nine months Russia exploded her own. Communist Dictator Joseph Stalin had died, but no one knew what new power play was in the making in the Kremlin. The Korean peace had been signed, but a new war was raging in Indo-China. Dienbienphu had just fallen to Red rebels. World peace was a tinder-dry powder plant with matches burning here and there. The powder in that plant was an unthinkable hydrogen nuclear concoction that could wipe out a city or a nation. Yet it was also a marvelous new power uncovered by modern discovery and invention.

Few had yet learned what had really happened to science, nor could any estimate what still lay ahead in the twentieth century. It had been a little less than fifty years since the seams had been opened on orthodox knowledge of the physical world. It had been less than ten years since the new concept had been proved in the atom bomb that loomed now so menacing or promising. The manner in which that development evolved was a classic example of vision and effect, with implications for technology of every sort.

It was a story that began in Berne, Switzerland, in 1905.

A young man who had taught himself calculus and analytical geometry, because he sought knowledge, was
working at the patent office in Berne, studying for his
Ph.D. degree at the University of Zurich. Albert Einstein didn't agree with those who said the discovery of
X-rays and radioactivity had left nothing more to be uncovered. He puzzled over a classic experiment done by
A. A. Michelson and E. W. Morley in Cleveland in 1881.
It proved that the speed of light wasn't affected by
earth's movement through the "ether" of space. There
appeared to be but two possible conclusions, one as dev-
astating as the other to accepted laws of physics and astronomy. Either there was no ether—no medium to sustain light waves—or the earth wasn't moving but standing
still.

The problem got Einstein to thinking about speed and
motion. Shouldn't the speed of light from a train head-
light be the speed of light plus the speed of the train, as
two plus two is four? But that couldn't be, according to
the Michelson-Morley experiment. The speed of light
was always the same, regardless of motion of the sender
or receiver. Something was wrong. Yet Einstein felt
within him the sure mathematics of a universal order. "I
can't believe that God plays dice with the universe," he
said. There had to be an explanation.

Speed was a measure of time as well as distance. Maybe
time had something to do with it, Einstein thought, and
he got back on his imaginary train. Suppose a lightning
bolt struck in front of the train and another struck behind it at the same instant, the same distance. It would be
the same instant for someone on the ground, halfway
between the two bolts. Would it be the same instant for
him, if he were moving on the train? He imagined himself riding precariously on the train top with mirrors to
see both lightning flashes instantaneously. He didn't think
he'd see both at once. Surely the lightning bolt ahead of
the train would seem to come first, because he was
moving towards it. How could he be sure?

Suppose his train were going at the speed of light, he
reasoned. Then he'd never see the lightning behind be-

cause the light could never reach him. Yet the man standing right beside the track, directly opposite him, would
insist that the two bolts struck simultaneously. He could
come to only one conclusion. Time varied with the
speed of the observer. For the observer traveling at the
speed of light, time stopped. Would anyone believe it?

Einstein knew he'd have to dig deeper. What was
time? he asked. He had to conclude that it was mostly a
comparison. Our clocks compared events with the turning of the earth, our calendars compared with the earth's
orbit around the sun. Those were measures of distance.
Would speed affect measures of distance, too? Sure
enough, just as with time, he concluded that his measuring rod of distance would shrink to nothing, if he could
reach the speed of light.

The theory, Einstein decided, would explain nicely the
enigma of the Michelson-Morley experiment, why light
always struck an instrument at the same speed, regardless
of the speed of the instrument. Because as the instrument
approached the speed of light, timing clocks slowed
down, measuring yardsticks shrunk. But it was hard to
believe.

"It goes against common sense," people argued.

"What is common sense but a deposit of prejudices laid
down in the mind prior to the age of eighteen?" Einstein
asked.

He kept on, year on year, realizing that in the Michelson-Morley discovery about light there was an opportunity to correct some big mistakes in theories of physics.
Not so much mistakes as limitations. Newton's law of
physics worked all right at speeds people travelled, but
not at 186,000 miles a second. Yet in radiation and light,
scientists were dealing with these speeds. New laws were
needed, as new laws were needed when speeds in airplane design went up.

"If time and distance are relative, not absolute, what
about mass, the other basic quantity of physics?" Einstein asked. Most people thought of mass as weight, but
the physicists knew it as resistance to change in motion.
A freight train was harder to move than a bicycle. Did

that change also with speed? It had to, Einstein reasoned, just like the other two quantities. Revolutionary, but his mathematics proved it true. Mass increased with motion. As a body reached the speed of light, its mass appeared to increase to infinity.

Interesting to contemplate, but of what value? Einstein didn't let go. His theory of relativity was leading to an inevitable conclusion. What was mass, he asked, if it was so expandable, if it grew with motion? What was motion? Motion was a form of energy. Mass and energy must be just different forms of the same thing!

Einstein's formula of the equivalence of mass and energy—energy was equal to the mass times the square of the speed of light—opened wide the doors of nuclear research. Laboratories proved his theory, bit by bit. In 1933 the Nazi regime, disliking the spelling of Einstein's name, stripped him of his property, his professorships, his German citizenship. He came to America as a haven of freedom.

The war approached. Scientific knowledge became a critical war commodity. According to Einstein's formula a pound of coal would yield eleven billion kilowatt-hours of electricity, if its mass could be converted to energy. Burning the coal used only one three-billionth of its energy. How could the rest be unlocked? The clue came in 1939 when scientists in England split a modified uranium atom, one of the heaviest of atoms, converting a small part of its mass to energy. It was then that Albert Einstein wrote to Franklin D. Roosevelt of the possibilities of the atomic bomb.

Twenty pounds of "heavy" uranium, a critically large mass, a trigger to start its atoms splitting, a chain reaction of atoms splitting atoms, and Hiroshima was destroyed. That was atomic fission—the A-bomb. But atomic fission released only one-thousandth of the energy of the uranium atom. The principle led on. Fuse two atomic nuclei together—atomic fusion—and the two would have less mass than before. The rest would be changed to energy. The decrease in mass of the neutrons had to be matched

by liberated energy to preserve the pure mathematics of
Einstein's equation, and this would be felt in heat and
light and blast. "Heavy" hydrogen atoms could be fused
together, but only at phenomenal heat. The energy of the
A-bomb could produce that heat. Now it was the fusion
bomb, the thermonuclear hydrogen bomb. At Bikini it
was proved.

The principle led on. After fusion, at terrific heat, the
nuclear energy could be used, the theory went, to split
more atoms, plain uranium atoms, unprocessed. That
would release more energy from fission. The process
could go on and on. There was energy to burn, as was
evident in the sun and every star in the sky. The creep-
ing realization of science in its frightening mid-century
decade was that it faced as never before a momentous
challenge—the challenge of control.

The threat of atomic aggression weighed heavily on
Lysle Wood, head of the Boeing pilotless aircraft division
in Seattle. Wood's division had been given the job of developing a long-range defense missile that could automatically intercept and destroy potential atomic attackers
before they appeared in the sky overhead. Sometimes,
when he was walking the beach on an evening at Cape
Canaveral, Florida, where test work was under way, he
would imagine those atom bombers approaching high
over the Atlantic in the darkness, unseen in the peaceful
Florida night. Just the thought was enough to shatter his
own peace, because the Bomarc missile his men were
building had not yet been successfully fired. The pressure he was feeling reached a climax on the morning of
February 24, 1955.

It was drizzling when Wood and his assistants George
Stoner and George Snyder left the Tradewinds hotel at
Melbourne, Florida, and drove northward before day-
break toward Patrick Air Force Base. It had rained all the
previous day, and they were praying for the break that
would make this the day they would prove Bomarc to
the doubters in the Pentagon. Bomarc was a pilotless
interceptor, about the size of an early pursuit plane but

much slimmer and longer—forty-seven feet from pointed nose to fire-belching tail. It would have a much longer range than existing defensive missiles, to hunt out and intercept high-speed enemy bombers while they were still far from vital targets. This called for intricate guidance equipment.

Keith McDaniel, the field test engineer, was preparing the missile on its firing pad, in hope that a change in the weather would bring the clear skies they must have for the tracking cameras.

Snyder was quipping that they'd "better see the Chamber of Commerce about this Florida sunshine." Nonetheless, Wood had the feeling that this was the day. Driving across the beach flats of low-growing palmettos on the approach to Cape Canaveral, Wood was thinking of the long, rough road by which the missile project had come. It had begun back in 1945.

Wellwood Beall and a delegation of engineers were on their way to Dayton. Bob Jewett, quiet, thoughtful head of the preliminary design unit, and Dr. Cecil Stedman, a former professor of electrical engineering whom Ed Wells had put to work on automatic-pilot and flight-test instrument development, were in the group. Beall had been talking with them about the possibilities of guided missiles. There had been recurring flurries of scientific interest in this subject all through the war. Then, when the Germans began launching their V-1 buzz-bombs in mid-1944, and later the V-2 rockets, Hap Arnold set up a crash program for 1,000 jet-propelled bombs a month, similar to the V-1s, to be built by the Northrop Company. Wright Field laboratories got busy on other related ideas, but nothing much was being done yet with defensive missiles.

"We know how to build a strategic bomber; why shouldn't we be the ones to build a defense against it?" Beall asked. Some day this new defense might become the country's greatest need, he thought. In Dayton they went to see General Frank Carroll, head of the experimental engineering section. "We're interested in getting into the missile business," Beall said. "What programs do you have?"

"How would you like to take on a long-range missile-bomb?" the General asked. He had been actively pursuing this subject.

"No, we want to develop something that will shoot down the bomber. Ground-to-air."

The General wasn't sure whether this would come within their jurisdiction or under the Ordnance Department of the Army. But the Air Force would like to get into the field, he said. It would have to be an aircraft, with aerodynamic qualities, not just an improved form of anti-aircraft gun.

"That's what we propose," Beall said, "a pilotless aircraft, a ground-to-air pilotless aircraft."

Carroll asked them to make him a written proposal for a study project on it, and he'd see.

The project GAPA, for Ground-to-Air Pilotless Aircraft, got started. By 1946, at a desert outpost on the great salt flats of Utah, Keith McDaniel and his men were firing needle-nosed GAPAs by the dozen. They'd watch through the armored glass windows of their dugout while the slender "bird," with a blast of smoke and a piercing scream, burned its way high in the sky, then fizzled out and plummeted to earth. Rocket-powered, the GAPA was guided by the pointing of a radar beam at its target. Tests were going well. But just when the missile seemed to be approaching the production stage, with ramjet power, the project was ordered cancelled. A Washington decision in 1949 put all missiles of less than a hundred miles range under Army instead of Air Force jurisdiction. The Army had a project of its own under way, called Nike.

Beall was asked to bring his GAPA people to Dayton to discuss the cancellation. There was a big meeting with Lieutenant General Ben Chidlaw, head of the Air Matériel Command, Brigadier General Sam Brentnall, deputy director of research and development, and others. Beall started to defend GAPA.

"There's no use talking about GAPA. It's dead. What else do you have to propose?" the Air Force officers asked.

Beall, caught flat-footed, looked at Bob Jewett. Jewett and his engineers had been giving some study to a new electronic guidance system that would work for a longer range defensive missile, but he wasn't prepared.

"Shall we tell them what we've been thinking about?" Jewett asked Beall.

"Go ahead."

The proposal was complex, involving a good deal of ground equipment. The officers were interested. "We have the University of Michigan working on something like that," they said. "Why don't you go and see them? You may be able to bring us a joint proposal."

They did. The result was Bomarc.

After the hydrogen bomb development and the knowledge that Russia was working on one, the heat was on U.S. missile projects. There was progress to report on Bomarc, but the Pentagon didn't seem impressed. The project was a tedious climb up a new technical path: guidance by electronic computers, automatic target-seeking, rocket take-off and then conversion to ramjet motors for supersonic flight. Thousands of devices had to play their roles perfectly without human aid.

Bill Allen had kept asking Lysle Wood about progress. "It's discouraging at times, but we're making headway," Wood had said. It was months since the last firing. No one had built a successful ramjet engine of the size needed. The ramjet was a big pipe that literally rammed air in the front end by moving ahead at speeds above the speed of sound, fanning a tremendous fire of fuel which would expand it and send it racing out the back in a mighty jet push. The plan now was to continue the testing with improved rocket engines while better ram-jet engines were developed. The rockets were simpler, burning a fuel mixture with built-in oxygen.

On August 5, 1954, the interim missile was ready, erected on the firing pad in Florida, with rocket motors charged for the sky. Wood, Keith McDaniel, other engineers watched. At count zero a mountainous roar of ground-pushing flame sent it sizzling upward. Then in a maneuver its wing pulled off and it fell.

Wood called Allen to report. "We didn't stay in the air very long. It's hard to take, but sometimes we can learn more from a failure than a success." Telemeter data was fruitful. To the engineers the flight was not lost. But they had trouble selling that viewpoint in Washington.

"Get us a missile that will keep flying," the men at the Pentagon demanded. They wanted to see it fly with ramjets, as it was supposed to do. Wood feared that to delay the tests until the ramjets were ready might kill the program; people lost interest and faith if something wasn't happening. But to continue making merely short flights might also kill it. He organized a blitz to get a new missile flying with ramjets by March 1955.

To Bob Jewett, heading up the team of missile engineers, the issue was plain. He remembered how the GAPA program had been killed just when he felt they were succeeding. There was interservice rivalry in missiles. Army, Navy and Air Force all were in it. A failure of the next critical test and they might lose everything—ten years' work.

The problems of Bomarc were profoundly technical. They were dealing with a shell tightly stuffed with complex upon complex of electronic, mechanical and hydraulic invention. There were thousands of gadgets, each tiny one monumental in importance. Threading through one of the systems in thought was like counting the dew drops on a spider's web without retracing a thread. When a system interrelated with another system interrelated with still another failed to work, and the designer came up for a decision between alternatives, it took the wisdom of Solomon to choose the right compromise, in the knowledge that the missile's success depended on not one but on every decision.

But those weren't the hardest problems, Jewett felt. The hardest were the unknowns, where there was nothing to choose between, no answer. The malfunction of one secret device was a riddle inside an enigma. Jewett prayed for X-ray vision to see through it, but there seemed no answer. Then when he was puttering in his basement shop at home one day, his mind free of Bomarc, the answer came. He took it back to the plant and things began to work out.

Other engineers were coming up with answers, the same way. "You aren't likely to find the solution by staying too close to the problem," George Schairer explained it. "You get all wound up in it and you don't see the obvious." It was significant, he thought, that the first Boeing pursuit plane was born in a Pullman car; the Monomail, first smooth-skin monoplane transport, at the Los Angeles air races; the swept wings of the B-47 Stratojet on a trans-Atlantic airplane ride; the final B-52 in a hotel room in Dayton; the low-wing jet transport in the Dayton office, engineers away from home on a Sunday afternoon.

The tortuous problems of Bomarc appeared to have been solved on February 24, 1955. The new ramjet engines were installed. The missile's myriad parts when last checked had been clicking in perfect order. Now Lysle Wood could see the glaring floodlights of the firing pad as he approached Cape Canaveral.

Test engineer Keith McDaniel had operations well started when they arrived. The Bomarc was being slowly raised, looking out at space with eyes that were hidden in a labyrinth of wires, tubes and transistors. Flight controls drooped in passive readiness on the missile's short wings and fins.

A man came up to McDaniel, shaking his head. "We just got the weather from Central Control. It's putrid."

"Any hope in the next three or four hours?"

"Not much. Maybe this afternoon."

General Yates, commander of the base, had said he wanted to fire a Matador missile if the Bomarc wasn't ready. It was a test that wouldn't require clear skies for photographic recordings. It would tie up the firing range for four hours. McDaniel told the General to go ahead. Then in an hour or so beautiful Florida blue was breaking overhead, but a heavy overcast approaching in the distance. They waited nervously while Matador was set up, and while it ran into delay. Finally it was fired and the range was free for Bomarc at two o'clock, but now the sky was covered again. McDaniel dashed off to Central Control to see if the General would keep the range open overtime, should the weather clear. Yates agreed to keep it cranked up until five.

Keeping the range "cranked up" for a missile firing was something of a grand alert. There were fire crews, ambulance crew, security guards, crews attending radar batteries, some making sure the air was clear of traffic, others manning the tracking radars. At fringe locations were the theodolite operators, "sky surveyors" ready to plot the course of a man-made shooting star. Close in were the automatic cameras and, at more remote locations, manned photographic stations, all necessary for the engineers to piece together the story of the missile's short life. Ranging at sea were B-17 Flying Forts with great horns protruding from their bomb bays to bellow a warning to any boats which might enter the prohibited area. All these—a 275-man team—stood by while the group on the firing pad waited, watching the sky.

It was after four when George Snyder spotted a blue patch to the south. "Maybe we're going to get a break." They watched the hole widen, but it remained off to the side.

"Coax it over," Wood said. The blue sky seemed slowly to open. The clouds were thinning. The theodolite crews said they thought they could track. Now it was 4:15.

"Let's take a run for it," McDaniel proposed, and Wood nodded. There was a quick dispatching of people. The firing pad became a burst of activity, like the deck of a flat-top being readied for a raid.

"Minus forty-five minutes," came the authoritative voice of the countdown man on the PA system, signalling that the final race was on. Mechanics took away the support wagon that kept the missile from being upset in event of a sudden squall. The firing crew was busy in the blockhouse, a strongbox with walls and ceiling of thirty-six inch reinforced concrete. Close under the viewing window was the "push button," not a button but a console where a white-shirted operator sat ready to play his electronic notes of command. Green lights were coming onto the big panel as various preparations were completed.

"Minus forty minutes." Out on the pad the photographers made pre-launching pictures. "Minus thirty-five." A top mechanic set the destruction system in the missile that would blow it up if it ran wild in the air. Others left on the firing pad were gathering up kits and hastily vacating.

At minus thirty the last man climbed down into the hatch in the concrete, closed the heavy lid over him and retreated through the long tunnel to the blockhouse, inserting plugs in wiring circuits as he went along. He appeared in the blockhouse at minus twenty-five. Bomarc was out there alone. "It's armed and ready," he reported.

Everyone was cleared from outside the blockhouse area to Building C, two-thirds of a mile down the road. Wood and the Seattle party joined a crowd of a hundred or so there, made up mostly of men who had finished their part in the preparations and now awaited the show.

"Minus fifteen." Automatic operations had begun in the blockhouse. The men at the big panel were watching a pair of dials come up.

"Pressures are O.K." It was McDaniel's voice on the loud speaker. Then the count-down announcer: "Minus twelve."

"Electronics is on. Checks O.K." Telemetering reception from range stations was monitoring O.K. "Minus ten." At their unseen posts military and civilian technicians were tensing for kick-off.

"Minus nine . . . eight . . . seven. . . ." McDaniel had his clearance from the range safety officer. Shipping lanes were clear. "Six . . . five . . . four. . . ." The range was a symphony of readiness. The great eyes of radar scanned the sky in their measured rhythm. Bomarc sat erect on her explosive tail. Even veteran crewmen began to tighten as the announcer intoned: "Minus one hundred eighty seconds." The dials on the big board verified that the missile had gone on automatic control. The automatic watch and sequencer had taken over. "Minus one hundred seventy . . . one hundred sixty . . . one hundred fifty. . . ."

Outside Building C the conversation was dying out. At minus one hundred twenty the sequencer switched the missile onto internal power. Batteries began paying their short, powerful life to run the ship. The monitoring crew in a trailer outside the blockhouse worked machinelike, snapping switches, watching tape roll out of a recording machine; one minute to check autopilot and telemetering mechanisms on internal power.

"Hold!" the announcer shouted at minus thirty seconds.

The intercom went silent. Wood at Building C was on needles.

McDaniel's voice came back on in reassuring tone. One of the battery voltages wasn't right and there was an automatic stop in the sequence. The machine would hold the kick-off if all the players weren't ready. When the voltage indicator drifted into tolerance range, McDaniel decided to override it. "Tell the range we'll resume," he ordered.

The announcer called fifteen seconds warning, then resumed his count. At Building C all faces were now in one direction. The seconds kept coming. "Ten, nine, eight, seven, six, five. . . ."

A belch of smoke out of the missile confirmed that the starting flares were lighted. It was committed now, no retrieve. ". . . Four, three, two. . . ." George Stoner had both arms high in the air with a stopwatch in each hand, thumbs ready to time whatever might come. It was his personal release.

". . . One, *Zero.*" Stoner's arms came down. There was a roar, a moment while pressures built up, then a great pot of smoke and flame obliterated the firing pad and the Bomarc shot straight up . . . upon a pillar of fire.

The announcer was still counting, ". . . Four, five, six, seven, eight, nine, ten," then there was only the continu-

ing roar as the missile pushed on through the light overcast and flattened on its course toward the blue area
down-range. Every eye on the base was another tracking theodolite, glued to its progress. Wood was bent toward it, straining to see what was going on up there, if
the ramjet was cutting in as it should. He could hardly
distinguish the trail behind the broken cloud screen.

Then it pushed right out into the blue, with a heavy
column of brilliant sun-lighted vapor trail behind. That
meant ramjet full-on. Wood's head began to swim with
joy. Straight as a die, Bomarc was pressing along on its
track. It disappeared over the heavy cloudbank in the distance and left them standing there for a moment, staring
into that cloud.

17

The long, drab reels of paper that came out of the telemetering recorders at Patrick Air Force Base told a story that was good news about Bomarc. Fed through electronic computing machines and analyzed, the figures held the key to more work ahead, more progress toward a system for H-bomber defense.

Every advance in defense called for a like advance in offense, and vice versa, as the grim game of keeping ahead of potential enemies was played. Hence there was a parallel quest for new concepts in strategic weapons that would be more difficult to intercept. The B-52 was just entering production, both in Seattle and at Wichita, Kansas, when a serious effort was started to look well into the future at weapon possibilities for the 1965-70 time period. Ed Wells and George Schairer had obtained an Air Force study contract for this purpose in 1953, labeled MX-2145. Schairer had appointed Ben Ruffner, a relative newcomer to the company, who had a master of science degree and had been teaching aeronautical engineering at New York University and Oregon State, as chief of a systems analysis unit to conduct this and other studies.

Adventurously, the group gave consideration to a range of far-out possibilities, including nuclear-powered aircraft and an uncanny craft that would be boosted by rocket to extreme altitudes, there to glide like a missile to its target. They looked also at ballistic missiles and improved guidance systems. Chiefly they looked at supersonic bombers. In charge of this latter exploration, Ruffner placed "T" Wilson, a rapidly-advancing young engineer with an advanced aeronautical degree and just back from a year's study at M.I.T. as a Sloan Fellow in industrial management.

Convair had won a competition for an advanced medium bomber—the B-58—that would be capable of a supersonic dash over the target. The task of developing a future airplane that could fly at supersonic speeds all the way to the target, at strategic ranges, seemed formidable; enormous quantities of fuel would be consumed. But Charles Grotz, the power plant engineer in the group, had found an exciting prospect in supersonic engine theory. They could get higher supersonic jet engine performance by putting less demands on the compressor that furnished the air for combustion to the engine, he held. It sounded like a contradiction, but at higher speeds the air would be compressed also as it was rammed into the engine inlet. That sudden squeezing would heat it. Then, if you ran the compressor-turbine in the engine at its usual rate, it would add more heat than the turbine blades could stand. The air would become so hot, in fact, that you couldn't get it much hotter by burning fuel in it, and the whole cause would be lost. The answer would have to be in doing more compressing in the inlet and less in the engine, was the conclusion. With the use of some General Electric data that confirmed this theory they were able to get startling results in performance calculations.

There was another theory, intriguing to Bob Hildebrand, a master aerodynamicist on the team, that the skin friction which generated the "drag" on the airplane would grow less as speed was increased to between three and four times the speed of sound, because of the heat generated at the surface of the wing. Hildebrand was enthusiastic over a set of experiments at Ames Laboratories that confirmed the theory. Added to the new engine approach the possibilities were sensational. "It means we can go farther at Mach 3 than we can at Mach 2," Hildebrand exclaimed. That would be three times rather than twice the speed of sound.

But they would be exchanging a drag problem for a heat problem, "T" Wilson reminded him. "Aluminum poops out at just over Mach 2."

"We can always use steel," Don Cox, the structures and weights man on the team suggested not too seriously. It seemed preposterous because of the weight. But when he ran his calculations and saw the gain, he became convinced it could be done.

It was a daring concept, but worthy of presenting, they all thought. But outside the study group there were questions. The assumptions were too great. Management's job was not only to probe ahead, but to do so with responsibility. Even if the tremendous problems of heat and material could be overcome, the range would be insufficient to meet Air Force requirements. The general view was that there would be another round of bomber development to follow the B-52, but not at this extreme speed. The radical idea did not sell.

More exotic still was the boost-glide concept for a future strategic weapon. It was not a new concept; it had for some time been the subject of intriguing contemplation within limited circles, but the talk had seemed on the verge of the space-fantastic. Now the subject was getting serious consideration. The approach was prompted in part by the projected Bell X-2 experiment, which was to attain speeds in the neighborhood of 2,000 miles an hour by lifting a craft under the bomb bay of a B-52 Superfortress, then letting it go in a blast of rocket power at high altitude where it would be clear of the heavy drag of low-level atmosphere.

Unlike the jet the rocket needed no air, carrying its own oxygen supply for combustion. Nor did it need atmosphere to push on; all the push was within itself. The mightily expanding gases of its burning fuel had an irresistible urge to get out of the combustion chamber by nearest exit, which was a jet nozzle that squeezed the hot gas to an even higher speed. All this had the effect of a tremendous backward kick against itself, to drive the rocket forward. The less atmosphere in the way of its mad dash, the better; therefore, to take advantage of rocket power you should get up as high as possible—beyond the capability even of the X-2.

If once the device got far enough out of the earth's cloak of atmosphere, when its thrust was cut off it could sail along without power until gravity pulled it back. If it could get going fast enough, it would defy gravity and stay up there almost indefinitely, because its speed would keep trying to drive it in a straight line while the earth's curvature would cause the surface to be dropping farther and farther below. This would mean, in effect, that the vehicle would want to be going *up*, increasing its altitude in terms of the earth's curved surface. So there would be a point—at a speed of about 26,000 feet per second—where the force driving it upward would just offset the force of gravity pulling it down. That balance would hold it in orbit.

No rocket had yet reached the speed this would require. But there was a trick that could be used to get to the higher altitudes that would permit these speeds. The ascent you could get would depend on the velocity of the jet blast and the weight of fuel and structure you had to lift. So you could take it in steps. Just as the X-2 could go faster by taking off from a mother plane at high altitudes than it could by taking off from the ground, so could the rocket. The hardest push was up through the thick, base atmosphere and that was also where you'd have the heaviest load of fuel. So you could use one big rocket to push a smaller one up to high altitude, let the heavy fuel chambers of the big one drop away and take the lighter one on from there. Then you could let that rocket boost a still smaller one to a great altitude, there to drop away and allow the lightest rocket to race on across the top of the atmosphere. This multi-stage principle was to be used to give a ballistic missile intercontinental range.

Walter Dornberger of Bell, from his rocket experience in Germany, had been urging the Air Force to try boosting a special light bomber to extreme altitude by rocket, then let it glide to the target at the hypersonic speed of this push. That was the boost-glide concept. If the friction of the air heated the vehicle to the danger point, it could zoom to higher altitude to cool, skipping in and out of the heavier atmosphere to slow down, as a flat stone would skip along the surface of water.

General Bill Irvine, now deputy chief of staff for matériel, was among those fascinated with the idea. He could see the possibility of rocketing a bomber high enough to reach a distant target, then let its momentum carry it on around the world to get home. It was a startling plan, dependent on much development, but encouraging enough to warrant more work, Irvine thought. Boeing was given a contract to continue the study under the code name ROBO—rocket bomber. But it seemed something far out in the future. There were neither the power nor the materials available. The cost would be prodigious.

The nuclear-powered bomber that was studied under project MX-2145 appeared even less realistic, enticing as was the contemplation of the light-weight fuel load made possible by the use of a nuclear reactor. Unfortunately, all the weight saved would have to go into heavy shielding to protect the crew from deadly radiation, and into the energy-converter itself. Then the landing gear would have to be beefed up to land that weight, making it still heavier. The plan did not work out.

All these efforts attested the fact that Boeing wanted to stay with bombers as strategic weapons. Engineer Ben Cohn, whom Wells had stationed in Los Angeles, was questioning this premise and urging that the company get into the long-range missile business. In Los Angeles General Bernard "Benny" Schriever was heading the secret Air Force branch sponsoring intercontinental ballistic missile developments—the Convair ATLAS and Martin TITAN. Both Wells and Schairer felt Cohn was right, but there was still a prevalent view that a missile aimed at such a far away point could not be as accurate as a bomber, and certainly would not have the reliability and flexibility of an airplane with man at the controls. "What are you trying to do, kill the bomber?" many would ask. Further, the ICBM projects were staked out; there appeared to be no big jobs in the field yet unassigned. Boeing had earlier elected to take on the defensive missile—BOMARC—this was maturing into a substantial product line. With test firings successful the Air Force was ready in 1955 to order BOMARC into production.

While the consideration of future weapons went on, the Air Force was increasing its orders for B-52 jet bombers, the materialization of Curtis LeMay's dream of an effective global "big stick" to deter aggression. It seemed clear that the country's retaliatory strength in case of war would still depend on bombers for a long time to come, and that the next immediate development in this field would have to be a supersonic bomber capable of replacing the B-52—capable of matching its long range. When an Air Force competition loomed in this category, it became at once the principal new business goal.

An all-out engineering attack was launched on the new bomber objective. Work centered on a large airplane of slower supersonic speed than the earlier study group's superheated "Mach 3-1/2" proposal, but with "afterburners" on its jet engines that would give it a thunderous roar of extra power by pouring new fuel into the burning jet stream, to add sensationally to the speed at the target end of the run. As with the B-58, it was a compromise to add range; the after-burners would be too extravagant consumers of fuel for use on the entire trip.

Study was given to increased power possibilities with faster-burning jet fuel mixtures. Coming forward in its aura of mystery and secrecy, the aircraft was guardedly referred to as the "chemical bomber." But the best design they could develop was still short of the needed range. They thought of putting special fuel tanks out on floating wing-tips, supported not by rigid structure but by the air stream going by. Other approaches were tried.

A big engineering crew was at work on the design. Every other major company in the country was now developing its own idea for a supersonic bomber, all assessing this as a major opportunity and a major step forward in the state of airplane design. It was evident that the competition would be intense.

Bill Allen spurred the effort. When the time came for the B-52 to be replaced, it must be Boeing who would replace it, he said.

The giant B-52 itself was becoming a tremendous production effort, with the first of the Seattle-built series emerging from Plant Two early in 1955 to fly to Moses Lake for test and delivery, and the new production line at Wichita scheduled to roll out its first airplane by the end of the year. The Air Force interest in a jet tanker version of the 707 to refuel the B-52 was confirmed by a production commitment in March of 1955. Air Secretary Talbott announced that the Air Force would standardize on the new tanker, the KC-135, to follow after the KC-97s. With performance like that of the B-52 the new refueling plane would enable the jet bomber to reach any target on the globe. The gamble of the prototype was paying off.

After the tanker order came through Bill Allen named as the No. 1 project for everyone, "to put the 707 on the airlines." Douglas was now promoting a jet transport proposal of its own, and Lockheed a turboprop version. But cost accountants at work on a price tag for the commercial 707 said they could come nowhere near the $3½ to $4 million per airplane that the airlines regarded as the limit of their financing ability. Instead, it would take $5½ million per plane to support a production order of fifty.

"We can't sell them for that," Allen protested. "We'll have to go at it the other way around, start with a price the airplanes can be sold for, then figure out how we can build them for that." The price was worked down to $4½ million, rock bottom.

On June 5, 1955, before the figures had been given to prospective customers, sales manager Ralph Bell brought troubling news. "Don Douglas is going to start building the DC-8," he told Allen. "It's almost identical to the 707 —a little larger." Allen shook his head. "You've got to admire him for his courage, now that we have the tanker business."

Sales teams, racing with Douglas, made presentations to Pan American, United, American, Eastern—quoting price and deliveries, talking special modifications and equipment to suit each airline's need, making performance comparisons with the planned DC-8. Airline delegations came to Seattle to fly in the prototype, then went down to Santa Monica to compare offers with Douglas. The DC-8 would have a larger wing area. With an advanced-model Pratt & Whitney engine, it claimed more range than the 707. The Douglas cabin would be three inches wider.

"Our prototype is our biggest asset, but it's also our biggest obstacle," salesman Bell fretted. "Douglas has a rubber airplane. It's easy to stretch on paper."

To meet the competition the 707's gross weight was increased from 225,000 to 245,000 pounds, permitting a payload of up to 150 passengers. Then Douglas went up. It would take so many design changes to increase the 707's weight again that they could lose all the advantage of earlier delivery and a lower price made possible by the prototype development.

Pan American, the foremost prospect, was satisfied with the 707 price and schedule, but wanted the added range of the Douglas. The airline sent its key pilots to Seattle for a flight. The sale might turn on their evaluation.

In Tex Johnston's office the pre-flight briefing was simple. "Just fly it as you would any airplane," Tex said. "Anything special you'd like to try?" One of them wanted an emergency descent from high altitude in case of cabin supercharger trouble. They wanted to try some stalls and a high "Mach number" approaching the speed of sound.

They took off from Boeing Field, the landscape receding at jet speed as they headed out over Puget Sound. They climbed quickly to 20,000 feet, 30,000, then leveled off at 33,000 with the Pacific Ocean and the crisp wrinkles of the Olympic range below. Tex Johnston was demonstrating some high-rate turns, maximum-rate rolls, letting the airplane cavort like a swallow. Test pilots weren't interested in plain flight; they wanted to try things out.

"Watch along the right wing," Tex said, gathering to maximum straight-away speed that was discernible only by instruments. "You may be able to see a dark shadow forming—the wing's shock wave." It was the old mystery of "compressibility burble" of Eddie Allen's day, now no mystery, no longer unruly, but visible speed-of-sound waves gathering neatly off the wing.

They did the stalls, power on, then power off, with everything coming to a seeming stop in the air—no sound, no vibration. Then came the heavy buffeting that was the pilots' warning of less than flying speed, a neat dip and recovery on even keel. The visiting pilots were pleased. They made the emergency descent, air brakes out, heading down, sinking forced-draft from 33,000 feet to 20,000 feet in sixty seconds. Tex looked around and grinned. "No problem."

Enthusiasm was mounting in the Pan Am group. They shut off two of the jets and flew on the other two. When they had run out of emergency conditions to try, they came in straight, like a passenger flight, toward the airport. "Just land it as you would a Stratocruiser or a DC-6," Tex said. The airplane was built to handle according to conventional rules at the terminal, to give the airlines an easy entry into the jet age.

Other Pan American executives came out for flights. President Juan Trippe wanted his airline to be the first American line to introduce jets. On October 13, 1955, he announced his decision. The airline would spend $296 million, buy 20 of the 707s to be delivered starting December 1958; also 25 Douglas DC-8s for a later delivery. It meant Douglas would be in the race from here on.

Negotiations with United and American were at a crucial stage. Both lines had been flying Douglas propeller-driven planes; Allen and the sales force had the uncomfortable feeling of being "outs" trying to get in. On October 25 United announced it would buy 30 DC-8s. Bill Allen, hard hit, gave his team a fight talk. "The test of an organization comes when we are knocked down. Now let's see if we can get up and come back swinging."

American and Eastern were both about to make a decision. TWA was holding off. If American and Eastern followed United's choice, the tide would put the 707 at a huge disadvantage. The fewer of them built, the higher the cost per plane. There were the European transatlantic lines, but the longer range of the Douglas was making the competition for that market tough. The sales team assessed the situation with Ed Wells in a New York hotel room.

"We've got to have a bigger airplane, if we want to sell on the overwater routes," sales manager Ralph Bell urged. "It's getting pretty desperate." Wells shared Bell's view. With aerodynamicist Jack Steiner he made some quick slide-rule plans for a larger model. It was Saturday. Bill Allen was due on Sunday. They wondered how he would react, with the original model still a gamble, and now the question of whether there would be orders enough to support a new model.

Allen didn't hesitate long. "It will increase our risk, but we've got to have what the market will take," he said. Wells flew to Seattle to get up a detailed proposal for the airplane that would be called the "Intercontinental." It involved a determined surge of new engineering effort. Then to win American Airlines they agreed to increase the body width also, making it a shade wider than the Douglas.

American announced on November 8, 1955 that it would buy 30 707s. That made 50 sold. The program appeared to be heading for success. A sales team set out for Europe to present the new *Intercontinental*. "United's Douglas order may have been a blessing in disguise," Allen said, encouragingly. "Now we have an opportunity to show what we can do."

They did show it in the weeks and months that followed. Continental, Braniff, Sabena of Belgium ordered the 707, then Air France, TWA, British Overseas, Lufthansa of Germany, Qantas of Australia, Air India, Cubana and Varig of Brazil. Others ordered Douglas DC-8s: Eastern, National, KLM of Holland, Scandinavian Airways System, Swissair, Trans Canada Japan Air Lines, Delta, Panagra, UAT and TAI of France.

Convair came into the market with a new rival jet, the 880. De Havilland in England was selling its new model jet Comet, the airplane that had started it all. In the space of a few months every major airline in the world was making decisions to re-equip. A transportation revolution as great as the science revolution brought on by nuclear power was taking place, suddenly growing to overwhelming proportions, as revolutions do.

A realization was dawning—the astonishing capabilities of the jets. One 707 could carry as many people across the Atlantic as the *Queen Mary* ocean liner could carry in the same time, by shuttling back and forth at jet speed—6½ hours from New York to Europe. There would be the equivalent of hundreds of *Queen Mary*'s flying the skies. The capacity of the airlines would be doubled. People of moderate means would begin to think of travel to far-off lands not as a fanciful yearning, but as a real prospect in their lives. At jet speed you could circle the globe in forty hours. The world was shrinking to half size.

The competition for a supersonic bomber called "Weapon System 110-A" was narrowed to Boeing and North American. November 1955, both firms were awarded contracts to complete their studies, then the Air Force would choose. This was a contract that "Boeing must win," Bill Allen reiterated. To support the effort, research went forward on the combined effects of great pressures, friction and heat, on the problems of supersonic control, manufacturing techniques with the heat-enduring metal "titanium." Construction of a big new $30 million Development Center was rushed, intended to make certain that the Seattle plant was best equipped to build the new plane.

The pressures on designers were building, with the time for Air Force decision approaching. When the decision came March 11, 1956, it was in unexpected form. Neither competitor had turned in a plan the Air Force was willing to buy. Both would go at it for another round.

In Seattle there was concern. The question was raised: Was North American, a late comer in the heavy bomber field, only being kept in to provide competition, or did it have some formula that was technically ahead? Assistant chief engineer George Schairer, who was overseeing the project, called for a whole new start. "Forget what the designs up to now looked like," he told Ed Gray, a versatile engineer who was chosen to head a fresh design team. "See what you can come up with. Anything goes."

The team made a range of designs, from twin planes hooked together at the wing-tips to shapes looking much like folded paper airplanes. Shape after shape was analyzed. The choice rested on a design not far different from the one the systems analysis group had brought in two years before, and like that early conception, built of stainless steel and able to reach Mach 3, three times the speed of sound. But it would also have the needed intercontinental range. By using sharply swept-back wings and high-powered chemical fuels, they found it could, in fact, be designed to fly a mission at that speed all the way, not just in a spurt over the target. It would mean taking a radical step forward.

But the Weapons System 110-A program was running into stiff competition with the rapidly emerging intercontinental ballistic missile. By early 1957, Schairer had developed a genuine concern as to whether the 110-A could reach production in time to compete with the ICBM as the next strategic weapon. Information he was getting while serving on a technical committee in Washington, advisory to the director of defense research and engineering, and continuing reports from representative Ben Cohn in Los Angeles, emphasized the threat. They ran a study, completed March 29, 1957 at which time Schairer went to talk with Allen about it.

"Bill, it's beginning to be quite clear that the ballistic missile is going to replace the manned bomber as a carrier for the nuclear warhead," Schairer said. "There is no crucial problem of guidance or anything else. It's just a matter of building it."

Allen was plainly disturbed. "Curt LeMay is certainly convinced there's got to be another round of bombers, isn't that right?"

"Yes," Schairer acknowledged. There was a live competition for that next bomber nearing its climax. They had better not take their eye off the ball.

A decision was made to concentrate production of the new model B-52G at Wichita instead of continuing it at both Seattle and Wichita. It would mean a record production buildup in Wichita to 35,000 employees, nearly 6,000 above the peak of World War II. But it would cut costs and leave the main Seattle plant ready for the 110-A, dependent on the winning of the 110-A.

September 1957, deputy chief of staff Bill Irvine came with an Air Force group to check progress on the supersonic bomber. Irvine chewed his cigar enigmatically. "We have two awfully good horses to bet on," he said. "Both companies have made major technological breakthroughs."

October 4, abruptly, astonishingly, the Soviet Sputnik I, a 184-pound satellite, was fired into orbit to circle the earth every one and one-half hours. The shock of its impact circled with it. The space age had arrived, and it was not the United States that had ushered it in. People gazed at twilight to see the new star crossing the sky. Four weeks later Sputnik II, weighing 1,120 pounds and carrying the dog Laika, was in orbit. Those who could calculate knew that the power which put it there could readily thrust a ballistic missile from Russia to American shores.

In the quickening rivalry and renewed defense worry, new plans were made to extend the usefulness of the B-52. Provision for air-to-ground missiles would be added, giving the airplanes the potent role of a missile-launching platform not having to expose itself to defenses over the target.

The entries were in on the 110-A and a decision was awaited. There were rumors both that Boeing had won and that it had lost. Ed Wells was getting a feeling in the pit of his stomach.

"What would we do if we lost?" Schairer asked him. "There'll be hell to pay." During the wait Schairer set up a new product research office, taking Ben Ruffner off the

110-A to head it. Again going into the ballistic missile, a study had been done by an industry engineer, Bill Bollay, showing that the missile would be more effective with a solid-propellant rocket, packed like jelly, than with the liquid propellants of the Atlas and Thor and Titan. It countered the general belief that the solid would be too expensive. On the contrary, it appeared destined to be both cheaper and more reliable. Wells and Schairer felt it surely meant another round of ICBM development, beyond the Atlas and Titan—and an opportunity for Boeing to get in.

December 17, 1957, at Cape Canaveral, the Convair Atlas was fired, the first successful firing of an American ICBM.

December 23, the 110-A contest decision was announced. America would have a new supersonic bomber —the North American B-70.

18

The two-day Christmas holiday that followed the numbing blow of the supersonic bomber loss was a time for reassessment. Almost unthinkably it appeared that the line of Boeing bombers would not continue beyond the B-52. It had been broken by a process that had not been encountered before—a protracted paper competition. There was the disconsolate after-questioning. Had they not presented their case well enough? Had they been defeated by too-conservative performance estimates, in their effort to be realistic? But that was past. Bill Allen called a meeting the day after Christmas. The urgent thing now was to go after new business, he emphasized; there was a big hole to be filled. All the planning had been based on anticipation of success.

A recital was made of near business prospects, but it seemed lame. George Schairer spoke out. "I think there are only two basic questions. The first is, does Boeing intend to maintain a position of leadership in the industry?" The looks around the room indicated the answer was obvious. Schairer continued, "Then the second is, does this mean we are going to go after the ballistic missile business?" There was silence. All looked at Bill Allen. He twisted in his chair.

"Let's hear how you propose to do it."

Schairer sent for the presentation he had prepared concerning the potential for a new solid fuel ICBM. The case was impressive. "All right," Allen said. "You all think this is what we should do. You get together and come up with a plan—what has to be done, how we can do it."

The company had been divisionalized to facilitate its growth. The need for business now was in the Seattle Division, headed by George Martin—the division that would have built the B-70. The Wichita Division was busy with the B-52, the Transport Division with the 707s and KC-135s. The Pilotless Aircraft Division, getting the Bomarc into production, had its own pressing need for every technical skill in the missile field—the kind of men who would be needed to launch a ballistic missile effort. It was decided the only way to give the new effort the power it needed was to establish an advanced projects proposal team that would have its pick of men from all the divisions.

In the Seattle Division, preliminary design chief Harlowe Longfelder was remembering his work on the ROBO rocket bomber. Thinking this effort might be carried forward he selected for the role Ed Gray, who like many, was still dazed by the letdown from his strenuous 110-A efforts.

"Ed, I had a feeling all the time in the 110-A that we were stretching the conventional airplane as far as you could stretch it with today's technology," Longfelder confessed. "Here is something that is a whole new beginning. I want you to see what you can do with it. He handed Gray the files on the boost-glide vehicle concept, and watched for the reaction. Gray scanned the charts. When his eye caught the speed—not Mach 3 but Mach 23—twenty-three times the speed of sound—he took a quick breath and whistled. Then he grinned. "Why not?"

It was not long before they were getting reports that an Air Force competition was soon to be announced for a development project in the boost-glide field, and further that it would be for a manned vehicle, whereas the later trend in ROBO had been toward an unmanned one. Ed Gray saw at once that his opportunity was real.

But he also knew it would take a tremendous amount of qualifying work to win a competition in this uncharted field—a big commitment of money and engineering manpower. He realized that few Boeing people were acquainted with the studies or aware of the possibilities. That in itself was a handicap. The time would be short. Immediate, all-out top management support would be essential, if there were to be any chance of winning, Gray was convinced.

Longfelder and Gray were en route home after discussing prospects with Wright Field. Waiting between planes at Midway Airport in Chicago, Longfelder saw a familiar figure coming up to the United Air Lines' counter.

"Isn't that Bill Allen?"

They found Allen had a half hour between planes, asked him if he'd mind spending it with them. "We're really excited about a new business area and we'd like to talk with you about it."

"Fine," Allen said.

Literally backed against a wall by the two eager advocates, Bill Allen got the latest word on boost-glide. "We ought to go after this one with all our resources," Gray told him, unreservedly. "It can be the beginning of a whole new era. You can only compare it with the step the Wright brothers took when they first learned to fly. It may be even more significant."

Longfelder added his reassurance. "It's really the first step of man's exploration into space. We don't see how there can be anything but a bright future for it. Wright Field is taking it very seriously."

"Have they asked for proposals?"

"Not yet, but they plan to very soon. We think we should get geared up for it right away. We think we could win if we decided to really put a first-class effort into it." Allen caught their enthusiasm. It was the spirit he wanted to see.

There was as yet no Air Force requirement set for a solid-fuel ballistic missile; it was agreed that the advanced projects proposal team would go after the boost-glide contract first. George Stoner, a key man in the Pilotless

Aircraft Division and a space enthusiast, was picked to be manager of the new team. He was a resourceful engineer, the holder of several patents, and most recently had been leading the further development of automatic control on Bomarc, with a system that would make it independent of the "SAGE" radar network on which its guidance currently depended. While Stoner was pulling together his top-talent staff from throughout the company, January 1, 1958, the Air Force's "request for proposal" for the project arrived. It would be called Dyna-Soar, for dynamic soaring—the picturesque new name for boost-glide.

"First," Stoner told his assembled group, "we've got to admit there are a lot of companies that know more than we do about some of the things we'll need. We're going to try to bring the best of them in as partners in this effort."

There were discussions of strategy and design. It was agreed that they should concentrate on keeping the vehicle as small as possible. Thereby, they could reap the advantage of the work already done on unmanned boost-glide devices, and minimize the cost. The thing would be fantastically expensive at best; if it weren't kept within reason it might never be built, Stoner feared. Moreover, he thought a small craft would make it possible to use solid-propellant rockets, the newest promise.

By far the largest problem appeared to be that of cooling the vehicle. Most of the energy consumed in boosting it to the top of the atmosphere, by a law of conservation of energy, would be recreated again in friction heat when it came racing back down. If you pictured the flaming torch it took to drive it to the sky, you would have a picture of the heat it would generate on the way back. That heat had to be cast off to keep the whole thing from burning up, as a meteor does when it shoots from space into the earth's atmosphere. This was where the glide phase came in. Wing surfaces, even if scanty and finlike, could stretch the descent into a long glide path, but still the heat generation would be tremendous because of the speed.

For the wings it did not appear practical to use a process of ablation, charring the surface material and letting it gradually drop away. The objective was to have a vehicle that remained in condition to fly again, like any other aircraft. The surfaces could be cooled with a system of plumbing, but this would be too bulky and heavy for a compact design, and would raise questions about reliability, it was felt. "We're going to find a better way," George Stoner insisted. There was always a spark of conquest in Stoner's eyes, peering through thin-rimmed glasses from under heavy, dark brows. "We've got to know how hot every part will get, then choose the materials and the way to put them together to withstand that heat."

Vigorously, ardently, Stoner would each day send his engineering groups scurrying after answers, then each night convene around the table to report their progress. The subject matter was so unique and stimulating that the discussions would continue into late hours. Because the Air Force requirement called for a winged device it was assumed that the Dyna-Soar would operate within the earth's atmosphere, or at least where there'd be some slight atmosphere for the surface to bite into to gain support and control. But when engineer Bob Hildebrand put the speed calculations on the blackboard, a startling fact stood out.

If the device were ever to be used for a bomber, it would be hard to drop a bomb. At Dyna-Soar speed, up where there was little atmospheric drag, the bomb would want to stay up where the airplane was. If you put a motor on it to drive it to its target, the added speed would make it go up instead of down, because speed would always add to the upward force offsetting gravity. You'd have to put reverse motors on the bomb to get it to go down at all. Otherwise, it might climb right up into orbit and stay there.

That suggested something to Stoner about Dyna-Soar itself. "Here we are boosting it to a speed of 24,000 feet per second to soar just at the fringes of the atmosphere," he said excitedly. "You'll only have to increase the speed four percent to make it an orbital system. Let's think of how many things you could do if you could keep it up there for as many trips around the earth as you wanted."

The challenge set the designers into far flights of imagination in the days that followed. They could hang missile platforms in the sky, reconnaisance planes, antimissile defense, weather observers, space commanders—whatever you wanted—to stay up there, simply riding the orbit. Dyna-Soar would even make it possible to build space stations up there, as in the comic strips. It could be the taxi going back and forth to earth. They wondered if they were dreaming.

It would take an exorbitant amount of power, unless they could hold the package to absolute minimum size. No one had boosters that were nearly large enough. The satellites the United States had been putting into orbit were being derided as "oranges and grapefruit" beside the Russian's 11,000-pound Sputnik II. Still, by clustering rockets and firing them in a stair-step of stages, it could be possible.

Models went into the hypersonic wind tunnel. The first ones looked like hydroplanes for racing on water. Gradually they changed, as the wind tunnel's blast told its story. The intercompany team George Stoner had lined up was brought together for collaboration—General Electric, Ramo-Wooldridge, Chance Vought, Aerojet-General, the Autonetics and Missile Development divisions of North American. Competitors had been grouping the talents of other companies in like manner. Bell and Martin were teaming together and were being regarded in the trade as a shoo-in for the contract award —Bell with all its background of Dr. Dornberger's boost-glide research, Martin with its Titan booster rocket.

Bell had been working long on a means of cooling the vehicles with coolant tubes, and was openly advocating this method. George Stoner's structures' engineers faced the task of meeting his insistence on a lighter means, tackling the problem of reducing the huge stresses that would tax the structure when the outside was white-hot and the inside cool. The goal was to make the temperature uniform and to separate the structure into pieces that would minimize the problem.

They were planning to use "refractory" metals that would radiate much of the heat from the wings back into the air, with mercury vapor in tubes to equalize the temperatures within the diamond-shaped structure of the wings. Engineer Max Braun was studying drawings of the arrangement when suddenly he saw it differently.

"You don't have to equalize the temperatures," he said, "if you change to a triangular pattern. You can expand any side of a triangle without affecting the other." The principle went into the plan, enabling them to eliminate the cooling tubes.

March 27, 1958, the competitors paraded before the judges at Wright-Patterson Air Force Base with their voluminous proposals. In the one hour that was allotted them Stoner and his group made their oral presentation. Again there was the suspense of awaiting decision.

Systems analyst George Rounds had been dispatched in January 1958, to discuss the need for an advanced ballistic missile with engineers of the Ramo-Wooldridge Corporation of Los Angeles, a firm which was doing basic system engineering for the Air Force in support of the development. Rounds returned with positive word as to the solid-propellant missile opportunity, but his principal finding had to do with another aspect.

"They say none of the present contractors grasps the weapons systems concept," he reported. "The Atlas, Thor and Titan are all plagued with problems of integrating the whole system. The aircraft companies have always centered their thinking on the flying equipment. They fail when it comes to putting the rest of the system together—the ground support; the testing and check-out equipment; the operational facilities and installations; the maintenance and logistics concepts and all the rest. There's good reason to believe the Air Force would like to get a new contractor into the field for an advanced system of this type."

It became clear that the new requirement was systems management. Boeing had been learning the importance of it in its Bomarc program, where the need had been to create a whole defense system where none existed before, to bring the capabilities of other companies together, to put in whole bases, make them operate. There was hope that this experience would serve Boeing to advantage.

At the Air Force Ballistic Missile Division the plan for the new weapon was taking form. Minuteman, it would be called, and General Schriever's expectations of it were vast. Buried in silos in the ground, on farms, on deserts, in distant hills, ready with its own self-contained solid propellant, not dependent upon the pumping of high combustion fuels, it should be capable of being dispatched within a minute, if the day should come. It should be "hardened" or bomb-proofed to take a blast without damage. It should have close accuracy at intercontinental range. It should, besides all this, be less expensive and more reliable than any predecessor missile. In its instant readiness and nuclear deadliness, it should be a total deterrent to enemy nuclear aggression. Therefore it should be brought into existence quickly, without delay.

In Seattle there was urgent discussion as to the needed organization to go after the Minuteman business—should it be with the existing proposal team that was competing for Dyna-Soar, or a new one? Ed Wells felt permanent management should be built into the group developing plans, and that the lack of this was one of the reasons for the loss of the B-70. Allen decided to enlarge the advanced projects proposal team into a Systems Management Office, placing Ed Wells at its head, Dyna-Soar and Minuteman to be its current twin objectives. "T" Wilson, who had become project engineer for the B-52, was chosen to head the Minuteman effort.

June 23, 1958, an elimination decision came on Dyna-Soar. The competition was narrowed to the Boeing and the Martin-Bell group, each to be given contracts to develop their articles for a new round of competition. There was the chance to win. Bill Allen was exuberant, intent on taking the final heat of the race. "We will undertake it with all the vigor and ingenuity at our command," he told the Air Force.

The preparations for a Minuteman proposal had been going forward, but the project was not in the Boeing tradition. The basic designing was already done. The program would be divided into a number of packages—first stage booster, second stage booster, third stage booster, guidance and control section, warhead section, assembly and test contract. All but the last, assembly and test, had been committed to companies specializing in the particular fields. Many felt the "assembly and test" portion alone would not provide enough work to be a worthwhile endeavor, but George Schairer again disagreed.

"If we're willing to go in and assist the Air Force in managing this," he said, "—if we're willing to take the viewpoint that it's their program, not ours, and just help them do the job, I think there'll be plenty of business in it for us."

Schairer and Wells were sitting on the front steps of the Ballistic Missile Division, where the proposal was to be submitted, discussing this subject for hours one warm Los Angeles evening. Industry people had been complaining that "outsiders" were directing the Air Force programs; the Space Technology Laboratories, an outgrowth of Ramo-Wooldridge, was to provide engineering supervision for Minuteman.

"I don't see why we should fight them," Schairer maintained. "They're part of the scenery. We can work with them. We've got to get our people to quit this 'not invented here' complex."

Wells agreed completely. "The thing we've got to get across in Seattle is that we have to be responsive to the requirement. That means being responsive to the customer's view as to what the system should accomplish. They want to overcome the shortcomings of Atlas and Titan, in terms of readiness, reliability, reaction time, ability to be either hardened or mobile, ability to be maintained over a long period without constant attention. Our job will be to bring an understanding of these needs, and how we can help to meet them."

The advice took root in Seattle. The whole concept of Minuteman was analyzed, with attention to both technical and management sides. A 1/20th scale model was constructed and fired in an underground silo at the north end of Boeing Field. The approach was as thorough as they could make it, covering plans for economical "hardened" silos; underground control cubicles with their automatic equipment; a launch site installation system with missile handling devices; checkout and maintenance gear; the integration of the missile itself; a plan for management of an assembly and test plant; construction of installations; plans for the research required in support of each aspect of the program.

October 10, 1958, Ed Wells was working late when a teletype came in from the commander, Air Force Ballistic Missiles Division, Air Research and Development Command: "Reference your proposal submitted in response to our request for proposal for the assembly and test of the Minuteman Weapon System WS-133A. Your proposal has been evaluated as being the best submitted. Contract negotiations will be scheduled for a date in the near future." Four days later in Los Angeles Bill Allen signed the letter contract.

Amid the jubilation over the win, representatives of an agency that had been engaged to do a Minuteman study for the government gave "T" Wilson the admonition of their report: The commitment to Minuteman as an unmanned strategic system was an act of utmost courage. Every action and reaction had to be automatic throughout. If the system should prove to be unreliable, it could be the greatest fiasco of all times. With the nation's atomic might embraced in it, failure could be catastrophic.

It was soon evident that there were major aspects of the Minuteman program analyzed in the Boeing presentation that were yet unassigned by the Air Force, and that these would logically attach to the assembly and test responsibility. They involved work similar to that Boeing had done on Bomarc: the ground environment including launch control system; electronic sequencers and readiness monitors; the security system; the means of transporting the missile into place; the brick and mortar of base installations. These were added to the Boeing work package. The dimensions of the total task loomed larger. It was a responsibility for making the Minuteman work, for putting together all the pieces of a complex and undeveloped technology and integrating them into a whole.

The competitive Dyna-Soar development was moving deeply into the problems of an even more exotic technology. Test, test, test, was the requirement at every turn, according to a pattern that had been laid down in Bomarc. But there was also the urgent need for new knowledge, out at the frontiers of capability. Guil Hollingsworth, who had been leading the company's technical push into electronics and astronautics, was convinced of the need for more basic research. Sooner or later there'd have to be new materials that could not be found in nature, he contended. Hollingsworth pressed his views with George Schairer who had just been made director of research.

"We need to be able to say, here's the kind of molecule we want, now by golly we'll make one," Hollingsworth said. "If we're going to do this, we'll need to understand a lot more about solid-state physics. The same is true of plasma physics and geo-astrophysics. We ought to have a laboratory staffed with top scientists doing free research, not geared to any product."

Hollingsworth was rushing to a meeting in Los Angeles, having spent much of the night compiling slides and data on a recent piece of investigation he'd been asked to present.

"I'm sorry we don't have you cleared to go in," the receptionist said on his arrival.

Hollingsworth made it clear that there was a meeting inside where he was expected. "I'm the speaker. They invited me."

"I'm sorry, there's nothing I can do."

He suggested a verifying call to Seattle, but the receptionist said they were allowed only three long distance calls per day on security, and the quota was used up. Totally vexed, Hollingsworth turned. "That's all right," he said, "there's a lovely davenport here and I was up a long time last night. You'll find me horizontal, whenever you get the thing straightened out." He reclined and feigned reading a copy of *The Saturday Evening Post*, but he was giving more thought to the basic research laboratory he had been proposing to Schairer. While the girl was "straightening the thing out," he was seeing a new requirement for such a laboratory located away from plant gates, where doors would be always open, where top scientists from all over the world would come and go and contribute to each other's quest for new knowledge. At best a corporation could produce perhaps one percent of the ideas in a rapidly changing field, he felt. The other ninety-nine percent would have to be brought together from many sources, through exchange.

Later Hollingsworth was talking with Dr. Walter Brattain of Bell Laboratories, asking if Brattain felt a basic research laboratory, not geared to any product, would pay out.

"I think I know what you want me to say. I can give you a very specific example," Brattain said. He told how, several years before, they were doing fundamental studies on the nature of materials like silicon which were only semi-conductors of electricity. The electrical measurements kept varying, depending on the condition of the surface. It was extremely troublesome. When they put the whole thing in a liquid to try to keep the surface conditions uniform they discovered—almost by mistake— an effect they hadn't been looking for.

"What resulted," Brattain explained, "Was the transistor. Now it's in use everywhere."

The Boeing Scientific Research Laboratory that was recommended to management by George Schairer was consistent with the vigorous new start Allen had called for in 1958—the rebound from the 110-A loss. It was established without delay. Guil Hollingsworth was named its director.

There were other new starts in the wake of the 110-A. Schairer had Ben Ruffner in the product research office looking at other product areas that might be developed. The Defense Department's increasing concern with the "limited war" problem was bringing new concepts of mobility in the Army, and Ruffner reasoned that the helicopter could become the "jeep" of these limited wars. Schairer, who had done his Master's thesis on the subject, felt the rotary wing device had by no means been developed to its full potential.

Seeking to identify the people in the organization who had had experience in the field, Ruffner ordered out an IBM run of coded skills in the technical personnel files. The machines spit out the names of Ruffner and Schairer. Ruffner took the information smilingly to his balding boss.

"I guess you and I are going to have to do it."

They concluded that the way to get in the helicopter business was to see about acquiring an organization that was already in the field. With encouragement from administration vice president Jim Prince and with Bill Allen's interest, they began the quest.

But the more advanced concepts of vertical lift were being explored within Boeing engineering. The Seattle Division's preliminary design unit was working on a vertical lift plane with twelve engines, four on the wing-tips, four in the body, all capable of being pointed either straight aft for cruising, or straight down. Air Force people were unimpressed, however, with this "showerhead," as they called it. A group from West Germany on a survey trip took special interest in the work, appraising Boeing as being ahead in the field and suggesting joint development of an aircraft on an experimental basis. But that approach had no appeal at Boeing, and the Germans left disappointed. They said they might undertake it on their own.

In the Transport Division, a quiet, contemplative engi-

neer, Ken Holtby, who had been at the Wright Field end
of the B-47 development, was heading the aerodynamics
staff, having moved there after holding a similar staff
role at Wichita. Holtby went to talk with the technical
staff chief, Bill Cook, about supersonic airplanes, which
he couldn't get out of his mind after the 110-A experience. "If there's going to be any work done on a supersonic transport, it's going to have to be in the Transport
Division," Holtby said. "Shouldn't we pick it up and get
a group started on it?" The thought had been that if
Boeing won the B-70 supersonic bomber contract the
men who had done the initial development could move
on to apply their talents to the supersonic transport, if
it were decided such a project should be undertaken.

The prospect had been studied at various times. In 1952,
before technology had made its steep ascent in the supersonic direction, engineers Dick FitzSimmons and Bob
Hage had turned in a report both alluring and discouraging. "In man's ever-present quest to conquer time and
distance, he will not be content with spending four hours
flying coast to coast, if there is any way of doing it in two
hours," they had written at that time. But when they got
into the question of economic feasibility they found the
hope forlorn, unless there were to be technical breakthroughs. "We should take another look at it in thirty
years," they had concluded.

In 1956, with reports of British interest in the supersonic transport, preliminary design engineers had been
put to work to survey again the possibilities. In 1957
there had been further stimulus with an inquiry from the
Air Force regarding a possible supersonic military transport, and Ruffner's product research unit had done an encouraging study.

It was early in 1958 that Bill Cook went to chief engineer Maynard Pennell with a proposal for Transport Division action. "This is a job that calls for a 'critical mass' of
at least fifty people," Cook told his chief, enumerating
the many aspects requiring study and test before any conclusion could be reached. He proposed a group consist-

ing of half project people—designers, and half staff people—the technical specialists.

Pennell's interest ran intuitively toward the next step into the unknown, from his own long experience in preliminary design. He expressed his conviction to Bruce Connelly, the division general manager, that this was something they must actively pursue. Connelly agreed to the plan with the understanding that the purpose would be to determine the feasibility of such an airplane. Promptly Cook assigned Holtby to head the staff side; preliminary design chief Don Finlay in turn assigned Lloyd Goodmanson, who had been project aerodynamicist on the 110-A, to lead the project side, and the supersonic transport became a long-range goal.

They were not alone in the effort; the rest of industry was making like moves, following the B-70 go-ahead. North American, Douglas, Lockheed, Convair were all beginning to talk supersonic transport. In the flare of this competitive excitement Pennell spent repeated hours with Cook on the subject, but the maturing of a commercially practical airplane seemed a long way off. Pennell valued Cook's reputation for thoroughness, his insistence on step-by-step exploration in the wind tunnel and other test laboratories before each move was determined. This, if ever, was a project that would require just that, Pennell told him. July 17, 1958, increasing the pace of activity, Pennell asked Cook to assume responsibility for the SST development, dividing his time between it and the technical staff.

There was another source of supersonic experience. Boeing had been told that its work was advanced in the field of the light-weight stainless steel structures that were proposed in the 110-A competition. As a result a subcontract was sought and obtained from North American to build the wings for the B-70, involving extensive "honeycomb" panels—sandwiches of stainless steel sheets between which were to be brazed a light core of thin-walled honeycomb cells to provide the lightness and strength required. The same technology, it was felt, could be applied to the supersonic transport.

Meantime a still more advanced materials technology was being emphasized in the pursuit of the Dyna-Soar contract. The new Development Center, filled with elaborate heat-and-stress testing equipment purchased in anticipation of a 110-A award, was turned over to that use. The Dyna-Soar competitive study was to be submitted by April 1959. With 600 engineers assigned to it the work was progressing with all the "vigor and ingenuity" that Bill Allen had promised; also with a throat-choking yearning. A Dyna-Soar win was needed for Boeing's entrance into the space age.

19

The 707 jet transports were scheduled to go into service in the fall of 1958. There was yet the unanswered question: would the public take to them, or would there be hesitation and fear? Airline orders for the airplanes had mounted satisfactorily, and a further market was being found for a somewhat smaller Model 720 with the same wings and engines. But the costs of developing and manufacturing the airplanes had far outrun expectations, partly because of a multiplicity of changes required to meet individual airline desires and gain sales in the close contest with Douglas and Convair. The prospect of serious financial loss was casting an accounting office shadow on the high-spirited exhilaration over a bold forward step in air transportation.

One of the men caught in the contradiction was Jack Steiner, the tall, intense engineer who had been Maynard Pennell's aerodynamicist and project man on the preliminary design of the 707. Steiner was now working on proposals for a small jet transport intended to reach the short-to-medium range market. The assigned model number was 727. It was not yet determined whether a two-engine or a four-engine plane would best meet the need, though work was continuing on the two-engine as showing the most promise.

One problem was that the fast jets could not get into

the smaller fields of short-range routes; another was that the jet was most efficient at high altitude, and there wasn't time to climb high between short stops, nor would this be economical. It was in assessing this problem that Lockheed had chosen to hitch the turbojet engine to propellers, using the slower bite of the propeller blades for lower altitude flight. Two British turboprops, the Viscount and Vanguard, were doing well, and Lockheed's plane, the Electra, though not yet in service, was selling rapidly. Steiner sought the advice of the division's market research people as to prospects in the field despite this situation.

"There should be a free world market for five hundred short-range planes up to 1965," the market research head, Harry Carter, told him. "The question is, what is going to move into the vacuum? Very likely the turboprops will be shifted on down to shorter ranges as the heavy jets go in above. The same will be true of the piston planes that can no longer compete on the longer routes. If we are serious about offering a short-range jet we're going to have to come up with one that can operate as economically as the turboprops and into the same short fields."

That was not an easy assignment. Yet the new French Caravelle, with two jet engines astride its aft end just ahead of the tail, was selling in Europe for short-range use. It was selling speed. "The Electra can't hold the market—it hasn't the speed," said sales engineer Art Curren, who had made a test flight in the Caravelle and had come back enthusiastic. "We'd better watch that Caravelle. It's going to have the same effect on the small airplane field as the big jets will have on the long-range."

Curren's words were the encouragement Steiner needed. Neither he nor Pennell, when they had talked about it, had been able to gather any enthusiasm for the turboprop as an answer. The Electra was promising 400 miles an hour. The Caravelle could go 500. But the 707s and 720s could do 600. Wouldn't the Caravelle itself have to give way to a faster plane? Steiner asked. The report was that de Havilland was considering three engines, an arrangement that Bob Rummel, engineering head of

TWA had also suggested, not too expectantly, in a conversation with Steiner. Adding a third, middle engine, would involve many more design problems and much greater development cost than two or four engines. But the news meant that there was already a competitive threat in the proposed Model 727 category.

Then word came via the Boeing European office that Douglas, too, planned to enter the market with a two-engine, scaled-down DC-8. Pennell and Steiner, convinced that action must be taken at once, went to see Bruce Connelly. The division manager was highly interested, but he made it clear that it would be difficult to launch a new uncertain program in a competitive market when the present programs were losing money. Nonetheless he was anxious to see the subject thoroughly explored. May 6, 1958, a few days after he had authorized the supersonic transport effort, Connelly signed a directive establishing a 727 planning committee of representatives from various departments, Jack Steiner as chairman, "to establish the feasibility of a Model 727 type airplane."

Almost everyone in the division was skeptical. One executive confronted Steiner with a direct challenge. "It simply isn't feasible. We can't get into any such gamble," he argued. "Which is better, to recognize it now, or after it's too late? Another loss like the one we are taking on the 707 and we're out of the airplane business. You want to be responsible for that?"

But Steiner had a strong feeling the airplane could and should be built. It would fill an air travel need; it would fill out the Boeing line.

Immediately his exploration encountered difficulty, however. A two-engine design was working out to best advantage, but at a meeting in San Francisco, United Air Lines, the most likely initial customer, showed no interest in a two-engine jet. The reliability of jet engines had not yet been fully established. Passenger acceptance required four engines, United felt. Douglas apparently was encountering similar reactions, because it was switching its planning to a small four-engine DC-9. But the operating economy United Air Lines sought would require a

two- , not a four-engine plane. Further, a four-engine
727 would come too close to the medium-range 720 that
Boeing already had on the market, and the Sales Department was guarding its fort against any such intrusion.
Finally a survey trip by Steiner in Europe showed no
interest there in the four-engine plane. The whole study
was turning out to be a riddle.

There were other problems. Cost estimates pointed to a
price of $3.25 to $3.5 million dollars, even for the proposed twin-engine airplane. The smaller turboprop
Vicounts were selling for $1.27 million, the turboprop
Electras for $2.1 million, even the Boeing 720, twice the
size of the proposed 727 but based on the 707, for $3.5
million.

Sales engineer Art Curren, too, was tormented. "Are
we using a Cadillac mentality to set prices for Plymouths
and Fords?" he would ask. But the cost estimators cited
the unknowns. There was no inclination to take a risk of
enormous loss.

By the spring of 1959 the 727 prospect had nearly
faded. The Renton plant was a sea of rushing activity,
with 707 delivery schedules for Pan American, American, TWA, Continental, BOAC, Braniff, Sebena, Lufthansa. The flying public was responding with high enthusiasm to the first planes on the lines. The DC-8 was yet
to come out, and Boeing was jostling Douglas from its
long-held place as leading supplier of transport airplanes.
A new fan-jet engine was planned for future models that
would cut operating costs and make the jets still more
attractive to the carriers. But against the prospective
passenger prosperity the financial loss from production
was deepening with the multiplicity of models. There was
little time or disposition to start a completely new 727,
certainly not without larger orders than appeared in prospect.

Yet United Air Lines was moving toward a decision on
short-range jets. There was the chance that Douglas
would go ahead with the DC-9. If it did, it would not
only kill a 727 but could badly hurt the 720. Art Curren,
genuinely disturbed, brought Steiner a sales-and-work-

load forecast. "It drops off too damned abruptly for comfort the end of '62," he moaned. "We're in a really bad hole in '63 and '64. If we're going to sit in on the poker game, we've got to put up or get out."

Vice president Bruce Connelly wanted the new product line, but he was in the vise of his dilemma. "I don't think it's going to be any different for Douglas," he said. "Maybe de Havilland can go ahead with government backing, I don't know. But if it's going to take us 200 airplanes at $3.5 million each to make a program, that's a pretty fast poker game to be in. You can lose a lot of money." Connelly turned to Steiner with a considerate but quizzical smile. "Besides, we don't have an airplane to offer yet, do we?"

It was true, and Jack Steiner was smarting. He had been pondering the contradictions of the design quest. What they needed for short-range operation was low operating cost. They knew how to get the airplane's speed and efficiency up, and at the same time increase its riding comforts by keeping the wings small in proportion to the weight they would carry, then sweeping them back sharply as on the 707 and 720. But for landing on short fields it was axiomatic that the wings should be larger and have less sweepback, to give them more lift for landing and takeoff. That spoiled the performance and the operating cost. Steiner puzzled over the enigma with Joe Sutter, Bill Cook's head aerodynamicist and an old friend—they had worked together on the 707. They could only conclude that what was needed was a whole new design formula: a high-speed wing still capable of getting into short airports. Sutter regarded this as not impossible. "We ought to be able to have our cake and eat it, too," he said, smiling.

George Schairer had been urging Cook and Sutter to start a new comprehensive study on wing "boundary-layer" control, using trick devices to add to the suction of the layer of air that moved over the curved upper surface of the wing and gave the airplane its lift. The wing curvature could be increased by extending flaps from the trailing edge, as had become customary for landing, but there was a limit to how far this device could go without causing the air to become unruly and dissipate the lift.

Cook laid out a plan of research, to try a whole series of alternatives in the wind tunnel and on the 707 prototype, which had been converted to a flying research laboratory. He wanted particularly to try the effect of multiple flaps, one behind the other, each with a slot ahead of it to help with boundary layer control.

The prospect gave Steiner a surge of hope, if the development could be completed in time. Still there was the perplexing question of size of the airplane and number of engines. Steiner had two men making parametric studies on computers, weighing all the advantages and disadvantages of every feature and combination. But the computer spun out on the one perplexing question of United Air Lines' requirement. That line had now set up a target "Airplane X" that called insistently for low operating cost, plus the reliability of four engines, the latter especially needed for its operation into high airports such as Denver. The parametric studies still called perversely for a two-engine airplane to meet the economic goals.

Steiner went with Pennell to see Bruce Connelly. "We need rather desperately to put some more engineering time into really studying the alternative designs," he said. Connelly, back from a conference with Bill Allen at which the whole situation had been reviewed, was prepared. A budget was set up, a full-out product evaluation study authorized. Steiner as study director was to report directly to Connelly each week, and bring in a finding for corporate decision by August 1, 1959.

That was just two months away. Steiner knew it was the chance he needed, and he was not going to let it slip. With staff assigned he moved urgently, setting first priority on the two-engine design development, second on the four-engine. He went to seek Ed Wells' opinion as to the prospects with United, knowing Wells had remained close to United people.

"Do you want to know the truth," Wells asked him, "or what we'd like to believe?"

"Go ahead. We're bruised and bloody already."

"They're talking about an understanding with Douglas by the first of July."

Steiner was stung. Only a direct contact from Bill Allen to United's president William Patterson could save the day, but Allen first had to be sold himself, and that awaited the study.

But Wells was encouraging about the 727. "Let's really project the potential through the next ten to fifteen years," he told Steiner. "We have to realize that the important thing is how many can we sell altogether. The profit comes from staying in the market, not with the first ones you build."

"How do you feel about competing with our own 720?" Steiner asked, feeling that this was the concern which was holding the 727 down.

"That's what I mean, we have to look beyond the present. We ought to be in a position to sell whatever is in the best interest of the customer. Try to get there just by cutting costs, and you may not get there at all."

"You aren't concerned about the cost problem?"

"Of course. But my point is let's not compromise on getting the product we can sell."

Steiner pondered the problem through the night. Douglas was ahead with a four-engine version, in fact, had a tie-up with Pratt & Whitney to provide engines for it; de Havilland was ahead on three engines. The field was left for a two-engine airplane, which appeared the best answer, anyway. But it would mean losing United. It was still a miserable choice. Even the engine location was in question. They had been studying aft engines, as in the Caravelle, but almost no one in Engineering was for the aft location; there'd be too much restriction in loading the airplane for good balance, it was thought. On the other hand the favored location of two engines in the wing was developing problems as to flap arrangement, and a structure and weight distribution question had arisen that would have to be determined by further flutter tests in the wind tunnel.

June 25, Maynard Pennell called from New York.

"I've talked with Charlie Froesch at Eastern. He's very interested. He says a Caravelle-type airplane, preferably with three engines aft, would be ideal for them."

Steiner was caught off guard. "He does? What does he say about two versus four engines?"

"He thinks they would buy the four rather than the two, if that were the only choice. He says they may be forced to consider the four-engine DC-9, because of availability."

American Airlines, on the other hand, was only interested in the smallest possible plane for short hauls—nothing more than two engines. The puzzle grew more complex.

Bill Allen was now following the development with high interest. He talked with Patterson of United about the study under way. "We expect to be able to talk with you definitely in the month of August," he told the United president. Shortly after that conversation Douglas publicly announced its plans for the four-engine DC-9.

Amid the pressures and uncertainties Steiner made his presentation in Bruce Connelly's conference room July 28, 1959, giving all the alternatives with pros and cons. The finance people went into the matter of cost, explaining that the group had had to cut out all allowance for contingencies and plan on 20 to 25 percent reduction in overhead and engineering, in order to get down to what the Sales Department thought would be the maximum saleable price for either model. Eyebrows were raised at the assumption, more so at the estimated cash requirements of $130 million before deliveries. It was plainly unlikely that any such amount could be made available. The meeting adjourned inconclusively.

Jack Steiner, weary and distraught, could see the program slipping away, yet he felt more than ever that the short-range market was one Boeing should enter, and that it was up to him to find the way in which it could be done. He had been given that assignment. He found himself wondering if the answer could not be in a three-engine version that they had included in the study at lowest priority. He had been going along with all the oth-

ers in Engineering who felt a three-engine design should
not be given serious consideration, because of the many
difficulties it would involve—the tail design, the higher
cost, the longer development time in a competitive race.
Except for Maynard Pennell, almost everyone had
viewed it negatively. But weren't they trading a design
problem for a bigger problem of the program itself?
Steiner asked himself. The three-engine version was the
common ground between two and four. The parametric
studies, when he looked back at them, showed almost as
low operating cost for three as for two engines. The
plane could meet United's economic requirements and
still give them the extra engine reliability, plus Denver
takeoff capability. It would suit Eastern and TWA. If
United would come down to three, might not American
come up from two to three? Here was a prospect of getting all four prime airlines, the prospect of a 200-plane
program, which was just what was needed to permit a
reasonable price.

But there was one defeating hitch. There were no engines available of the right size to make the three-engine
design work out. Steiner discussed the problem with
George Schairer who came by his office regularly to consult.

"There's no reason you should be held up for want of
the right-size engine," Schairer said. "You don't have to
take an engine that's on the market, just because it's always been done that way. Write your own specification."

Afire with hope and resolve, Steiner went in September
to the Rolls Royce plant in England, which was building
engines for the de Havilland Trident, now announced as
going into production. By arrangement he met representatives of the Allison Division of General Motors which
had agreed to build the Rolls Royce engine in America.
Would Rolls be willing to design a larger special version
of their engine on speculation for the 727? he asked. "I
think I can say that our development of a three-engine
airplane depends on this."

Rolls wanted to get into the American market. In two

days he had a commitment. Back in Seattle he was vibrant with hope as a new effort went forward to perfect a three aft-engine design.

But the financial problem in the Transport Division had reached crisis state in the fall of 1959. By October figures were in on the first year's production of 707s. The projected loss for the program at the end of the year would be just over $200 million, an amount equal to the company's entire working capital. Other companies introducing the jets, Douglas and Convair, were coming out the same way. Whether a 727 program could be undertaken at all, despite the enthusiasm for a new three-engine design, was in gravest doubt. Bruce Connelly, wanting to make it possible, asked assistant general manager Tory Gamlem to lead a rigorous cost-reduction effort in all aspects of the proposed program. Department by department Gamlem sought savings and commitments to specific targets, to make it possible to set a reasonable price. Then a go-ahead decision would be faced.

It was regarded as fortunate that the large-scale production of B-52s at Wichita, of KC-135 jet tankers at Renton and Bomarcs in the new Missile Production Center at Seattle were bringing income enough to more than offset the commercial airplane losses. But these lines could not be counted on as extending far into the future. Across the path of the B-52 there was the controversy over bombers versus ballistic missiles. Washington was now riddled with accusations over the "missile gap" that had been revealed between the U.S. and Russia. In the alarm, the big supersonic B-70 itself, scarcely in the incubator, was becoming a center of controversy, and there were Boeing sighs that it was better to have won Minuteman.

The Bomarc defense missile, which had become the largest Boeing production program and was being rapidly installed in a ring of twelve U.S. bases as well as two in Canada, was coming into its own political crossfire. Its performance was not in question. It had made effective intercepts against both subsonic and supersonic targets, and even in salvo against multiple targets, all by automatic remote control. The missiles had cranked themselves around at supersonic speed like fighters, and zeroed in for the kill. With the 250-mile radius of the current Bomarc model, a single base could provide effective defense for an area of 196,000 square miles. The new model with solid propellant would increase the range to 400 miles. Twelve thousand people were working on the Bomarc production, putting together the miniature electronic gear and other intricate parts by production-line methods, and a thousand more men were out building bases.

But a question was being raised as to how far the country should go in the defense against bombers when ballistic missiles were the coming thing. There was concern about the vulnerability of the Air Force SAGE network of "semi-automatic ground environment" which blanketed the whole area with electronic detection and dispatch signals for fighters as well as Bomarc interceptors. The independent ground control system of Bomarc which had been worked out had not been accepted; the commitment to SAGE was too great.

On top of all this there was rivalry between the Army and the Air Force over the defense missile role. The Army had its short-range Nike which could be deployed at many points for close-in anti-aircraft defense; the Air Force Bomarc could umbrella a whole group of Nike bases, as well as intercept farther out to sea. The Air Defense Command pleaded strongly that the need for the Bomarc system was based on a Russian bomber threat that was real. But Congress was confused by the duplication and alternatives. After hearings in June, 1959, it trimmed $162 million from the $540 million that had been budgeted for the next year's Bomarc program, but the program as a whole would go forward.

For Lysle Wood, heading the Pilotless Aircraft Division and shuttling constantly to Washington in Bomarc's behalf, the shakiness of the program was putting new importance on Dyna-Soar, for which his division would be operationally responsible if the competition were won.

The full technical plan for Dyna-Soar had been submitted in April 1959, but the contest was still undecided. Most recently the Air Force had asked for data covering potential military applications of the system—a request that put proposal manager George Stoner's imagination actively to work. Stoner pictured a network of Dyna-Soar trails that could be wound around the world like yarn around a ball, providing global surveillance, command operation, multiple military uses. The report went in on June 30; then came the standby. From a thousand people Dyna-Soar went down to a nucleus of forty awaiting verdict.

Overall employment had come down in 1959 from 100,000 to 80,000. Bill Allen was clear about the change that was taking place in the business, and its implications. "We have to recognize that the day of the long production run, particularly in the military heavy aircraft field, is coming to an end," he told the management staff in a review of affairs. "Programs such as the B-52 from now on are going to be few and far between. In place, we have products that cost infinitely more to design, but will be needed in much smaller quantities and will require fewer people to produce. For this business the competition is becoming more intense by the day. I might say more desperate."

To meet the situation Allen listed the principles that he felt must guide the effort ahead:

"In order to obtain business," he said, "we must *earn* the opportunity to compete for it. In order to compete we must have a better product to sell. In order to develop and offer a better product we must have superior product conception, design capability and a demonstrated cost performance.

"In order to be superior in those fields, we must invest capital to sustain the people who will accomplish product conception and design, and we must put capital into research and development facilities and efforts. In order to have that capital we must either earn it through our profits, or attract it in the money markets."

The principles were being applied by putting 80 percent of earnings back into research and new kinds of facilities, latest of which was a new Mach 20 hypersonic wind tunnel, the most advanced in the country. In a further move to fit the new character of the business the Pilotless Aircraft Division, the Seattle Division and the Systems Management Office were combined into a single new Aero-Space Division, with Lysle Wood as general manager and George Martin, assistant general manager. "The purpose is to multiply our technical strength—our strength to compete in a new and decidedly different market," Allen said in announcing the change.

The new division name meant that the company's sights were turning toward space. At an earlier date a competition for NASA's earth-orbiting Mercury capsules had been passed up, with only six capsules to be built and the Minuteman and Dyna-Soar competitions requiring priority attention. Now such a contract would be welcomed.

A contract had been obtained to do a Mars Explorer study, but it was only a study, typical of the new business opportunities that were long on engineering time and short on hardware to be built. Another contract was awarded by the Air Force to Boeing, and a similar one to North American, to study means for getting man to the moon and establishing an outpost there, an expedition in which the Air Force might follow the tradition of the Navy in its expeditions to the Poles. Dr. Walter Hiltner, who had a side interest in astronomy and had long been a space enthusiast, was given the task of heading the effort.

It all seemed unreal, but Hiltner's group laid out a plan that involved the use of three rocket engines with cryogenic fuel—hydrogen stored at extremely low temperature, lighter and more efficient than kerosene—and a vehicle small enough to get to the moon in one straight upward shot, without the need for rendezvous in lunar orbit or earth orbit. This would be the most reliable way to do it, Hiltner felt. First they would make unmanned probes to take pictures with soft landings, then go for a manned landing.

They even established an experimental station on the 14,408-foot top of Mount Rainier, simulating a landing on the moon to see how personnel would react in long and hazardous isolation. This developed from a conversation between Hiltner and Dr. Maynard Miller, a Columbia University geologist interested in a foundation for glacial research, when Miller was speaking at a meeting of a Northwest mountain climbers' club. The professor was engaged as a consultant on lunar topography problems. When he could find no documented studies on the psychological problems to be encountered, he proposed the mountain base for the purpose and was given a subcontract to set it up.

Miller's party made the tortuous two-day climb up the glaciers with special instruments that the Boeing space medicine department had developed for the measuring of human effects. In the frigid winds of half the atmosphere of sea level the men set up a two-tent camp beside an ice wall on the pumice rock that sloped down from the outside edge of the crater. They established radio-telephone communication with the Boeing Flight Center. Hiltner, himself a mountaineer, was strenuously up and back to check progress at intervals.

The outpost study went on from May to September 1959. But a visiting glacialogical research professor from Western Washington State College—Dr. C. T. Bressler, who had asked the opportunity of doing research work from the base, took sick from complications of altitude effects. Harold Horn and Charles Carman, two Boeing men, took off in a private plane in the night, September 2, 1959, with oxygen bottles to be dropped, but the plane disappeared in the darkness and did not return. Dr. Bressler had expired before morning. Six days later searching alpinists found the airplane upside down at the 14,000 foot level, the two flyers dead in the wreckage. The first three fatalities of a lunar landing had occurred, it might be said, on the icy summit of Mt. Rainier.

20

The "missile gap" concern was converging on Minuteman, barely started in 1959. Intelligence disclosed that Russia would have a missile force in being in the early 1960s that would seriously threaten United States security. Five repeated attempts at long-range Atlas firings had met exasperating failure. The press was crying for a "missile czar." Subsequently the Atlas came into success, but it was Minuteman that was looked to as the means of moving ahead of Russia. The hope in the new missile was summarized by Air Force chief Thomas White: "It will be the backbone of our future strategic missile force —and a most economical backbone. The unit cost per operational Minuteman on site will run less than one-quarter of that of the Atlas or Titan."

Although Minuteman would not have the titanic blast of the larger liquid-fuel missiles, it would have more than fifty times the power of the bomb that was dropped on Hiroshima. The theory was that Minuteman would permit production-line techniques, and would require a minimum of trained men to launch it. A two-man launch team with electronic monitors would be responsible for 10 missiles. Launch sites could be prepared in less time than for existing missiles. Therefore, when Minuteman was deployed—went the argument—Russia could not hope to match its force without prohibitive cost or by changing over to a similar missile itself.

The plan fit the U.S. policy that America would never strike the first blow in a nuclear war. Minuteman could take a blow and still belch back from across the land with instant catastrophic effectiveness. It offered a solution. Air Secretary James Douglas, in the pressure of the "gap," asked the Ballistic Missile Command if he could not tell Congress the Minuteman operational readiness date would be moved up from mid-1963 into 1962. The question reached Seattle, where program manager "T" Wilson gravely assessed the prospect with his staff, then consulted with the associate contractors. In a mixture of perspiration and zeal Wilson said it could be done.

General Schriever proposed to his superiors that the schedule be stepped up a full year, with first operational deliveries in July 1962. This would mean the overlapping of testing and production and site activation, all with a new system yet to be proved, its first test flight still a year and a half away. The schedule would call for more than 100 missiles to be in place and operational by the middle of 1963, and 400 by 1964.

When the proposal was approved Major General Osmund Ritland was given the job of administering the program as new commander of Ballistic Missile Division, with Schriever moving up to head the Air Research and Development Command. Colonel Sam Phillips, named Minuteman program director in August 1959, made it clear to "T" Wilson: "We're going to have to take the bold approach."

It was decided that an early trial would be made from the simplest possible hole in the ground, to discover whether there would be any defeating problems. By this time Boeing had run some 1,400 one-twentieth scale tests in Seattle to learn of heat-effect problems in a silo launch, and one-third scale firings had been tried at a leased test area in the Tulalip Indian reservation north of Seattle. There were still numerous questions to be determined in an actual Minuteman silo launch, with the missile enveloped in its full inferno of flame. They needed to measure the effects of pressures from the storming exhaut gases and the effects of the noise generated in the silo, to determine whether this would batter against the missile at dangerously high levels, whether the resonance and vibration would foul the delicate guidance system.

For the first full-scale tests Wilson had been getting a pair of dummy Minutemen ready—with steel cases in true configuration, but containing ballast to simulate part of the load, and without guidance equipment or warhead. The first of these was scheduled to be fired September 15, 1959. Out of a force already built up to 3,500 men nearly 500 were at Edwards Air Force Base, California, preparing for the full-scale tests.

On schedule September 15, hole No. 1, sixteen feet in diameter and 86 feet deep, was ready with silo instrumentation and mechanical equipment. Caisson electrical work and land lines were all complete. Test missile No. 1 was inside, ready to be fired. In the square blockhouse the countdown had a special element of weirdness, with the Minuteman out of sight. When it reached zero an excited ring of white smoke and then yellow heat preceded the missile out of the ground. The pointed bullet-nose of Minuteman emerged, lifting slowly at first, then accelerating rapidly on a rocket column of flame and roar. At 250 feet, before its short fuel supply was burned out, its triple-cable tether suddenly caught the missile and snapped it angrily over. It sizzled to the ground.

There was the quick check of instrumentation results, the eager inspection of the silo and—half buried in the loose, charred sand—the bent casing. No major problem appeared. In fact it was decided that the hole could be narrowed to twelve feet for the next trial, and the Mexican "sombrero" flame deflector changed to a simpler flat-plate type. The missile and silo for the second test would be ready in two weeks, the Boeing crew reported to Colonel Sam Phillips. The Colonel was smiling the rest of the day.

The next test went well, and those that followed. The time allowed for the test series, and the number of missiles required, could be cut in half, they found.

It was in the glow of the encouraging test results on Minuteman that Bill Allen got a call, November 9, from a different Air Force branch. General Beverly Warren was on the phone from the Air Matériel Command, where a decision had been awaited for weeks.

"Congratulations," the general began, and Allen felt a quick rapture of relief. "I expect you'll be glad to know that your company has been selected as system contractor for the Dyna-Soar program."

Bill Allen was more than a little awed at the thought of the bizarre, sledlike wings of Dyna-Soar glowing white like a meteor, as its pilot shot it down from space to use the atmosphere as his cushion in the world's most exciting toboggan ride. Allen wrote a message to all Boeing management on the winning of the contract. "It is a prospect that captures the imagination. What we have won is an opportunity. What we do with the opportunity is entirely up to us."

The spirit of that win had its stimulating effect throughout the organization. Now two immensely challenging programs had stemmed from the resurgence that followed the 110-A loss—Minuteman and Dyna-Soar. A third proposed program, the 727 short-to-medium range jet transport was having its struggle for existence, but with improving chances. A fourth project, and the one most directly derived from the 110-A work, had been started knowingly with a long trail of development ahead, before it could claim its right to a future—the supersonic transport.

Maynard Pennell and his men leading the supersonic transport effort all felt an intuitive optimism that the SST would materialize, certainly by the late '60s, though there was admittedly yet no clear engineering path in view. The problem was the extremely adverse "lift over drag" ratio. Where the subsonic transport had twenty times as much lift as drag, the supersonic had only seven. When you translated this into range the tripling of the speed would help offset the poor "L over D"—lift over drag— but then the structure required to withstand the forces of increased speed would add to the weight of the airplane, decreasing the payload that could be carried for a given take-off weight. The economics were maddeningly poor, yet there was the lure: this was the way aviation was heading.

On the technical staff side of the SST project there was constant effort to find new ways to improve that disappointing L over D. It had turned out that North American had promised a somewhat better L over D than Boeing, in winning the B-70. But the engineers who had made the 110-A proposal didn't think the North American figures were right; they didn't think the B-70 would reach them. New theoreticians were brought in, to search the wilderness for new approaches. They looked at wings of high camber or curvature, and at twisted wings, shooting for a lift-over-drag ratio of 10 or 11. There were theoretical gains but always some practical limitation. They could get an L over D of 10 in the wind tunnel, but with a configuration that left no place to put such essentials as engines and landing gear.

But the group was getting away from the delta triangle wing of the B-70. A continued cross-stimulation of three top aerodynamicists—Cook, Ken Holtby, Lloyd Goodmanson—was giving rise to an alternate design. In the delta they had found that the base of the triangle across the back accounted for a large amount of surface that did very little work. So they tried cutting away the center aft portion of the delta wing beside the body. This gave them what looked again like conventional airplane wings, but much more highly swept. It became more of an arrow wing in shape, with a thinly spreading wedge like an arrowhead.

The sweepback helped immensely in one way. You wanted to get the air that crossed the leading edge of the wing to move at subsonic speed even though the airplane was going supersonic. High sweepback would accomplish this very efficiently, but with the embarrassing problem that the thing couldn't take off or land. You'd have to almost stand it on end to slow it down enough to land. There was a crying need for a breakthrough.

Researchers at NASA's Langley Field laboratories, constantly whittling at airfoils to advance the state of the art, were working down the same line toward the arrow wing approach in early 1959. In March, John Stack, director of research at the Langley Laboratories, called George Schairer. "We have a new invention we're showing to industry. Can you send someone back?"

"Sure, what is it, John?"

"We have some new ideas on variable sweep."

The idea of changing the sweep of the wings in flight had been tried. Stack had encouraged the interest of the Bell Company, which in the early '50s had built and flown an airplane with variable sweep, under an Air Force experimental contract. The purpose was to gain the advantage of high sweepback in flight, then to move the wings up into a position to make possible normal landing. But it had been necessary to change the location of the wings, fore and aft, at the same time as changing the angle of sweep, to preserve the stability of the airplane. The Bell craft had its wings not only hinged but mounted on tracks, walking backward and forward along the body. It was a cumbersome and heavy device, and it had cooled the whole industry on the magic promise of variable sweep.

But Stack at Langley Field had continued working. More recently he had been consulting with the British on a new fighter project that had reopened the subject of variable sweep. He had also been talking with his friend and neighbor General Frank Everest, head of the Tactical Air Command, about the development. With Everest's encouragement he had run more wind-tunnel tests.

On receiving Stack's call Schairer arranged for Bill Hamilton, who was head of flight technology in the Seattle Division at the time, and John Aydelotte from Wichita aerodynamics to respond to the invitation. Representatives of most of the other aircraft companies also arrived at Langley to get the new information.

"We can solve the problem of stability," Stack told the visitors, "with a hinge in a fixed position at the side of the body, if we have it in the right location, and if we have a horizontal tail of the right size in the right place." He distributed papers with calculations and drawings. The NASA researchers had devised a fixed extension reaching forward from the root of the movable wing alongside the body, to improve the aerodynamic effects. But there was no enthusiasm among the visitors, most of whom had done their own work on the problem.

"I think your weights are too optimistic," Hamilton told Stack. "But we'll go home and give it the old college try." Others expressed their views. They didn't think it was going to work. The consensus was that the wing joint sliding on massive circular tracks was heavy and impractical, leaving mechanical difficulties unsolved.

Reporting back to Seattle, Bill Hamilton acknowledged that there was probably a certain "not invented here" aspect to the industry's reaction to the NASA proposals, but he was still skeptical, he said, until they could run some tests. He went over the material with those in the Seattle Division who were particularly concerned—Vaughn Blumenthal, in charge of development of advanced military airplanes including tactical fighters, and Hamilton's own men. Together they became a brainstorming group.

The skepticism changed gradually to guarded enthusiasm as they began to get results from the wind tunnel. They tried different variations. One day aerodynamicist Bob Brown came in with a design nicely blending the wing and body, a step ahead of what NASA had done, employing a more refined variation in areas. It made Hamilton whistle. "Say, that looks real sexy." With computations and wind-tunnel trials the enthusiasm was growing solid. "Let's take it back and show it to John Stack," Hamilton said, seeing its possibilities, as did Blumenthal, for an advanced, variable-sweep tactical fighter.

Ed Wells who, on the merging of his Systems Management Office with the new Aero-Space Division was given a post as vice president for development engineering, had concluded that the next important market was going to be for a high performance fighter-bomber, because of the "limited war" problem. His conviction put force behind the new development. By October 1959, comprehensive wind-tunnel studies were well under way, and all types of wing pivot joints were being explored. Engineer Phil Whitener came up with a joint that was clean and straightforward, not too heavy, simply a large double ring that would serve as a circular bearing. Construction was started on a full-scale model of the pivot for tests under load.

When more wind-tunnel results on the newest aerodynamic shape came in, there was general excitement. The engineers were back and forth with NASA, moving ahead with the detail problems of a fighter-bomber design.

To provide space for more men, the Seattle Division fighter group under Vaughn Blumenthal was moved to a new location on the fourth floor of the Puget Sound Power & Light Building in Bellevue, on the east shore of Lake Washington, and Bill Cook's supersonic transport group from the Transport Division was relocated at the other end of the same floor. As a result an informal but constant intercommunication began between the two groups. Ken Holtby and Bob Brown, heading aerodynamics on the two staffs, were close friends. Holtby was following the fighter work to see how it would apply to the SST. Blumenthal, in turn, wanting to get an outside check on the findings of his group, arranged to borrow three of Cook's men to work for two months on the fighter. In that 60-day period the three men became converts to variable sweep.

The new feature, when combined with the arrow wing shape, would provide just the answer that was needed for the supersonic transport, Holtby and his aerodynamicists were contending. If it could be worked out satisfactorily it could outclass the delta not only in high speed and cruising efficiency but especially in takeoff and landing.

Bill Cook's reaction was characteristic of his method. "Let's find out," he said. "We aren't going to get there unless we really go after it." He split the group into two teams, fifty-fifty. In three months of competitive effort both teams came to the same conclusion. The variable sweep made sense; it could be competitive with the delta in weight and would begin to solve the operational problem of getting in and out of airports with an acceptable angle of attack—without the need to use the delta piloting technique of pitching up the nose and landing like a leaf. Cook changed the ratio of effort, putting more than 80 percent of the men on the variable sweep development, the remainder to carry forward the delta alternative.

Not only did the new approach solve the riddle of landing the arrow wing, but Maynard Pennell thought it had another virtue that would save them all manner of future difficulty. His conclusion resulted from experience in another quarter.

The strategic controversy in Washington over the North American B-70 had resulted in the cancellation of all but the experimental models in that program. The Boeing subcontract for B-70 wings was accordingly cancelled. But the work of fabricating and brazing the stainless steel honeycomb panels for those wings had been sufficient to reveal the difficulty and expense. Pennell wanted to avoid it as much as possible on the SST, for commercial practicability, and the variable sweep was providing a means to do so. The new wing could be built in almost conventional manner with spars, skin and stringers, but with titanium parts instead of aluminum for added lightness and strength and heat resistance.

Other structural problems were being resolved. From the pivot joint for the fighter, a satisfactory application to the transport design was developed. Load tests of the pivot were proving successful. By early 1960 the supersonic transport was making firm headway.

On the fighter side, meanwhile, Vaughn Blumenthal had an invitation from a special project office of the Wright Air Development Command to participate in a briefing at which industry comment would be sought as to the feasibility of a vertical or stationary take-off fighter. Separate meetings were held with industry in

Dayton in February 1960. It was quickly evident that WADC, with NASA encouragement, had become en-amored with the prospect of a variable-sweep fighter. The companies were being asked if they were ready to undertake such a project. In response to the query, Blu-menthal was eager.

"Yes sir. We can start immediately," he said.

He learned that he was the only one to so volunteer, and he went home throbbing. They were out in front, he was sure. Wells and division engineering director Bob Withington, enthusiastic over Blumenthal's report, au-thorized the construction of a full-scale mock-up. They went to Washington to help Wright Field gain accept-ance for the new idea. There should be a new experimen-tal tactical fighter program, they were convinced. The new technology made all existing fighters obsolete.

The supersonic transport staff was making its own rounds, talking with engineering heads of TWA and Pan American. The airline men were impressed with the tech-nical feasibility, but their companies were by no means ready to talk SST, they said. The economics were too out-of-reach. They had first to digest the heavy investments in jet transports.

There was, however, a quickening threat of rivalry from Europe, as had prodded the jet transport develop-ment. Both British and French industry were beginning to discuss supersonic transports, with the possibility of government-sponsored projects.

Schairer and Beall discussed the possibility of a joint SST venture with both the French and the British. There was a certain appeal to the idea because the project was so mammoth it could not possibly be undertaken with company resources, and an early U.S. government pro-gram did not appear likely. But the whole prospect was so tenuous, the transatlantic liaison so formidable that it did not seem practical. Then Sud-Dassault of France an-nounced it intended to proceed to build a supersonic transport. There was every indication that the race would become a reality.

France had already moved into the lead in the medium-range jet transport field with the Caravelle, and the possibility of a Boeing collaboration with the Sud company on an advance version of that airplane was a more serious consideration. The argument was that it would provide a production item for a known market without the huge gamble that a three-engine 727 development would involve, at a time when there were no funds to gamble.

The whole question of whether the jet transport business was dragging the company down or building it up was moot. The transports were being celebrated, revolutionizing travel, but the financial struggle was still acute. Allen told a meeting of New York securities analysts: "The competition is intense enough from a performance capability standpoint, but it is more so from a sales price standpoint. It is not limited to a basic asking price; it involves extending credit to the purchasers or taking trade-ins of used airplanes, or both. This is competition at its severest. Where it will lead is most difficult to predict. The break-even point becomes more and more difficult to reach. The prospect of hitting the profit side of the ledger moves, time-wise, further and further to the right."

Acting to strengthen the company's divisions in the face of such challenges Allen was moving top corporate executives into division positions. He made vice president-controller John Yeasting general manager of the Transport Division. Bruce Connelly as vice president and assistant general manager would be freed to give top executive attention to sales that were mandatory to salvage the future.

Yeasting wanted to see the Model 727 project go ahead, but he told the persisting Jack Steiner he was concerned about the combination of financial risks on 707 sales, the 707 development costs still being absorbed and the disturbing difference between estimated cost and proposed sales price on the 727. "If we go into it I want to be sure that it's priced rationally, not just to sell," he said. "It's going to have to make sense with the cost estimates and the market."

Vice president Tory Gamlem's cost-reduction campaign on the 727 had brought results. There was a firm determination to keep as many parts as possible common to both 727 and 707 in order to hold down costs, but it was inescapable that new development costs would be high.

Chief engineer Pennell had finalized the decision in favor of the three-engine over the two-engine version. "We could build either and make it a good airplane. I have no doubt of that," he told Steiner when they met to establish the design. "But now that United and Eastern have both stepped up their size requirements it would take overly large engines with only two. The other thing is the practical fact that American isn't ready to move and Eastern and United are. So, I think it's already decided."

Pennell agreed also to the aft engine location, which had now been studied from every angle, and satisfactory balance had been obtained with an extension of the tail. Now, with the Boeing design set, the question of whether to accept Sud Aviation's offer to go in on the Caravelle was crucial. United Air Lines, to everyone's surprise, had just placed an order for the Caravelle.

"Is it better," Ed Wells asked, "under the circumstances we're in, to start out with a new model or join forces with someone already under way?" While Jack Steiner waited, quaking, a delegation left for France to determine it.

Allen summoned a Sunday meeting in his home on the subject, when they got back. He said he would have to give an answer the next day to the head of Sud. "I'd like to hear what each of you thinks about it."

There was a rallying to the home product. Carl Dillon, the new Transport Division director of finance, raised the problem of making all the changes of measures to the U.S. system and manufacturing the airplane economically. Yeasting didn't think two production lines would be justified. "It would have to be in one country or the other. We've thought about making sections here and shipping them over, but it gets pretty complicated from an engineering standpoint."

Pennell said there'd be a great deal of engineering to be redone to make a product with which Boeing would be satisfied. Schairer backed the 727. "I think it's too good an opportunity for us to miss," he said.

When Allen came to Jack Steiner he grinned. "I don't suppose there's any use asking you."

Steiner was ready with a card presentation of technical comparisons with the Caravelle. "If you take the basic Caravelle at $3 million and then add the changes—reverse thrust, cockpit revisions for better vision, improved flaps, a non-inflammable hydraulic fluid system—the price will be up to our own."

Bruce Connelly, who had headed the mission, seemed as relieved as Steiner as he summed up the obvious tenor of the meeting. "I don't think we should give it any consideration," he said.

Then Sud aviation itself said it had concluded the Boeing 720 was too near to being competitive with the Caravelle for a partnership. It signed an agreement with Douglas to become U.S. agent for Caravelle sales.

But there was another alternative—joint production with de Havilland of England on the Trident—an airplane still in development stage, in the same class as the 727, but with an advantageous time lead and possibly better keyed to participation in the growing Common Market of Europe. Schairer and Connelly went to examine this possibility in mid-February 1960, leaving the hard-pushing Steiner again on edge.

Steiner felt that technically the 727 design was constantly gaining ground. Bill Cook, who had consistently expressed concern that the competitive sales timetable did not allow sufficient time for the difficult flap development and the tail development for aft engines, had given head aerodynamicist Joe Sutter a charge, once the three aft engine configuration was set: "Joe, you make that a good airplane."

Sutter was confident, relaxed, and he teamed easily with Steiner. He had agreed with Cook that there would not be time to complete an exotic development of boundary-layer control by blowing air on the surfaces. "But

we don't need it," he assured Steiner. "We can do the
job with mechanical flaps." Wind-tunnel results were
showing that triple-slotted flaps, each extending behind
the other, plus a leading edge flap, would deliver the results they needed aerodynamically. There remained for
Steiner's men the knotty job of working it out mechan-
ically.

The object was to move the successive flaps out into
place so as to add 25 percent to the total wing area and
change the contour into a big umbrella for landing. Then
they'd have a combination such as no other airplane had
—a small, efficient wing for high speed but with a high-
lift device that would make it docile for landing—just
what was needed for the short-haul operator. Sutter was
highly enthusiastic about it.

"No competing airplane will have it," he said.

Steiner grinned. "I hope *we* will have it." He put his engineers to work on the mechanical linkage.

Connelly returned from England no more enthusiastic
about a de Havilland tie-up than he had been for the Caravelle, but the possibility remained an alternative if the
Boeing program could not be launched. February 29,
1960, the Transport Division had its presentation ready in
Bill Allen's office. Steiner, with a fresh set of 55 graphic
charts, showed how the jet success had obsoleted all other
aircraft, how the lines would have to add jets on their
smaller routes. "But operating a 50-aircraft fleet of 720s
instead of 727s costs an additional $30 million per year.
A one percent decrease in direct operating cost means $1
million gross profit per year for a fleet of sixty."

The Sales Department showed encouraging market
forecasts. The target had been for a price of $3.5 mil-
lion each for a minimum quantity of 100. Carl Dillon of
Finance said this was wholly unrealistic, but that $3.8
million each for a 200-airplane quantity was possible. "It
would mean a very substantial loss if only 100 were sold."

Two hundred airplanes at $3.8 million would be a
three-quarters of a billion dollar program. Bill Allen reminded them that it would exceed the risk of the 707
venture. It would be the biggest gamble the company

had ever faced. "The Electra is out and flying," he said. "It's designed to do the very job the 727 is intended to do. As far as we can learn the operators are very happy with it."

Steiner countered politely that the Electra would be obsolete as soon as the 727 became available.

But Allen was concerned, too, about the European competition. "Their wage rates are only a fraction of ours. In the case of the French, at least, the enterprise is government-owned and they can set their price without relation to cost if they want to."

He kept referring to the risk of loss and what it could do to the company. Finally he said he'd give the Board a "progress report." He asked Connelly and sales director George Sanborn to continue to press the sales campaign to see if starting orders could be obtained for a hundred airplanes. "I'd like to set as a goal—I admit this may be hard to achieve—that we sign Eastern and United simultaneously. I think that's the minimum we should do to reduce the risk."

The question of go-ahead waited.

21

Surrounding the 727 decision were other uncertainties of 1960. Chief of them was Bomarc. The fact that Bomarc "A" was operational and had just scored an impressive test intercept against a Navy supersonic Regulus missile two hundred miles out was less noticed than the five successive test failures of the new Bomarc "B." Actually the new solid-fuel booster rockets in the Bomarc B were working well. The trouble was in the valves of the Marquardt ramjet that was already working satisfactorily in Bomarc A, but this fact was less noticed than the fact that the firings at Cape Canaveral *did* fizzle.

The timing was awkward. The House Defense Appropriations subcommittee, which had slashed $162 million from Bomarc the year before, was looking for places to cut the new appropriation, encouraged in part by the relative harmony that had developed between the United States and the Soviet Union. Khrushchev had visited America and a Paris Summit meeting was in the offing. Furthermore, critics of Bomarc still pointed to the fact that it could not stop an intercontinental ballistic missile —though neither could anything else—and that it was dependent on the vulnerable SAGE. The Air Force proposed to "harden" SAGE by putting the centers underground, but Congressmen were balking at the heavy expenditure this would require. Instead, there was talk about whether the economy could adjust in the event of disarmament.

The issue between Bomarc "area defense" and the Nike missile's "point defense" remained unsettled. Appropriations subcommittee members told the press that they would use the Bomarc test failures as a basis for demands that the Bomarc B program be cancelled as "wasteful duplication."

The Air Force replied promptly, "The Bomarc B has achieved all its primary objectives."

Representative Dan Flood commented dourly that the Air Force claims reminded him of the old saying, "The operation was a success, but the patient died."

But new revisions in Air Force planning beat Congress to the ax. General White told the subcommittee March 30 that the service planned to slash both the Bomarc and SAGE programs, the money saved to be used for other things—one of them expeditious developing and testing of Minuteman. A cut of $381 million would be made in the Bomarc allocation for the next fiscal year, leaving just $40 million, compared with $394 million in the current year. Further, said the chief of staff, the program would end in 1963. "Technology and the enemy threat are constantly changing," he explained.

In Seattle and along the eastern seaboard, where base installations were being completed, 10,000 worried employees were working on the Bomarc program. They would not be affected at once, Bill Allen assured them, but there would have to be a gradual reduction of 2,700 by the end of the year. It put new stress on the need for other new business.

The start-up of the Dyna-Soar program was with certain reservations. First, the amount of money expected to be available was severely slashed, giving the program a longer paper period. Second, a "Phase Alpha" was ordered by the Defense Department to re-examine the basic concept and evaluate other alternatives, including the alternative of a ballistic-shaped re-entry body instead of the tuck-winged glider. Phase Alpha became a free-for-all that could upset or redirect the program. In a meeting at the NASA Ames Laboratory in California the Avco Company came up with an inverted parachute drag brake, Lockheed with a fold-out wing, Chance-Vought with a medium lift-over-drag approach, Goodyear with an inflatable design.

In April 1960, Phase Alpha was ended, the glider concept confirmed and "Step 1" begun—the analysis, planning and development of initial hardware for a supersonic sub-orbital research and test vehicle. Step 2 was to later introduce a larger booster to obtain orbital speeds, Step 3 to cover a weapons system based on the knowledge learned by that time. There was no commitment to Steps 2 and 3.

The Boeing lunar excursion study report, with its outline of steps to be taken to get to the moon, and human factor findings from the Mt. Rainier base, was turned in to the Air Force and accepted with compliments. The study was extended to June 1960, but no one expected a production contract to follow.

The moves toward product diversification were giving new impetus to the marketing of gas turbine engines in the Industrial Products Division that now occupied the original Boeing Plant I in Seattle. The little turbine, which could apply the turbojet principle to wheel power, had been first built in 1947 in the research work that preceded the jet transport. The Navy had taken an interest and by the time of the Korean war had ordered a 250-horsepower version in quantity for auxiliary power in minesweepers. Now the turbine was being sold to the airlines for field carts used in starting jet engines, to the Navy for a radio-controlled anti-submarine helicopter, and to the Swedish Volvo Company for use in a series of Army vehicles. A number of other uses had been tried, always with the dream of cashing in on a revolution in automotive power, but also with the realization that that day would not come until the turbine could match the fuel economy of piston engines. The product development was kept going on a long-term hope.

In Morton, Pennsylvania, the Vertol Aircraft Corporation with 2,300 employees became a Boeing division in the spring of 1960, to add to the Boeing product line the helicopters that Schairer and Ruffner had sought. Vertol was flying a tilt-wing experimental vertical take-off airplane that showed ingenuity though no immediate promise. But three new-model helicopters showed definite promise—the big Chinook, of which the Army had ordered ten for carrying thirty-three troops or nearly six tons of equipment, a smaller craft, the Sea Knight, that had just won a Navy Marine Corps competition and a civilian version called Model 107 that had been sold to New York Airways. The final engineering and test of these aircraft was still ahead. Payroll and production facilities would have to be expanded. There would be a big investment required before the Vertol Division could turn in earnings.

An exploration that had been begun into the field of anti-submarine warfare equipment had taken a new and interesting turn. Engineer Bob Bateman, who had been two years at Strategic Air Command Headquarters in Omaha as senior engineering representative, was rotated back to Seattle in 1959 to head an office established for the evaluation of new systems development. Reviewing the anti-submarine question he had concluded that it would be better for the division to pursue the vehicle side of that field than to get into listening devices and small equipment. He recommended a more serious look at anti-submarine warfare aircraft, advanced surface vehicles and undersea vehicles. Shortly afterward, when the Aero-Space Division was formed and jobs were being shuffled, assistant general manager George Martin called Bateman in, asked him what he'd like to do. Bateman deferred to Martin.

"All right," Martin said, "how about taking on the project you've just proposed."

A study group was set up with a half million dollar budget for a one-year exercise to see what could be done. But market projections showed the opportunity in anti-submarine aircraft to be doubtful, with Lockheed already in possession of that field. The group looked at the prospect for light, fast, aluminum submarines akin to aircraft construction, and hydrofoil boats. Then the two were put together with a result that was intriguing—a "flying fish"—a light submarine that could be equipped with hydrofoils to fly over the surface of the water or duck down when it needed to hide. Bateman could see the possibility of mass-producing it in hundreds.

Learning that there had been consideration for such a device in NATO Bateman went with customer requirements manager Airo Gonnella to talk with military officers in the European countries. The response was high enthusiasm, particularly in Germany and Italy, but no action. Bateman's group had meanwhile entered a bid, with the assistance of the Martinac Shipbuilding Company of Tacoma as subcontractor, on a 100-ton U.S. Navy hydrofoil patrol boat to be capable of 40-knot speeds. Division manager Lysle Wood had agreed that the entry would provide a useful test to see if they could manage a fixed-price contract for a marine craft under Navy rules, with the Navy furnishing most of the design. No one greatly expected the bid to win.

Then, as a result of the European trip, an inquiry came from Fiat of Italy, asking if Boeing was really interested in the hydro sub. A decision had to be made whether to continue with this and other marine efforts, as Bateman's year of investigation neared its end. It was early June 1960. A major management conference was convened, Bateman urging continuance, but the consensus was that the division should drop out of the marine field. It would mean withdrawing the Navy bid.

Bill Allen reviewed the recommendation. "Let's wait a month and see if Bateman has us committed," he said.

June 14, the news came that they were low bidder for the Navy hydrofoil boat. The European hydro-sub prospect vanished, but a second Navy contract was obtained for a 15-ton twin-hull test craft for advanced hydrofoil work. Boeing was launched in the marine hydrofoil business, knowingly with a misty future, developmental and undefined.

The situation had suddenly changed on Bomarc. The Bomarc B with a Marquardt valve fix was pronounced

"100 percent successful" in new test firings at Cape Canaveral. Almost simultaneously an American U-2 reconnaissance plane was shot down over the Soviet Union and Nikita Khrushchev's rage made the Paris Summit meeting impossible. The old concern over U.S. security returned. Reacting promptly the Senate Appropriations Committee took the lead, and the House concurred in restoring $244 million for Bomarc B procurement. But it was over the head of the Defense Department—the end was in sight.

From Wright Air Development Command a study release had gone out to all industry on the proposed experimental tactical fighter—TFX—with variable sweep wings. It meant that all the companies would be getting to work on the plane, but the year's effort that had already been put in on the fighter could give Boeing a big lead, it was felt—if the competition were called for soon. There was a high hope that it could mean a substantial new field.

But the opportunity nearest at hand, though also the most fraught with apparent financial hazard, was the 727 short-to-medium-range transport. The trijet had now been given project status for engineering purposes, with Jack Steiner as chief project engineer, but the program go-ahead decision was still pending.

Eastern Air Lines was insisting on ability to use the 4,980-foot runway on New York's close-in LaGuardia Field, which had been outmoded by the jets. The new triple-slotted flap development, along with leading-edge flaps, would make that possible. United Air Lines' Caravelle order had proved to be only a stop-gap, their major short-to-medium-range needs yet to be filled by the hypothetical economic airplane they called "Airplane X." United's engineering vice president Bill Mentzer had been contributing ideas to the 727 design, regarding it as their best chance of achieving "Airplane X." TWA was not ready financially. American had been holding to the Electra turboprop for its shorter routes; its interest was increasing with the evident increased popularity of the jets, but it still wanted a smaller airplane than the 727 was turning out to be.

The airlines in general were against the wall with debt, and sales were slowing on the 707 and 720. It would take sales of approximately a billion dollar's worth of airplanes to make the 727 project profitable, Bill Allen now estimated, with a development and tooling cost alone of nearly $100 million. He was still highly concerned over the question of the 727's ability to meet British-French competition in the world market in order to gain the required sales. "The French labor rate is about forty percent of ours, and the British about fifty percent," he said in a speech in St. Louis in June 1960. "The price of both the French and the British airplane will be lower than ours. Unless we can overcome this differential by offering a substantially superior product, at least a billion dollars in production will be lost to American business and its employees. If we want the business we must earn it through better performance."

Still, there was need for future production in the plant, and there was an opportunity. Allen recommended to the Board in late August 1960 that a firm production go-ahead be authorized, if there were starting orders for one hundred airplanes under contract. The Board approved. The action sent chief project engineer Jack Steiner and his forces into a do-or-die final effort to meet airline requirements. Eastern and United wanted the engines changed to Pratt & Whitneys; the change was made. It would take at least United and Eastern together to make an order for 100 airplanes.

Allen and a Boeing group were in United Air Lines' Board room in Chicago, with board chairman William A. Patterson well aware of his strategic position. But Patterson relieved the tension. "We want the 727," he said. "I'll give you a letter you can take to Eastern."

Boeing attorney Lowell Mickelwait and United's attorney drew up a Letter of Intent with the provision that Boeing could withdraw if Eastern didn't agree to go along, or if total orders fell short of one hundred by December 1, United holding a similar withdrawal privilege.

After continued negotiations Eastern signed for forty airplanes, but United decided it was able to enter firm contract for only twenty, with twenty more to be subject to cancellation. That was well short of the one-hundred-airplane target, as the December 1 deadline neared. The decision load was back on Allen, the Board willing to leave it in his hands. He was tortured by sales and development risks, aware that cost estimates were drum-tight, but he felt a confidence in Engineering, and John Yeasting had encouraging forecasts for future market growth. The 707 red-ink line appeared to have reached bottom and turned upward, though there would have to be a long climb before it could come to the break-even point.

Allen could not turn back. November 30, 1960, one day before the deadline, he signed simultaneous contracts with United and Eastern for eighty airplanes—twenty of United's still provisional. At a combined cost, with spares of $420 million, it was the largest single commercial aviation transaction ever to have been made. The 727 was a commitment.

There were delays in the announcement of an Air Force TFX competition which had been rumored to be imminent through the fall of 1960. When the November elections brought a change in the Administration Secretary of Defense Gates decided to leave the program determination to the new Secretary, Robert McNamara. On his arrival in the office McNamara ordered a new thorough study begun within the department, with the objective of seeing if the fighter requirements of the Air Force and Navy could not be combined in a single type as an economy move. With still no request for proposals forthcoming to industry, the Aero-Space Division's TFX study group was trimmed to minimum crew, marking time, chafing over the fading away of the strategic lead it had prized.

The B-52 and Bomarc programs would both end in 1962, it was now known. But Minuteman and Dyna-Soar were growing in importance. Minuteman had the status of the Air Force's No. 1 program, and with this came the same feeling of consequence as had accompanied the B-29 and the B-52. The Dyna-Soar, in its break with tradition, seemed more like the B-47, a development program with uncertainties but with the possibility of substantial production, if it turned out to be a military system. The KC-135 jet tanker, less glamorous but effectual, had meanwhile turned out to be a staple, rolling up a production of 400 airplanes to date, with never a schedule missed. It was counted an all-around successful program, turning in its regular earnings.

The military programs were carrying the commercial on their shoulders, as far as corporate finances were concerned. Bill Allen was appreciative of this fact, and reflective on the high value of responsible engineering and management of big government programs, which he felt had become the company's tradition and capability. This was not to say that he regretted the purposeful push into jet transports. Always he had held the desire to see the airplane find its basic use as a commercial carrier and a pacer of civilian progress. Likewise he had held as a goal the balancing off of government work—so subject to sudden guillotine—with business that was based in the civilian economy.

Allen as a young lawyer had helped Bill Boeing and Phil Johnson organize the Boeing Air Transport system in the '20s and had seen it grow into United Air Lines. He had suffered, with Boeing and Johnson, the company's split-off from the airline business. He had a genuine interest in air transportation and the aspiration to see Boeing the leading supplier of air transport equipment. That position had now been reached, but the satisfaction had its sense of emptiness, even of alarm, if it had to be written in red ink. The goal was to do it at a profit on which a future could be built.

The fact that this goal had not yet been reached made concurrent military success more mandatory. With the B-52 and Bomarc coming to the end of the line the challenge now rested with Minuteman and Dyna-Soar and the hatching TFX.

The compressed schedule for Minuteman had called for the first firing of a completed missile by the end of

December 1960. The pressure of that commitment had grown through the past year. It was not a total Boeing responsibility, but shared with other companies, yet the task of putting it all together and making it work, made the Minuteman now seem almost as much as any before it a Boeing product.

Much of the stitching that was required to sew the Minuteman system together, they were finding, was in the field of electronics. As a result a big electronics manufacturing facility was being activated on Boeing Field in the area vacated by the exit of the B-70 wings. From the Bomarc program, as fast as they could be released, and from elsewhere, electronics engineering and fabricating skills were being brought together for the big push to make schedule.

A mounting sequence of problems had been keeping the December firing date in jeopardy—late equipment deliveries; design changes; the matching of all the functions between the three stages of the missile that would fire successively; the working out of the gimbaled nozzles that would give directional control; the shortages from late engineering drawings where stumbling blocks had been encountered.

Scheduled dates for start and completion of the dynamic and static tests had to be slid further down the calendar, reducing the amount of structural information that would be available to assure success of the first flight. Simultaneous work was under way at high priority in developing a system for a mobile Minuteman to be constantly switched along railroad lines to keep the enemy guessing. A plant for final assembly of production missiles and for later recycling them to keep them current and in constant readiness after their silo hibernation was being established at Hill Air Force Base in Ogden, Utah. Sounding holes were being driven in widely separated places to determine locations for the underground silos and launch control capsules. The first sites had been picked in the area of Malmstrom Air Force Base in Montana. The next were to be in South Dakota, then New Hampshire and other states would be surveyed.

Transportation problems were being worked—how to get the big equipment and the missiles themselves across country roads and frail bridges. At the Atlantic missile range on Cape Canaveral strikes were delaying construction of ground facilities where the test firings were to take place. The pads and blockhouses and towers and underground silos and telemetering system all had to be built and installed in five months. Computer systems were being devised for the tests to transmit data to recorders at the rate of 350,000 separate bits of information per second.

The pressure on December was monstrous. The plan had been to prove out all equipment in Seattle before its transfer to Florida, but time did not permit this. The test group at Cape Canaveral was receiving it by the truckload and planeload, hot from the creative ovens, and having to take the burden of checkout. To hold schedule they had to group functions together for simultaneous tests, where a more conservative schedule would have provided for separate testing of each. It was the marrying of the work of many companies—North American Autonetics, Thiokol, Hercules, Aerojet, Avco and many others. It was the "bold approach" that Colonel Sam Phillips had called for. But the whole nation was now watching. You couldn't fire a national Minuteman in private.

In mid-December, with compounding problems of compatibility of equipment, Colonel Phillips reset the launching date for late January. A first firing could not be frantic, it had to be orderly and sober; a delay was better than failure.

One of the inevitable problems of an initial firing was that the launch consoles, instrumentation and support equipment all had to be on hand in complete form, but these were always the last ordered into construction, because their design was dependent on completion of the detail engineering of the missile itself. A further trying circumstance was that everything was new. There were all the check-outs to be made to show that the thousands of items could behave as one, when the button was pushed. Electronic gear was called upon to check and doublecheck itself through programmed computers. If one thing was out the computer would stop.

There were problems of getting the air-borne guidance system to talk to the computers on the ground. Because the Minuteman in operation was ultra-lethal, everything in the system was so designed that if it were not functioning correctly and in proper sequence, it would not go, so the problem was to get it to fire at all. If the current got below or above a certain point during countdown, it would shut off. In the assembly building there were twenty-eight switches in series, any one of which could shut down the operation. There was a switch on the panic door. When someone accidentally leaned against it, it would turn everything off. Twice the test was started; the countdown went within seconds of the firing, then stopped.

The month of January was expiring, and the target date was rescheduled for February 1, a month behind the schedule set in October 1958, but still almost a year ahead of original estimates. The remaining flight test dates were re-programmed to recover the time, keeping the first silo launching on August 23, 1961.

Primary objectives of the initial launch—which was to be from a surface firing pad—were to be the testing of first-stage ignition, lift-off, pitch-over and launch techniques, plus the manufacturing sequences, the missile assembly, the pre-launch check-out and instrumentation. But in keeping with the "bold approach" it was hoped to get data at one stroke on second and third-stage performance also, and the overall operation of the missile. If this could be accomplished it would be the first time a new missile had combined in its maiden flight all three live operational stages. It would be the first time for operational guidance equipment to be functioning in the initial flight. The compact inertial guidance system of Minuteman was itself a "first," built up by North American Autonetics with micro-miniaturized components.

On February 1, 1961 in tenseness the countdown went to zero. A burst of flame hit the pad and smoke boiled upward. In a roar the Minuteman was rising quickly, racing before its red torch into the sky. It continued: first stage . . . separation . . . second stage . . . ignition . . . separation . . . third and final stage out over the Atlantic. A zealous reporter in the press group shouted, "There goes the missile gap."

22

The first Minuteman had traveled to its planned impacting point 4,200 miles down-range. It was pronounced by the Air Force as an "unqualified success." The problem now was production of the intricate system against the forced schedule that had been set up. But it was not to be production in the previous sense; it had to be an integration of the work of a half-dozen major associate contractors, and delivery not out of a door, but in the form of a comprehensive installation at hundreds of sites across the northern states—nuclear-laden capsules of intercontinental power with all the accessories, controls, wires, elevators, doors. And it had to be delivered underground.

It would be a production line stretching from Seattle to Ogden, Utah to all the field installations, a management task as much in geography and logistics as in technology. The problem was how to make it as efficient as a factory, so schedules could be kept and costs held down.

Youthful, square-jawed "Tex" Boullioun, who had been installing the Bomarc bases, devised a plan with Howard Hurst, a veteran in managing airplane production lines. They decided to organize it, despite the geographical spread, just as a factory line but with one exception: instead of bringing the work past the men at their stations, they would march the men past the work, each to perform his expert operation. There would be 8,000 men required in the field, working in 50 or 60 holes at a time, as though they might be working on 50 or 60 airplanes or cars on a line. Every task would be broken down into 8-hour increments, so that the skilled men could put in a day or days and move on. The 8,000 men would be divided into three crews, so that 2,700 would be cycled through to take a job from beginning to final button-up. It would be a new kind of mobile work force with men and families living in trailer homes scattered across the midwest.

The concept was exciting. The whole basis of low-cost quantity production in an airplane factory was that if a man performed the same operation on each airplane in large production runs, he would build the last part at one-tenth the cost of the first, because of the learning process. Boullioun reasoned that the same should apply in the field, even though it meant a daily stream of men across half the farms of Montana. There were those that thought it couldn't be done. Boullioun convinced program director "T" Wilson that it could. They set up a control room in the Developmental Center at Seattle with the whole pattern on big wall charts, with colors to represent crews and cycles, to make sure that each was moving according to plan.

In another part of the plant the strange shape of Dyna-Soar was going into mock-up, with an apparent much longer road to travel to operational status. It was 45 feet long, with probing nose and wings in a narrowed delta shape, like an almost-closed Japanese fan. The back tips of those wings were turned up for control surfaces, between which was the rocket nozzle. The whole thing was chopped off at the back, as with a cleaver.

"The simple shape is deceptive," Dyna-Soar manager George Stoner told perplexed visitors. "It isn't that simple. But it has to be a plain shape to survive all the conditions it must go through."

The fact was that the Dyna-Soar in the course of its design refinement was in the midst of the most extensive wind-tunnel program ever undergone by any aircraft, in subsonic, transonic, supersonic, hypersonic and plasma jet tunnels. "It has to fly like an airplane at speeds of Mach 15 to 25—where the meteor glows," Stoner explained. "It must fly hypersonically at speeds from Mach 4 to 15. The fastest present rocket airplane is the X-15 which travels about Mach 6. Then it has to fly satisfactorily through the sound barrier and in the supersonic region from six or seven hundred miles an hour up to Mach 4, about 3,000 miles an hour. Finally, this same simple shape has to fly satisfactorily when approaching a landing field and landing like an airplane."

Even the simplest change in an angle on the design had to be re-checked in all the different wind tunnels for effects in all these ranges of speed. They had encountered the question of how effective the control surfaces would be at a high angle of attack—nose high and tail low. At the upper fringes of the atmosphere this steep angle would be required just to maintain level flight, because the air would give so little support. Finding the controls less effective at hypersonic speeds at these angles, they had to change to larger, different shaped controls.

The direction of the aerodynamic development, along with overall engineering, power requirements, electronics and guidance, life sciences and military applications, fell to senior project engineer Harry Goldie. By the spring of 1961, Goldie was able to report to George Stoner that most of the major structural and aerodynamic design features of Dyna-Soar had been settled. Most of the 1,600 engineers on the project were turning to subsystem design—hydraulics, electronics, control and generating systems.

They were still working the temperature control problem. By using "refractory" alloys with a high content of molybdenum—the material that had been discovered ideal in the manufacture of steel safes, because it defeated the robber with acetylene blow torch—they were able to re-radiate 99.8% of the heat back into space.

They faced the problem of how to get rid of the .2% of the heat that would still be absorbed by the vehicle—enough to make the cockpit an oven. Insulation and then cooling with liquid hydrogen appeared to be the answer.

The liquid hydrogen in a "cryogenic" tank could be stored at 420 degrees below zero Fahrenheit, then passed through the cooling system to be warmed by the heat absorbed through the cockpit walls. As its temperature was raised to 100 degrees above zero it could devour a phenomenal amount of heat per pound.

"A four-foot tank of it will make the greatest heat sink in the world," the designers told Harry Goldie.

"Of course you'll have to get rid of it as it's heated," Goldie pointed out.

"We can run it into an auxiliary power unit, mix it with oxygen and burn it to generate our electrical power."

"Now that's a real cunning system," Goldie said. But he cautioned that it would take great care in design.

Not all parts of the craft would be so cooled. There was a need for electronic wires to go to sensors in the wings, where they would be subject to 3,000 degrees. The electrical suppliers laughed. Goldie gave the problem back to the project group. "We'll have to invent our own."

They developed a wire made of platinum with ceramic insulation. To meet the problem of the cracking of the brittle ceramics when the wire was bent, they devised ceramic beads, stringing them on the wire as insulation.

The creative work was continuing when, on April 12, 1961, from the Mayun-Kun Desert of Kazakhstan, a two-stage giant rocket shot through the sky and the Soviet Union announced that Major Yuri Gagarin had orbited the earth. From that day the pressure for U.S. space accomplishment rocketed, and every program entered a new light.

NASA had been fighting technical problems on the Mercury program, a tight one-man capsule to be boosted by the existing Army Redstone rocket, well-proved but insufficient for full orbit. Later an Atlas booster was to make possible the step into orbit. From the first, Mercury had seemed tentative. "At best it is a technical stopgap justifiable only as an expedient," NASA's chief of manned space flight, George Low, had told the Senate space committee in the summer of 1960. "It is no substitute for what is needed sooner or later—a maneuverable spacecraft similar to the Air Force's much hampered Dyna-Soar."

The trade press had been critical that Dyna-Soar was being kept on the national back burner when it should be an all-out program. Said *Missiles and Rockets* magazine in October, "There is some high-level sentiment in DOD to drop the weapons system requirement on Dyna-Soar in order to speed its development. The hitch is that the Air Force under Administration policy must now justify Dyna-Soar as a weapon, to get the necessary funding. If it drops this requirement, the wolves will move in."

Boeing was proposing in late 1960 that the booster for the program be changed from the sub-orbital Air Force Titan to NASA's forthcoming Saturn I which would push it into orbit. NASA, serving as Air Force advisor on Dyna-Soar, proposed further that the program be identified as experimental so it could be voted funds without raising the question of manned military vehicles in space. The Air Force, on the other hand, was urging upon the new Administration that there be more military participation in space. It said it wanted "to be able to use space on a routine day-to-day basis, with equipment that would be re-usable after normal service." It said it needed the Dyna-Soar's lifting wing surfaces so it could maneuver to a wide selection of landing points, admittedly with the penalty of greater weight than a ballistic vehicle such as Mercury would have.

May 5, 1961, the nation was gripped by a TV view of Commander Alan Shepard's maiden U.S. space flight in the Mercury capsule Freedom 7. President Kennedy called for a program to catch up with Russia in space. The Air Force went before the House defense appropriations subcommittee to ask that the Dyna-Soar appropriation be increased by $160 million to save a year's time.

When the committee raised the question of the Air Force's not having a specific weapons system concept for Dyna-Soar, Undersecretary Joseph Charyk replied that this was not important in the early stage of development. "I believe that some of our major errors have been in attempting to hold back development until we could completely spell out a military requirement," he said.

Under the label "Project Streamline," the Dyna-Soar speed-up movement before Congress gathered impetus, with Boeing backing the plan. Then a new crisis ensued over Berlin. The defense-conscious House responded, July 7, by voting $86 million for Dyna-Soar beyond the Defense Department's request, along with additional funds for B-70s and B-52s. The Senate concurred.

But the space race was out-doing the defense race. While Secretary McNamara had the Congressional action under study, astronaut Gherman Titov in Vostok II sailed seventeen times around the globe, crying triumphantly "I am an eagle." Captain Virgil Grissom had duplicated Alan Shepard's space flight, but a Mercury orbit with Atlas boost would still be months off. In the public stir over space President Kennedy sent a message to Congress establishing an American Space goal—to put a man on the moon by 1970. It would ultimately cost billions, he acknowledged. The idea brought acclaim.

Digesting all this, and not to be stampeded by Congress, Secretary McNamara made the decision that none of the funds voted by Congress beyond the Administration's requests—Dyna-Soar, B-52 or B-70—would be expended. A direction of thought was beginning to emerge. The Dyna-Soar—a much more difficult undertaking than the orbiting of simple ballistic capsules—would be late for the orbiting role. The military had not yet proved its role in space. The big program ahead was going to be the race to the moon.

The President had turned over to NASA the Boeing study plan that had been prepared for the Air Force on reaching the moon. The Air Force was out of the moon business. NASA's Apollo mission was following a similar line of planning for a direct lunar flight, though there was under consideration an alternative plan. If the weight of equipment to be space-hoisted should be greater than at first expected, a two-step venture would be substituted —the first step going to a lunar orbit, there to lower an "excursion module" to the moon's surface and later return it to an orbital rendezvous for the Apollo trip home.

It was becoming evident, even before the President's pronouncement, that the NASA-Apollo mission was going to be big business. There were two aspects of the program—the Saturn launch vehicle containing the booster stages to power the flight, and the Apollo spacecraft to carry the passengers. The opportunity to compete in both of these arose at the same time, but there would not be a chance of doing both. The choice was weighed in a management meeting—whether the Saturn or the Apollo end would likely be more important. It appeared that the launch vehicle, once it came into being, might have an inherent work-horse life well beyond the Apollo mission. Boeing would pass up the Apollo competition for Saturn, it was decided.

Saturn was being developed by NASA's Marshall Space Flight Center at Huntsville, Alabama, the former Army Redstone arsenal, under Dr. Wernher von Braun. The design, construction and testing of the prototype Saturn C-1 were being done there, but industry was being asked to compete for the award of production contracts. The Saturn C-1 first-stage booster would deliver 1,500,000 pounds of thrust, four times that of Atlas, 19 times that of the Redstone that launched the first Mercury. There was also an opportunity to bid on a proposed still larger first-stage booster for a "C-3" Advanced Saturn, employing two of the C-1's rocket engines to double the power. While this was being built, the Marshall Center intended to work on a still larger launcher, the Nova. The Saturn C-1 would put 25 tons into earth orbit, the C-3 would lift 50 tons; the Nova a mighty 200 tons, but it would take much longer to develop.

At Boeing, familiarization study work on the Saturn program had been carried forward since 1958. A Boeing office had been opened in Huntsville to learn more about the requirement. Earlier bids had been made and lost for parts of the Saturn system, but in July 1961, a NASA contract was won to study use of solid vs. liquid propellants in both Saturn and Nova. The conclusion was that for these larger sizes the liquid was still best.

With the decision made on Saturn vs. Apollo, with the lack of acceleration on Dyna-Soar and the flaming new interest in the great adventure of getting to the moon, Lysle Wood named Stoner as Saturn program proposal manager, August 28, 1961. Stoner stepped up to the challenge with fervor; he was eager to get deeper into space. The man he picked as his assistant was big, strapping Swedish Dick Nelson who had been project engineer on Gapa and Bomarc and then manufacturing manager of the Missile Production Center in Seattle. With combined efforts they put together a proposal team.

The Government had determined that the Saturn production should take place in the old Michoud ordinance plant outside New Orleans, whence the big boosters, 138 feet long by 33 feet in diameter, could be barged to Cape Canaveral for firing. Stoner made clear to each man being considered for a place on the proposal team that those who wrote the proposal were going to have to do the job. "You're going to have to move down there to the southland and see that it is done," he said. "If you don't want to make that commitment tell us now."

In mid-September, with Nelson and others picked for key roles, Stoner was in the municipal auditorium in Huntsville, Alabama, in steaming heat. Wernher von Braun was on the stage before all the representatives of industry desirous of competing for the Saturn work. It was evident that the German-born scientist was at a peak of excitement, grasping the materialization of an ambition that had been burning in him since the early '30's. He re-stated the national goal that had been set by the President of landing man on the moon by 1970. Within the audience was the means to make it happen, he said.

"The Lunar landing is our present focal point—our big step into manned space travel," von Braun said, "but it will not end there. The Saturn does not care what its payload is. It is just a big truck to increase this country's capacity to carry cargo into space."

He outlined requirements for the Saturn C-1 first-stage booster, then for the Advanced Saturn. Although the latter should be quoted on the basis of two engines the contractor should be prepared to design a stage with four or more engines, von Braun explained.

Back in Seattle Stoner's team worked intensively on management plans and analyses for both proposals, determined to win one. Stoner wanted to take advantage of the possibility that the C-3 would be extended in size. "I think we should recommend the biggest one we can make," he told the proposal team. "The spacecraft people will have a hard enough time getting the Apollo light enough for a direct launch to the moon. Let's make their job easier."

It became evident that the goal Kennedy had set could not wait for the proposed huge Nova booster. On the other hand there was a practical limit to the amount the Saturn could be stretched. Could it be four engines, five, ten, twelve? They wouldn't want to get beyond the capacity of the biggest machine tools such as boring mills, or make the parts too big for boats or highways.

That last consideration got Stoner thinking. "Von Braun says the Saturn is a truck. It is; it's a space logistics system. Let's find out what are the heaviest pieces any other truck or boat or train has to haul. Let's see if we could build a Saturn that would lift that big a piece out of the earth's gravity."

They found that the typical payload compartment on a ship was limited to 100,000 pounds, on a train, about the same, truck transport, about 70,000 pounds, the biggest air transport, approaching 100,000 pounds. That seemed to be the biggest man-made chunk that needed to be hauled. If they gave the Advanced Saturn's main booster a cluster of five rocket engines, each with the 1-1/2 million pounds thrust of the Saturn C-1—and five would make a logical grouping, with one in the center—it could lift 90,000 pounds into escape velocity to the moon. Going just to earth orbit, which would require much less power than to escape the earth's gravity, it would lift 240,000 pounds—a substantial package. The five-engine cluster was feasible. Its big tanks, lying on their sides, would just go under the trusses of the 40-foot-high roof of the Michoud plant. They decided to strongly recommend this as an alternate to the specified two-engine design.

The first proposal for the C-1 Saturn went in. Chrysler was promptly announced as winner. That left the big job —the Advanced Saturn, the one Stoner really wanted. Their proposal was submitted and they were summoned for oral briefings. Stoner and the others passed in review, along with the teams from competing companies, each required to recite before the assembled NASA group. Then they went home and waited. It was worse than a countdown, awaiting such a decision.

The Defense Department's request for proposals on the TFX tactical fighter was issued October 1, 1961, calling for a version common to the needs of both the Air Force and the Navy. The two services had agreed to support jointly such a program, and a satisfactory "envelope" had been roughed out to contain the performance requirements of both, the Department announced. "Industry will be given as much latitude as possible in drawing up design proposals."

Engineers on the TFX effort were not altogether enthusiastic about the compromising of the design to the somewhat different operational conditions of Tactical Air Command and the Navy carrier forces, though they felt much could be gained by a reasonably high degree of commonality. They set to work to manicure their designs to best achieve that end, and to capitalize in every way possible on all the development work that had been done. The variable sweep feature, which by then had been subjected to thorough tests for both fighter and future supersonic transport use, was a requirement to meet the Defense Department's performance specifications. All competitors would be using it.

In a staff meeting Allen called the outcome of the TFX competition critical to the company's future business success. "The apparent decision not to order additional

B-52s, the completion of our Bomarc program, the declining of the additional Dyna-Soar funds, in combination, will be severely limiting to our future business prospects," he said. "The remaining opportunities for new business assume extraordinary importance." Allen stressed the responsibility heaped on both the TFX and Saturn proposal teams, and the need also for extending sales of helicopters and commercial transports.

In Morton, Pennsylvania, the Vertol Division's struggle to develop and produce its three new helicopter models was proving an expensive operation. In Renton the new 727 transport development was more costly than expected, though sales gains were gratifying, with orders from American Airlines and Lufthansa of Germany, raising hopes for wide airline acceptance. Recognizing that the commitment on the 727 was growing huge Wells and Schairer had urged the construction of a static test airplane for structural test-loading to destruction, and a second airplane for subjection to exhaustive tests for metal fatigue, plus the equipping of a special flight test airplane to measure and confirm the flight loadings in every speed and condition.

"With all the investment we're putting into it the only way we can come out on the program is by having enough sales," Wells told division manager John Yeasting, in advocating the admittedly expensive precautionary steps. "We'll be in a much better position to get these, if we're on the soundest possible foundation. We'll get our money back in the long run, if we get our changes in early."

Yeasting had been impressed that two competitors in the jet race had encountered serious engineering changes during production—one to meet performance guarantees, the other to remedy a structural failure. The added cost of the proposed test airplanes, on top of a full-scale control system test rig capable of simulating flight maneuvers, which they had already undertaken, were painful additions to the budget, but Yeasting approved them, as did Allen. The whole case for the airplane rested on its being right.

On the Dyna-Soar the Air Force was now considering a new Titan III to replace the Titan II booster. It would make the vehicle orbital, but it would mean much later launching than the Streamline Program had proposed. The dilemma of Dyna-Soar was that, if rushed, it would not go into orbit, when orbiting was the goal in the national eye; but if it was delayed for the new engine, the ballistic-type orbiters would be satisfying much of the need. The Air Force would have to come up with new reasons for Dyna-Soar.

The Minuteman program had become a titanic effort, with first operational missiles promised to be in place by mid-1962. The first base installation at Great Falls, Montana, was under way and on schedule. The launchings from surface pads had been successfully completed in Florida. Preparatory to the first silo launching the Air Force had inspected a test silo constructed in Seattle to final design—86 feet deep, 12 feet in diameter, with an 80-ton lid to be forced open by a ballistic charge seconds before the missile was to be fired, and with elaborate anti-sabotage protection, combination-lock steel doors, alarm systems. But when the countdown reached zero at Cape Canaveral for the first silo launch, there was an earth-shaking detonation and a rending eruption of debris as the missile emerged. The second and third stages had ignited almost simultaneously with the first, activating the command destruct system and exploding the missile. The second one was successful, November 17, 1961, but in the meantime an unexpected change-order had struck. A review committee from Washington, ordered by the Administration to make sure the Minuteman system was safe against the remotest possibility of erupting into war, had gone over the entire system and come up with a list of additional safeguards to be provided, along with changes in the target selection technique. The task was to engineer all the changes in the electronic system that would be necessary to accomplish the results they sought. It would be shattering to the work already being pressed at peak pace. But the request was for the alterations to be made without affecting the delivery schedule dates.

Ollie Boileau, the launch control system manager, had the task of finding the solutions, working closely with the Ballistic Missile Command and Space Technology Laboratories. The changes affected the whole ground control system. While involving only 10 percent of the functions, these affected ninety percent of the electronic equipment. They were overlaid in such a manner that it was necessary to redesign whole circuits and tie them all together in new ways. It was a major upheaval, calling for sixty and seventy-hour weeks without letup for the nine months before the first ten missiles were to be in the ground and working.

General Phillips, who himself had a Master's degree in electrical engineering, sat in Ollie Boileau's office to approve or disapprove, as Boileau's staff put diagrams on the wall. When they posted the master schedule the outlook seemed forlorn. The Air Force was highly concerned that the schedule would have to be changed. But Boileau said not.

"We can make it," he contended. "We have good guys."

The struggle of Minuteman had the sense of the vital. It dealt with the most awesome array of destructive power ever conceived—with the stern subject of life or death of a civilization. The struggle of Dyna-Soar was of a different order. It was a struggle for the life or death of a single man in space, a struggle in his behalf in trying to gain control over the ultimate forces of free speed and gravity. It could be in behalf of an exotic new military dimension, but this was not known. Or else, it seemed at times, it was a struggle for the life or death of a program.

Besides these two, there was the possibility, in the days that the Minuteman security changes were starting through, that still another kind of struggle would be in the offing, one having to do with the assembly of the world's largest package, not of explosive but of motive power, in the giant Advanced Saturn—if that contract should be won. It would be power with which to leave this world, not for an orbit still tied to the earth, but to depart for another orb. The full future significance of this capability was yet unknown, but it was by definition portentous.

The wait for word on the Saturn outcome was not long. Lysle Wood received a teletype December 14, 1961 from Marshall Space Flight Center. Boeing had been selected as contractor to build 24 Advanced Saturn first-stage boosters. A phone call and a following letter from von Braun answered the other big question. No, the booster would not be the two-engine version of 3,000,000 pounds thrust proposed in the Saturn C-3 specification. It would go the full way to the cluster of five engines recommended in Stoner's alternate proposal—a booster aggregating 7,500,000 pounds of thrust, to be known as the Saturn V.

23

While Dick Nelson, who was to build the Saturn booster, was surveying the dusty rafters and broken floor of the cavernous old Michoud ordnance works in New Orleans that he was asked to convert into a hygienically clean space-plant, Minuteman builder Tex Boullioun was slogging through knee-deep snow in Montana where crews were digging at the first 150 missile silo sites, scattered over a 20,000 square-mile area, each "a bomb" away from the next.

In deeper snow in Washington's Cascade Mountains a small group of electronics researchers was established in a solitary Weather Bureau station atop Stampede Pass, weathering winter blizzards intended to simulate Montana conditions. They were there to solve a perplexing problem of Minuteman: protecting the far-flung system against intruders. In every other nuclear-armed system, security had been maintained with guards. The dispersal and limited manpower concept of Minuteman required electronic guards instead.

At Titan sites they were using television. A crew in the control room could watch the screen to see if anyone was coming. For Minuteman they wanted electronic eyes. Nor could the electronics be subject to being foiled by an enemy agent bringing up another electronic black box designed to so perform that the Minuteman system would think there was no intruder when in fact there was.

The required development had begun in the Boeing antenna and radar laboratory on the roof of Plant 2 overlooking the Duwamish River in Seattle. But the detection devices that were being devised could see through the roof of the building to all the activity below. This cluttered the experiments. A development lab was then set up at Tulalip, along with other Minuteman testing. That, too, had its limitations.

It was not difficult to devise the means to detect human intruders, but all kinds of other activities might likewise set off the alarm—birds, animals, picnickers tossing beer cans, farm machinery going by, a low-flying airplane or tumbleweed blowing against a fence. All these had to be filtered out. A wind-blown fir tree laden with rain could cause a troublesome signal. They considered cutting down all the trees but that would require nine acres around each site, which was impractical. Worst of all, a heavy, wet snow blizzard could potentially blank out the system. That was what occasioned the winter station at Stampede Pass.

The problem was perplexing. What was needed was a clear detection of everything within a limited distance and nothing beyond—an electronic "fence" around each site. But you couldn't chop off radio waves in mid-air.

"Yes you can, in effect," said radar specialist Herb Williams. "There's a way we can do it." He proposed sending out electronic feeler waves in tiny pulses, cutting them off so fast that only those that bounced back from moving objects a short distance away would have time to get back to the receiving antenna before a synchronized receiver was shut off.

"We'll have to deal in rather small measures," Williams admitted. In truth it would be in nano-seconds, each of which was a thousandth of a microsecond, and a microsecond was a millionth of a second.

With an array of apparatus they made the tiny signals perform their staccato miracle of selection. It remained only to prove that the equipment could meet all challenges, then to reduce it from apple-box to cigar-box proportions.

The devising and experimentation continued. In January 1962, they reviewed the concept with the Air Force. By March they were ready to demonstrate it to General Phillips at Tulalip. They used every device to try to fool the electronic guards—a rifle shot at the antenna, pigeons flying, squirrels scampering by. A consulting zoologist had been hired to provide data the Air Force wanted on animal life of the Montana vicinity. A Boy Scout troop was sent to eastern Washington to bring live jack rabbits. Pheasants were tried. General Phillips' men wanted to try sea gulls. It took a clearance from the Department of Interior, which protects sea gulls, to get permission to catch one. There was objection—fear that the bird would be thrown into a jet engine, but the permission was obtained, the gull captured, the test run.

The system was approved. But the task ahead promised continued effort under hectic pressure—the detail designing, manufacture, test and installation of the system across the landscape of Montana, against a schedule which called for security by October 1962, seven months away.

The first production Minuteman was emerging from "Plant 77" at Ogden, Utah. In the final push toward delivery General Tom Gerrity set up a full-time Minuteman production board representing all the associated contractors, to meet regularly in the control room in Seattle, to chase problems and bring into close mesh the manifold assembly of talents. Minuteman was becoming a huge program—$2 billion worth in the 1963 defense budget.

Meanwhile the TFX tactical fighter project in the Military Aircraft Systems Division was moving toward a decision date that could make it, in turn, a foremost program of the company. Boeing and a team of General Dynamics and Grumman were announced in February 1962, as finalists in the competition. The Boeing proposal had recommended a General Electric engine; the Defense Department indicated its preference for a Pratt & Whitney, but other than that the Boeing technical entry was considered to have come out on top. Both competitors were given an extended study contract, Boeing to change to the Pratt & Whitney which General Dynamics had already included, the latter to make other revisions by April 1, when the new entries would be compared. Air Force Secretary Eugene Zuckert said the differences between the two proposals were narrow. The other four bidders "were not in the same ball park," he told the Senate armed services committee.

A source selection decision was expected in May. Then it was postponed to June, pending further study. The Navy had written a position paper expressing certain objections to the Boeing proposal. Both companies were being asked to re-submit to meet stiffer Navy requirements. Engineering director Bob Withington and his staff did so, and Wells reported to Allen that they had "dealt with these requirements responsively."

In July both competitors were given another contract for sixty days of further refinement. Bill Allen was getting nervous. "What is the effect of these delays on our chances?" he asked Wells.

"The competition is narrowing down," Wells said uncomfortably. "We've been trying to prevent this, but the ground rules almost automatically make for identical airplanes."

Contract commitments were crowding close on Minuteman. Operational readiness tests and crew training were going on at Vandenberg Air Force Base in California. The area surrounding Malmstrom Air Force Base at Great Falls was a vortex of activity. The work was moving through the sites of five flights of ten missiles each, the first planting of a 150-silo garden that would comprise the Malmstrom wing. Involved in all would be enough concrete to make seven Pentagon buildings, enough steel for 26 Empire State buildings. A network of roads was being laid for the monstrous 64-foot transporter-erector vehicles that would bring the charged global dissuaders and drop them quietly, tenderly out of sight.

The first operational missile arrived July 24, 1962, barely within the target that had been so audaciously set two and a half years before. The myriad installations and check-outs of silos and subterranean control rooms and wires and electronic cabinets continued. By October 15 the first group of missiles was in place, though without yet the supporting paper work and military readiness inspections for activation. The next day U-2 reconnaissance photographs revealing Soviet ballistic missiles in Cuba were placed ominously on the desk of President Kennedy.

In the week that followed the Cuba missile crisis went from confirmation to resolve and final confrontation. The world was quivering in the balance between peace and dread war between the two great nuclear powers. Strategic Air Command B-52s were circling in the air, ready to straighten toward their targets with H-bombs. Atlas and Titan missiles were on grim and potent alert. Minuteman readiness preparations were a frenzy of direst urgency. The missiles could be fired. Then Khrushchev backed from the consequences, and people breathed.

There was wonderment at the close call and the escape. There was occasion for sober pondering. The timing had so nearly coincided. Could it have been that the challenge had been paced to beat the hardened Minuteman force that the next two years would see installed across the face of America?

Lysle Wood's Aero-Space Division, charging ahead on Minuteman and Saturn while battling to keep alive the Dyna-Soar project—now slowed down to wait for a Titan III engine—was up to 55,000 people in the fall of 1962. Company employment as a whole had just reached an all-time peak of 106,000, including the rapidly expanding Vertol Division, getting its three helicopter lines in production.

It was a few days before the Cuba crisis that Wood had called his vice president and assistant general manager, short, hard-driving Bob Tharrington, into his office. "Bill Allen wants to talk with you, Bob."

"Do you know what about?"

"I think I know. I thought it had gone away, but maybe it hasn't."

In Allen's office, Tharrington learned immediately. "We need some help on the Vertol situation. Would you be willing to go there and take it over?"

Tharrington was spinning for a moment. Allen added, "You'll have to give it consideration of course, but I'd like to know pretty quickly. Take a look at it and then come back. Talk to Gracey about it." Clellan Gracey, corporate vice president for manufacturing, had been spending much of his time at Vertol. Its Army Chinook project was behind schedule, and the division was getting into heavy financial loss on the smaller model development—the commercial 107 with its Marine Sea Knight counterpart that was about to make its first flight. The Air Force had just made a survey of the operation and its report was highly damaging. Vertol had won an Air Force competition for helicopters, but on the basis of the results of the survey, the order had been taken away and given to Sikorsky. The division's cost trends were so bad that there was serious question as to whether it could survive.

Tharrington learned all this and went back to Allen's office. "Look, Bill, this situation is really a bad one. You'd better send the man you have the most confidence in, wherever he is, in the company."

"I think you're the best man for the job," Allen said. "I'll give you all the support you need."

"I'll need it." Tharrington accepted. When he got to Vertol he concluded that the division, built up of the former Vertol Company resources, did not have the depth of production, development and test capability that had been so traditional at Seattle. This would take more money, not less. The organization had been working valiantly, but was trying to put three programs into production at once with limited staff, and to solve design problems as they went into production.

George Schairer and Lee Douglas, Vertol engineering director, were in Vietnam; the prospect of a crucial need for helicopters was becoming apparent. Tharrington was back on the phone with Bill Allen. "I'm going to have to have the best men I can get from throughout the company. You said you'd support me."

The process began—painfully extracting key people from organizations loath to lose them, putting them to work in Vertol, amalgamating them with the organization there. The Boeingization of Vertol was under way.

In the Transport Division, where director of manufacturing Bob Regan was the man of the hour, getting the first 727 ready for roll-out just twenty-four months after its production go-ahead, Maynard Pennell was in less pressure and again thinking new product. He had had two competing studies under way, a "growth version" of the KC-135/C-135 series of military jet transports and a much larger 700,000-pound logistics transport idea. Engineer Dick FitzSimmons had been working on the latter, and it had been looking adverturously interesting. When Lockheed won a military transport competition in mid-1962, with the large C-141, Pennell's thinking jumped to the 700,000-pound giant as the airplane that could ultimately outmode the C-141.

As a part of the big-plane exercise the division's operations analysis group had started a computer study of Army equipment to be hauled. It found that 40 percent of the design payload of the C-141 was floor-limited—the full payload couldn't be put aboard because there wasn't room for it on the floor. Definitely there appeared to be opportunity for improvement. Pennell assigned Ken Holtby, just back from a year's graduate study on a Sloan fellowship, to do more work on the concept. They developed a plan that they felt could bring a radical improvement in the efficiency of airlift, making whole divisions and their equipment mobile, drastically altering military doctrine. They applied the 727 high-lift flap development and the continuing work on boundary layer control for short-field landing, then devised a "high flotation" landing gear that would so distribute the weight as to make it possible for the air leviathan to land on soft forward fields, to help meet the small-war need.

In November 1962, Pennell and Holtby took the plan to Washington, peddling their enthusiasm throughout the Pentagon Building.

"No one has ever dreamed of moving these big tonnages by air," said Colonel Jess Peaselee, one of those fascinated by the concept. "But why not?" The Defense Department had its contingency plans for large general-purpose forces in Southeast Asia. This fit the need.

In the hopeful atmosphere of the Pentagon there were rumors, too, that Boeing had won the TFX, an assignment that was expected now to become, with combined Air Force and Navy requirements, perhaps the largest single program of all time. The long-awaited announcement was due. In Seattle, where the variable-sweep fighter had been a dedication of four years, there was keenest expectation and suspense.

On November 24 the TFX announcement finally came, but the news was desolate depression. General Dynamics had won.

Bill Allen was nursing extreme disappointment when he got a call from Senator Henry Jackson. The Senator, just on his way to Hawaii, was highly concerned. He said he had learned that Boeing had entered the low bid by $100 million, and that all the evaluating groups in the services had recommended Boeing for the award. Allen was startled. Jackson said he thought he should call these facts to the attention of Senator John McClellan's Senate investigating committee, of which he was a member.

Allen hesitated. He immediately could see the spot the company was in. He didn't know what the situation was. "I think you should call Gilpatric," he said. "Undersecretary of Defense Roswell Gilpatric would have been in on the decision; it was he who coordinated aircraft procurement matters. Jackson, about to leave, said he would call Gilpatric from Hawaii.

Three days after the TFX blow, at noon between showers of rain, the trijet 727 emerged from the Renton plant. Hundreds of employees who had worked long overtime hours crowded around it after the official ceremonies, viewing in the daylight its unconventional shape with three engines at the back and its high "T" tail, regarding it as a child yet to make its way in the world, and containing all their affections.

There was now a company investment of more than $150 million in the program, and five airlines—TWA the latest—waiting and trusting in it with a $700 million combined commitment of their own. Engine and functional tests began. Just before taxi tests in early February 1963, two Australian airlines, Ansett-ANA and Trans-Australia, became customers. The plane was ready for flight on February 9, everyone on hand. On chief project engineer Jack Steiner's mind were many things, the airplane, finally a reality; his stake in the flight; all the performance guarantees he had committed to customers; above all these, the excitement of the day.

No fixes were required after taxi. Test pilots Dix Loesch and Lew Wallick were letting it roll, sweeping down the air strip, lifting off. There was a rush for cars and light planes to get to Paine Field where the 727 would land. In two hours of flying Loesch reported by radio that they had proved the controls, had done full stalls, would not need to follow the precautionary plan for landing but would come down normally, using the triple-slotted flaps. Bill Allen was at the front of the anxious little group that watched them lower toward the field. They landed lightly, rolled up to a stop and Wallick and Loesch came grinning from the airplane. Allen was on top of them, throwing his arms around them, pounding them on the back and laughing.

The airplane remained ready to fly. In five days of testing it covered what normally took four to six months of flying for a new type airplane—all the conditions of normal and emergency operation including steep-angle stalls. By late February it was up to 670 miles per hour—96.5 percent of the speed of sound. Jack Steiner was in the radio room at the Flight Center with Gerry Bowes, a performance engineer who was plotting curves on the speed at different altitudes and power settings, as the telemetered data came in from a flight. Bowes seemed to be secretive, hiding his work. Steiner asked what was the matter.

"You know how far off instrument calibrations can be," Bowes said. Steiner could see that the line was way off the predicted points on drag. They were getting fifteen knots extra speed. It seemed too good to be true. But more tests confirmed that it was. He went to Dick Rouzie, now the director of engineering, Maynard Pennell having been assigned to devote full time to the supersonic transport development.

"We're in trouble. We've made a mistake," Steiner said, then grinned to relieve Rouzie's worry. "I'm sorry, but we've got a lot better airplane than we're supposed to have."

It was partly low drag, partly better engine performance. They were able to issue a new performance document to customers and prospective customers, committing a 6.5 percent improvement in miles per pound, still holding some in reserve.

Everyone was exulting over total test results. In the rolling enthusiasm that swept through Transport Division, sales director George Sanborn was in Bruce Connelly's office urging a world demonstration flight.

"We could work it in as part of the FAA performance and reliability test," he said. "It would be a graphic thing. It would really have impact, out where foreign customers could see. That's what we need."

Connelly was enthusiastic; John Yeasting got behind the plan when it was proposed to him. They told Bill Allen it was feasible, could be done by late summer. Allen, immeasurably happy about the whole outcome of the tests, said yes; he wanted to go along.

Bill Allen had needed a refresher. The TFX hearings, which Senator McClellan was now undertaking, were deeply troubling. Most Boeing people had felt, from the indications in the press, that they should have been declared winners of the competition, but the decision was made. Allen feared most of all that the investigation would be attributed to Boeing and would impair future relations with the Department of Defense. He cautioned the staff not to become involved. But some, who had lived the project, were undeniably emotionally involved.

The hearings did not reveal irregularity or evidence of influence. They did reveal distinct differences of opinion. Air Force people, up to LeMay, and Navy operational officers felt the Boeing entry would have better met their requirements. The Secretaries, in their memorandum of basis for the decision, said that this was the view of the services, but that the evaluation scores were so close that either product would be acceptable and the judgment had to be weighed with consideration for other factors. Secretary McNamara had two scales that he regarded as particularly important. He had set as a goal, from the time he entered the office, the common use of the equipment by Air Force and Navy, for operational economy. His office testified that the General Dynamics design had 85 percent "commonality" in terms of identical parts for the two models, and the Boeing only 60 percent.

But Boeing had worked this problem so as to still come out at a lower cost in its fixed-price bid.

That was the Secretary's other scale. He was an expert and confident accountant in his own right. He simply did not believe Boeing could stay with its figures, when future orders came along. He had had uncomfortable experience with other developmental projects going up and up in cost. He thought, as did Secretary Zuckert, that the General Dynamics design avoided certain new features which could cause greater ultimate cost, or problems and engineering changes occasioning delays. One of these was in-flight reversible thrust, another the use of engine air intakes on the top of the airplane, another the use of titanium in major wing structure.

But these were among the items that had helped gain the performance which the operating people liked.

Bill Allen was asked to testify. He did not want to, he said, but how could he refuse? Ed Wells felt the technical questions needed clarifying; they involved the company's engineering reputation. On April 25, 1963, they both testified, Allen stressing Boeing's low bid, which he said was based not only on bomber and transport experience, but also on Bomarc, itself a complex supersonic fighter; Wells going into the Boeing design—the tests and experience behind all the advanced features.

"When large steps can clearly be taken in military capability, will the enemy permit us the luxury of taking a smaller step?" Wells asked.

For a time it appeared that the McClellan committee might request a change in the TFX decision. The committee asked Allen to comment on two possible courses of action: a reversal of the decision and an award of the TFX contract to Boeing, or award of two substantially identical contracts, one to Boeing and one to General Dynamics, under which the two companies would develop their designs so a source selection could be made by direct comparison of actual aircraft.

"We did not seek this investigation," Allen replied. "Nor do we seek redress in the halls of Congress. As between these two alternatives, however, we believe the second course of action offers the best possibility of meeting the objectives of the committee."

No one really thought it would happen. The hearings dragged on. Wells and Allen sincerely wished they would end. Finally, they did.

24

Work did not stop when a competition was lost. There was a certain stiffening of the fibers, a new bitter-strong ingredient in the draft of energy. In many corners of Boeing there were novel efforts under way, reaching for a future. Some of them would not see it, others would blossom in yet-unknown ways.

There had been the start on hydrofoil boats. Bob Bateman, managing advanced marine systems, had two Navy hydrofoils under test on Puget Sound and two Boeing research vessels on Lake Washington. The big High-Point patrol craft, to be armed with torpedoes for fast sub-chasing at more than 40 knots, made its first "flight" May 24, 1963, scudding over the water's surface, its entire 115-foot hull out of the water, attached only by three vertical struts to the submerged wings that supported it. The twin-hulled Navy "Fresh I," powered by an aircraft jet engine and first flown May 15, 1963, was a farther-reaching experiment, seeking speeds of 90 miles per hour, and later 115 miles per hour on modified foils.

But such speeds brought their problems under water. As the unruly "compressibility burble" had inhibited supersonic aircraft development until proper shapes brought it under control, so the hydrofoil at high speeds was subject to "cavitation." That meant a cavity or bubble was formed in the water when the negative pressure on top of the foil reached a point that would turn the water into vapor. The cavity in fact could get bigger than the foil itself, and work general havoc.

The cavitation could be endured if it could be controlled, but if boisterous it would pepper the foil with ultra-fine pellets of water at such high velocity and frequency that in a few hours the metal would be eaten away, all while the vessel was sailing smoothly through the air without feeling a ripple. "Fresh I" was a test craft intended to help in learning what could be done about controlling this phenomenon, to brighten the future of high speed hydrofoils.

Bateman felt there was much more to be learned about improved water transportation. The propeller had its limitations in water as in air. He had sold Lysle Wood on building the 20-foot research craft they affectionately called "Little Squirt" to experiment on Lake Washington with water jet propulsion, doing away with propellers. It had been the first Boeing hydrofoil to "fly"—May 15, 1963. It scooped up water and ran it through a high-speed centrifugal pump, expelling it through a three-inch nozzle at 3,500 gallons per minute.

Along with this craft, and fourth member of the singular Boeing fleet, was a pickle-fork shaped research boat, a hydrodynamic test system to test the foil shapes as airfoils would be tested in a wind tunnel, and particularly to test the control surfaces that were fitted like airplane ailerons and elevators on the foils of the Fresh I. With its electronic calipers for measuring drag, lift and other forces at water speeds above 80 knots, it was the only such moving tunnel in the world, eliminating, Bateman's engineer's felt, the construction problems of water tunnels that generally plagued marine engineers.

All this was early, experimental development, but with hope. By July the Fresh I was completing its high-speed trials preparatory to being turned over to the Navy. July 18, its crew brought it out of the water and it was flying haughtily across Puget Sound opposite Vashon Island. But its lift had been inadvertently mis-set. It kept right on climbing out of the water, its foils skipping. In an instant the rudder skipped out of a wave, the boat yawed, caught, and with a ripping of water was on its back. The crew was thrown free and escaped with minor cuts and bruises, but the hydrofoil program was blighted. Repairs would be needed, and redesign with a longer rudder that would not come out of the water. The Navy project was running short of money.

There were other fields of enterprise. Engineer Dick Truly, managing defense missile systems in Aero-Space, had been working for ten years on phases of anti-ballistic missile development. In the spring of 1963, he received a call from Vic Kupelian of the Defense Department's Advanced Research Projects Agency which was convening an industry briefing on hard point defense. The question put to Truly and the others at the meeting was daring: Could a defense missile be made to accelerate fast enough to catch an intercontinental ballistic missile as it finally approached its hard-point target? The feat seemed impossible, but Kupelian said he needed to know if it could be done. No one had ever tried.

In Seattle Truly met with assistant division manager Bob Jewett. With a piece of chalk he drew on the blackboard the path of the proposed missile's short flight. In the time he had taken to make the mark the missile itself would have to do it, he said. Jewett blinked his eyes and smiled. Together they faced the question of whether they wanted to bid on such a thing.

"It would be an opportunity to learn," Truly said. "It might have potential."

They decided to enter. Truly and his group worked up a proposal and Elliot Mock, who had been engineering operations manager for Minuteman and before that, Bomarc engineering manager, was asked to lead the presentation.

But Kupelian of ARPA, while impressed with the designs, said none of the companies understood how he wanted the experiments conducted. "We want a plan for a step by step development," he said. "Try something; if it works try something a little more difficult; then try something a little more difficult than that." It was to be the old, free style experimental approach, not defining the end product at the beginning.

Mock and Truly went back at the problem and came up with a four-phase program. In July they submitted it; September 5, 1963, they learned that they had won.

Elliot Mock and his project staff inherited the job of proving that HiBEX—for HIgh acceleration Booster, EXperimental—could be made to work. The program would have a low budget—$16 million, as though no one were expecting too much. But Mock was game, remembering the old GAPA that had preceded Bomarc, which had been started the same way. He gathered his men.

"If it can be done Boeing can do it," he told them, spiritedly. "What we'll have is a controlled explosion."

Casting about for other new activities, the Aero-Space Division recognized, somewhat self-consciously, that it was not yet in the spacecraft business, though it had the big Saturn booster, and Dyna-Soar was aimed at near-earth orbit. Lysle Wood discussed the further prospects with Bomarc program manager Bob Helberg, whose program was expiring. There had been continued conversations with NASA concerning new opportunities. One area which did not seem to be fully covered as yet was that of photographic preparation for the Apollo lunar landing mission. The Ranger spacecraft, taking a straight shot at the moon, could make pictures and telecast them back just before crash landing. The Surveyor spacecraft, which was planned for an unmanned lunar soft landing, would have the capability of making pictures of the immediate area. There appeared the need for much more comprehensive high quality coverage if a successful manned landing were to be assured. NASA had contracted with Space Technology Laboratories for a one-year study to decide the best way of accomplishing this task.

"I'd like you to look into it," Wood said to Helberg concerning the opportunity. "See if there is likely to be a competition and if you think we could win it."

Helberg went with the technology staff engineers who had been working in the field to discuss the possibility with NASA. They found there would be a competition for an advanced photographic spacecraft to orbit the moon. Helberg came back convinced that this was a role for Boeing, with the capability it had developed for integrating large systems, and its work with boosters on Minuteman and Saturn. "If we can bring together the companies that have the specific technologies, I think we can win this," he told Wood.

Already Ed Gray, heading a lunar systems study group, had made a verbal alliance with Eastman Kodak Company. Helberg went after RCA, which had the Tiros and Nimbus weather satellite projects and part of Ranger, and was Boeing's subcontractor on Minuteman launch control. At first RCA thought it would compete for the prime contract itself, then it agreed to join Boeing's team. When formal request for proposal was issued by NASA August 31, 1963 only five weeks were provided for preparing the technical proposal, but the preliminary work had been done.

With Eastman and RCA they planned a compact capsule that would orbit low to within twenty-eight miles of the moon with a double-lens photographic system, one lens for high resolution pictures to reveal objects the size of a card table, the other to cover a wider angle with less resolution. Eastman had designs already available for the photo equipment, but there would be the problem of reducing it from 400 to 140 pounds and to one-fourth its existing size. The plan was to process the negatives automatically as each was exposed. Unseen hands would pass each picture through a monochemical damp finishing process, dry it, then pass it before a scanner that would televise it to earth, speck by speck, as the spacecraft made its lonely cruise over lunar deserts and craters.

RCA solar panels and batteries would provide the power. A 10×10×9-inch computer, capable of storing 2,700 bits of information, would be built up by Boeing to serve as flight crew, camera crew, studio crew and laboratory crew, giving the commands to the various pieces of equipment. In fourteen days 200 pictures would be taken of the moon at close range.

The proposal was submitted to NASA, October 4, 1963.

More than once the question was asked: If you can direct these happenings at a pinpoint on the moon, why can't an airplane be directed to land in a fog on earth? The answer was to be found in the work of a technical staff group in the Transport Division—now renamed the Airplane Division—headed by a resourceful electrodynamics engineer, Ray Utterstrom. His work on automatic landing began at the time of formation of the Transport Division in 1956.

By 1958, in a joint project with the Bell Aircraft Company, Utterstrom's group had brought the 707 prototype hands-off to the ground, test pilot Jack Waddell in the pilot's seat. They used a Bell system with a narrow "pencil" radar tracking the plane, this linked to a computer to determine what the motion of the airplane should be to get a touchdown, and this in turn linked to the automatic pilot. Utterstrom's task was to analyze the relationships and determine what had to be done with the computer to bring Waddell down. It was a crude effort, Waddell having the option of not letting the equipment continue to operate if the approach wasn't working out right.

In 1959 the British began talking of equipping the Trident with automatic landing capability. England's Smith Aviation had been devoting itself to the automatic landing objective. Numerous trials had been performed at the Royal Aviation Establishment at Bedford. Prospective 727 customers began asking what Boeing was doing in this line. The question went to Utterstrom.

"We don't have enough faith in the electronics systems to talk about really blind landings," Utterstrom answered. "The reliability and performance is not such that we can come into pea soup. But we agree something must be done." He proposed that they set their sights on landing with a 100-foot ceiling and one-fourth mile visibility, as against the 300-foot and three-quarter mile minimums that the FAA was currently permitting. "We will accomplish this with equipment that will be high performance," Utterstrom said. "We will assume that it can fail, but if it fails the pilot will always be in command to execute an abort."

The British were saying that man couldn't take command at one hundred feet. They said they'd design to a requirement of absolute reliability with the pilot handcuffed—or, since nothing was absolute—to a figure of not more than one accident in ten million landings.

In the Smith Aviation effort it was proposed that this be accomplished by using three automatic pilots, any two of which would overpower a reluctant third. But it was not intended that the step be taken all at once. There would be some years of work first.

Utterstrom continued his development, working with customer airlines, the U.S. lines sharing his view that the pilot should be kept in command. He proposed, to engineering director Dick Rouzie, a system employing two automatic pilot channels, so set that if one went out, the other would neutralize it. Any failure would then be a passive failure, leaving the pilot free to take over. "But we'll set a goal of ten to the minus seventh power probability of failure," he told Rouzie. "That would be like the probability of two cars driving down the street both being Fords and both losing their distributors at the same instant in time."

"I could buy that," Rouzie agreed.

With encouraging results Utterstrom next proposed that the Boeing Company commit itself to the installation of this automatic landing system on its new equipment. An International Air Transport Association conference was scheduled for April 25, 1963 at Lucerne, Switzerland, for which Utterstrom had been asked to co-author a paper. "May we announce this at Lucerne?" he asked Rouzie.

Rouzie wanted to say yes. He arranged a meeting with vice presidents Tory Gamlem and Connelly to seek their approval before taking it to John Yeasting. A $4.5 million company budget had already been set up for the blind landing development, but there was no commitment to customers. Gamlem asked Utterstrom in the meeting, "Is it something we'll have to do in five years?" Utterstrom affirmed that it was.

"Why?"

"The trend of technology is in this direction. But more than that the problem of traffic growth and the lost revenue in weather cancellations is going to demand it."

Bruce Connelly was concerned with the immediate problem of selling airplanes. "If we don't do this Douglas or the British will," he said, recommending the commitment.

They took it to Yeasting. It was agreed that Utterstrom could state in his talk that all 727s contracted for since the first of the year would be equipped to land with minimums of 100 feet and below. Utterstrom made the announcement at Lucerne, but he felt the audience was skeptical that Boeing would follow through. Plans were going ahead on the Trident, however, to operate two of its proposed three channels so that a passive failure would allow the pilot to take over, as Utterstrom proposed; but the British were further promising to have the airplane at the triplex, fully-automatic level by 1969.

Federal Aviation Administrator Najeeb Halaby was taking the subject seriously. He urged that American industry carry the development to the goal the FAA referred to as its Category III A, with a 50-foot decision height for the pilot, and a system assuming survival of the airplane if the equipment failed at any time down to 50 feet. The FAA would then require a 50-foot ceiling for landing, and a failure below 50 feet wouldn't matter; the pilot would be in the right position and could see the ground.

Feeling that industry would not undertake the development on its own Halaby asked for proposals, and was about to announce a contract with Douglas when Utterstrom assured him, at an FAA symposium in Atlantic City, that Boeing planned to go ahead with such a development with its own funds. The 50-foot minimum was beyond what they had promised in Lucerne, but Utterstrom was confident they would have that capability with the system that was already committed.

As a consequence the FAA did not enter into the proposed development contract with Douglas. Back in Seattle Dick Rouzie said to Utterstrom, "I can't be mad at you." His action meant that Boeing should have at least a year's lead on Douglas in automatic landing.

The sub-assembly and assembly floor in Renton had become a sea of production logistics, with the 727 added to the other jet models. Including spares for older airplanes there were parts for 10 different models and 32 customers going through at different rates—600,000 different part numbers and some two million separate parts and assemblies per month.

"I don't think there's a manufacturer in the world that has anything like it," manufacturing director Bob Regan told a group of visiting editors in the summer of 1963. Regan had put it all on an electronic computer basis—everything was controlled from the computer center. Now he was glad the system had been installed in time. "If we didn't have it we'd go stark raving mad."

The editors were touring the plant while in Seattle for a convention of the National Editorial Association. Bill Allen spoke to them at luncheon. He was anxious to have a point better understood, because the country was facing up to probably the largest risk investment ever made in a single commercial product—the supersonic transport. It was a case of American enterprise in competition with two European governments, Great Britain and France, which were combining to bring out the "Concorde" supersonic transport.

Allen's question was: "Is America's long-held position of world leadership in transport aircraft manufacture in jeopardy for the future?" He spoke of the "critically expanding financial risk" involved in the creation and marketing of new aircraft products. "The really big financial risk comes when the manufacturer commits himself to build production airplanes," he said.

"The first airplanes are sold at far below actual cost. If the number sold turns out to be much smaller than the hoped-for number, or if the costs turn out to be higher than anticipated, the difference is a direct loss. It was this combination of lower than anticipated sales and higher production costs, rather than initial development costs, which caused the almost back-breaking loss to American manufacturers in the introduction of jet transports—a loss quoted by the Aerospace Industries Association as totaling $950 million. When the supersonic transport reaches the stage of being committed to production the required investment will be several times what has been necessary for the subsonic jet transport."

It would be essential that the U.S. government support the program, he said. "Yet we feel it is important that we retain the advantages of the private enterprise system of contractual responsibility which has proved so effective in the past."

Just how this relationship was to be worked out was not determined. But President Kennedy had called for a joint government-industry development of the American SST following announcement by Pan American Airways that it would purchase six of the European Concordes, due in 1970. August 15, 1963, the Federal Aviation Agency invited industry to submit proposals for an American supersonic transport superior to the European. It would require taking the much larger technological step to a titanium Mach 3 airplane instead of the European aluminum Mach 2, but this was a decision in which Wells, Pennell and Cook had already concurred.

At the FAA briefing in Washington, Donald Douglas, Jr. said that his company would drop out of the race. Douglas had just announced it was placing the DC-9 short-range jet transport in production—an airplane with two aft engines, a major venture in competition with the British BAC-111, and seeking the market in ranges just under the Boeing 727. This meant that Boeing, Lockheed and North American would be the supersonic transport competitors for whatever program the government might approve.

Boeing and Lockheed had each been given separate contracts by NASA, to evaluate four supersonic transport configurations worked out in the NASA laboratories, called SCAT 4, 15, 16 and 17, SCAT standing for Supersonic Commercial Air Transport. Ed Wells and Pennell reported on the results of this evaluation, as did Lockheed, at a three-day meeting at Langley Research Center. The conclusion was that SCAT 16, a variable-sweep arrow wing, and SCAT 17, a delta wing with small, finlike "canard" control surfaces well forward of the wing, both held commercial promise.

The Boeing group talked it over afterward. They had developed a three-year conviction that the variable sweep was the right answer, but they decided to give the question a whole fresh look. A team of engineers was again selected within the project to work on the delta wing. "I want you to come up with the best delta you possibly can," Pennell told the group. The effort went forward through the fall, the variable wing group meanwhile making its own improvements for the FAA proposal. When the results were in the variable design was better by 50,000 pounds.

"We'll submit the variable," Wells decided, and Maynard Pennell was glad.

The idea of a super-size logistics transport for Army mobility was gaining force in the planning councils of the Pentagon. Alain Enthoven, the assistant secretary for systems analysis, was writing it into budget proposals. Boeing people were back and forth to Washington throughout 1963, talking with Enthoven's staff and others. Wright Field was making a comprehensive study, labeling the project the CX-4.

Both Douglas and Lockheed were active, Douglas coming up with a full-scale mock-up of its own in June 1963. General Schriever was backing the giant ship philosophy, proposing that enough time be taken to make it an even larger advance. He wanted to see an improved "by-pass" engine developed to enhance the range and economy. The by-pass, like the fan-jets that had stepped up the performance of the 707s and 720s and helped make possible the 727, gained fuel economy by sending an extra quantity of air all around the driving jet stream, enlarging the column of hot gases that did the pushing. When the Air Force asked for performance estimates with the by-pass engine, Lockheed, Boeing and Douglas all came back promptly with new figures.

A big race for a big new program was shaping up, but it was not yet approved, because it required a major government expenditure. It appeared that the only way of making funds available for the development would be to take them from the latter end of the planned Lockheed C-141 procurement. If that were to be done, it would be necessary to get the program started in time to obtain deliveries in 1969. There were decisions to be made in the Pentagon.

25

The world demonstration tour of the 727 trijet was an exhilarating experience for Bill Allen and the others aboard. Starting from Seattle on September 17, 1963, the schedule called for the new airplane to be ready to fly every day, to land at unequipped fields, to make repeated guests flights at pre-appointed hours, to keep dinner dates.

The airplane responded like a trooper. There was nothing for the mechanics and technicians along to fix—Rome, Beirut, Karachi, Calcutta, Bangkok, Manila, Tokyo. Everywhere there was excitement aboard—flight guests enthusiastic over the sudden climb; the quiet cabin; the quick descent and settling to land with umbrella flaps; the short stop on 1,500 feet of runway; the instant right-about turn on the ramp that had made one startled tower operator in Miami cheer: "O.K. buster, now let's see you make it sit up!" When Allen got off at Tokyo he was soaring. The others continued on the tour to Australia, Africa, all the principal cities of Europe, on schedule, then home.

In the five-acre flight hangar on Boeing field, the static test 727 was trussed up in its bewildering harness of cables and festooned with instrumentation wires for its final load test to destruction. It had passed its 100% ultimate design strength loading—far beyond the maximum operating loads. On the control balcony the stress engineers in hard hats were peering from their controls as they added increment after increment of mounting hydraulic pressure. It was up to 105 percent, then 107, 108, the airplane holding fast together, still totally unyielding, the suspense among the spectators acute.

Finally at 110% in a sudden crack and roar the metal gave. Jack Steiner, overjoyed, went back to compute the gain. The added strength for payload, along with the performance jump from lower drag and fuel consumption, which had already permitted the mileage guarantees to be increased by 10%, meant a bonus in earning power of $2 million for each $4.2 million airplane over a ten-year period, he calculated. The 727 program was winning. The Japanese All-Nippon Airways, after examining the British Trident on a tour which followed that of the 727, chose the Boeing; then Japan Airlines, Northwest Orient Airlines, National Airlines.

But in another program there was heightening concern. The Washington controversy over continuance of Dyna-Soar would not be put down. All through the TFX hearings Air Force secretary Zuckert had been battling to save Dyna-Soar, already reduced to the status of an experiment. The view from the money side was that it was too expensive an experiment to carry on. Also, the policy had been stated in the United Nations that space would be used only for peaceful purposes. The agency for that was NASA, not the Air Force. This consideration had kept the Dyna-Soar suborbital for a time; then it became orbital but non-military; but having been laid down originally as a potential boost-glide military system, it was not equipped for multi-orbits. Those who had wanted to use it to get man into space were seeing "man in space" go in other directions. Further—though there had been a veritable harvest of technology gains from the effort—the weight of the vehicle had been steadily increasing as the design matured toward scheduled rollout in 1964, and first flight in 1965. On December 10, 1963, Secretary McNamara announced his decision. Dyna-Soar was cancelled.

There were many heartaches over the inability to see Dyna-Soar in actual flight after $400 million and years of effort had gone into it. There were also the internal consequences. In justice to the 5,000 men who would have to be laid off, beyond those who could be transferred to Saturn or other places of need, a great hiring-hall was set up in the Plant II cafeteria where all industry was invited to come. A minor consolation, but one that heightened the regret, was to be found in the comments of the competitive employers on the calibre of the people made available. "You mean to say these men you're letting go are from the bottom of your ladder?" a friendly counterpart asked industrial relations director Stan Little.

"Of course."

The visiting employer shook his head. "They look mighty good to me."

There were a good many technical fall-outs from Dyna-Soar not to be lost from sight. A contract was obtained to glean the advances and make them available for other government projects, or for the day when airplane-type re-entry from space might again be wanted. But that day was not in sight.

Two weeks after the Dyna-Soar cancellation Lysle Wood was notified that Boeing had won the NASA contract to build the Lunar Orbiter, an $80 million job, with five spacecraft to be built for actual flight missions and three more for tests. It was the plunge that Wood wanted, into the technology of outer space. NASA administrator James Webb seemed likewise pleased at the prospect. Boeing had submitted a proposal showing high technical and manufacturing capability, and reasonable costs for production, he said.

In the Airplane Division 500 engineers were rounding up their proposal to the Federal Aviation Agency for a supersonic transport. A three-day work-shop session had been held with ten interested airlines, in the desire to give heed to their operating requirements. The design submitted, Model 733, was the outcome of more than 500 configurations that had been worked out in the five-year effort. With variable-sweep wings moving back into a fast arrow shape it would be built mainly of titanium, would weigh 430,000 pounds—just under the B-52, would carry

165 passengers, would fly from New York to Paris in 2½ hours.

Lockheed and North American had chosen to enter delta-wing designs in the competition. Now there was a clear choice before the government. Maynard Pennell took his stand in the oral presentations in Washington January 21, 1964.

"The NASA research on the variable-sweep arrow wing, along with our own, has proved that aerodynamic compromise is no longer necessary," he said. "With the variable-sweep principle we can achieve superior supersonic performance in terms of payload-range and at the same time low-speed flying qualities better than present commercial transports."

He explained how the plane would sweep its wings to match its speed, much as gears were shifted in a car. It would climb to 20,000 feet in five minutes, keeping subsonic while close in to avoid the thunderlike "sonic boom" pressure disturbance of low altitude supersonic flight over communities; would be traveling 800 miles an hour when it reached 45,000 feet; 1,450 miles an hour at 50,000 feet; 1,800 miles an hour at 60,000 feet. All that would take about 20 minutes, during which time the SST would have traveled 200 to 250 miles. Its descent from 60,000 feet would be the inverse, in another 20 minutes. The operating economics, Pennell said, would be close to those of present jet transports, despite the tripling in speed, and a much smoother ride.

He stressed that the low-speed flying and handling qualities would be important in making use of the automation of airplane and ground control that would be available in the 1970 time period for all-weather landing. The variable sweep would minimize demands on the pilot. Even with the wings folded full back, however, the airplane could land and stop within FAA runway-distance requirements, he said.

The FAA began its work of comparing the proposals.

Boeing was by now deeply immersed in the commercial airplane business. An encouraging circumstance that had not been foreseen was the extent of repeat orders for the Boeing jets. Against 177 airplanes in first-time orders, 363 had been sold in repeat orders from the same airlines, as the appeal of the jets added to traffic growth. The 1963 traffic on the domestic airlines had jumped 14 percent over the previous year, and the airlines' profit had nearly doubled to $73 million for the year, putting the carriers in a better position to finance equipment purchases. With the improvement the Civil Aeronautics Board had authorized a lowering of fares which should bring further traffic growth.

The result of all this was that the 707-720 program was finally coming out of the red, with all the development costs and early losses repaid. But the heavy cost of entering the 727 program was an off-setting drain. The break-even point on that program had been pushed well out beyond original predictions, and to reach it would still require many more sales. Bill Allen assessed the situation before a top management meeting in March 1964:

"A substantial portion of the increased costs on the 727 were deliberate," he said. "The development programs were enlarged with greater testing—static, fatigue, flight. On the long pull I think that was good. It has reflected itself on our product. On the other hand a substantial portion of the increased cost was not anticipated originally. However, I am not dismayed about the 727. Far from it. Whenever you go into a fixed price contract it has an adverse impact during its early years on earnings. The 727 gives every indication of being a great airplane."

In the engineering theater at Seattle Plant II, looking out at the men who had fought a good many program battles together, he was speaking slowly and warmly, reminiscing. "I've had a few dreams in my life, not realized until this year. At least these two objectives of mine have been reached. One was to have a large airline customer call me up and, instead of giving me hell, tell me he was really delighted with an outstanding airplane, better than the one he had bargained for. That has happened with the 727. We have done an outstanding job on that airplane." Allen looked around for some wood to tap on, to safeguard the statement, and laughter broke the intense silence in the auditorium.

"Now, we can never be complacent," he continued. "But when one is getting older he has to have some satisfactions. The other objective was to see the Boeing Company end up with a profit on a commercial program during my presidency. Well, it has been a long, hard pull, but by God, we have done it." There was laughter again and a sharing of Allen's emotion. "It took two billion dollars and over twelve years, but you have seen the chart on the 707s and 720s. We have an unrealized asset as a result of this twelve-year period of effort—a program with substantial earning potential for a number of years. Looking back to the time of the prototype, with all of the blood, sweat and tears, it has been a good investment, a good thing for the Boeing Company. I think the same is true of the 727."

In the Vertol Division, too—the most recent scene of trial and financial reverse—the situation was improving. Chinook Army helicopter deliveries had been on schedule for a year. A vibration problem that had been plaguing the Marine Corps Sea Knight was being overcome and deliveries of that airplane were getting back on schedule. New facility construction had been completed; cost trends had turned the corner toward improvement. New orders were in from Canada, Sweden, New York Airways; and the Chinook and Sea Knight had been reordered. Employment was up to 8,000 from 1,750 in 1958. General manager Bob Tharrington was both grateful and candid, speaking at a management meeting.

"We've come through a most difficult and precarious period," he said, "a period which required tremendous efforts to get our production lines rolling while we were still in the process of testing six different configurations of the Model 107 and going through the critical period on the Chinook program. Every one of us has every reason to be proud of the achievements to date. I don't mean to imply that all our problems are solved. Our schedule position is still tight. We haven't yet completed all of our development and test programs. Our cost must be further reduced. But for the most part the job ahead involves aggressive refinement rather than the drastic action required a year ago."

Throughout the company there had been a heavy attack on costs, and it was continuing. On the 727 Steiner's men had devised a way to handle multi-customer variations in wiring and accessories by standardizing 90% of the systems and putting the other 10% in a "Sears Roebuck" catalog of options. A cost recovery campaign had been waged throughout the division. Value engineering was re-simplifying parts.

In Minuteman, Malcolm Stamper, with a General Motors background, teamed the entire electronics production management and employees in depth studies and problem-solving sessions to master changes and cut costs. For the Minuteman program as a whole, aggressive Bill Owens was put in charge of a "Minute-miser" drive to cut costs by $60 million for the year. In six months they had made the $60 million and were shooting for $100 million. The Air Force was getting money back, and the company was benefiting under the incentive features of its contracts.

The installation of Wing I of Minuteman, the Montana Wing, had been completed ahead of schedule in August 1963. The final delivery of Wing II in South Dakota was made in November, installed and operational and turned over to the Air Force three weeks ahead of schedule. Wing III in North Dakota was delivered ahead of schedule in April 1964, Wing IV in Missouri in June. Tex Bouillioun's moving-brigade production line was clicking like a clock.

But new kinds of Minuteman problems were arising, with more than two-thirds of the vast complex in operation. Winter snow loads had interfered with the quick ejection of the 80-ton silo lids. New tests with truckloads of snow at Tulalip were required, a rework of design. The Air Force wanted additional demonstration of the electronic security system in continuous snowfall. With all the available powdered dry-ice blowers that were used to supply cold storage in the holds of the Northwest fishing fleet, a two-foot overnight artificial snowfall on the half-acre security system layout at Tulalip was produced to pass the test.

A more bizarre emergency had arisen. Military safety experts had thought of a way in which a certain combination of irrational human behavior, although almost impossible to imagine, could conceivably cause an emergency despite the safeguards of the system. Frantic activity developed among the few who knew, both on the military and the contractor side. It appeared that six weeks' work would be required to make the necessary protective changes throughout the system, and they would be a harrowing six weeks. There had to be a better answer.

It was on a Friday that the shock had hit. Engineering manager Bob Plath pulled his key men into emergency session. "T" Wilson tried to cool them. "Let's just slow down and think it through." They traced every possible sequence of actions, looking for a shortcut, meanwhile starting shop crews overtime on the long fix. The think session continued straight through the weekend, without an answer. Finally, on Sunday, a light dawned on system design manager Dan Downey. A simple change could be made in the operating procedure that would propagate to every corner of the network, foiling even the most ingenius madman.

"I'd better leave this afternoon for San Bernardino," Plath told Wilson in a sweat of relief and urgency.

"Maybe you should phone."

"I couldn't explain it because of security."

Plath arrived at the Ballistic Systems Division to find the general and his advisors in grave session, every chair in the room filled. "I don't know that I'll need a chair," he said. "This may not take long." He told of the plan.

The chairman saw it at once. He turned to each of the others. "Do you see any reason why this shouldn't work?"

Three didn't. A fourth rubbed his chin. "I can find only one thing wrong with it."

"What is that?" There was the suspense of failing hope.

"Just that I wasn't the one to think of it."

Afterward they asked Plath, "Would you mind telling

us, just what was the management technique you used to come up with this solution?"

The Saturn branch was undergoing an urgent buildup to man the Michoud plant at New Orleans, involving the transfer of 6,000 employees and their families in one of the biggest industrial transplanting of all time, and the hiring of new people in the south to meet the 11,000-man requirement at New Orleans and Huntsville, Alabama. Wichita, also, was taking on major tasks in the building of the big Saturn booster. The Aero-Space Division was going after additional NASA work. It obtained a contract to do a study on a six-wheeled mobile laboratory for explorations on the surface of the moon, another for an orbital way-station from which men could assemble and service other spacecraft for far-away trips. There was hope of an Air Force manned orbital laboratory project, but as yet no request for proposals had been issued.

To move further into position to do advanced space work, Stoner was urging the building of a Boeing Space Center to pull together the space laboratories separately located about the plant and to add new ones. Aerospace technology director Nate Krisberg had been advocating particularly a fully-equipped laboratory for work in the newest micro-electronics field of "integrated semi-conductor circuits"—the science that could put a radio set in a tiny chip of solid matter. Krisberg felt it was going to revolutionize not only space technology but many of the devices of ordinary living.

Lysle Wood took the Space Center plan to Allen, who agreed it was an essential step in preparing for the potential of space, but more specifically for the prospective Air Force competition for a manned orbital laboratory. On land that had been purchased in the Kent valley, south of Renton, construction of the center was begun.

The big logistics transport plan for the Air Force had moved into live competitive proposal stage. Contracts went to Boeing, Douglas and Lockheed in June for three-month detailed studies. In anticipation Wells had set up a 500-man proposal engineering team. Flight tests of slow-speed landing devices for the purpose were continuing as a background for development of the airplane. The 707 prototype research ship, outfitted with "blown flaps" for boundary layer control such as had been envisioned in early 727 days, was being landed in tests at Langley field at less than 100 miles per hour, compared with 150 miles per hour for conventional jets. Experiments with soft-field landing gear were under way, employing an expandable set of multiple wheels for the purpose of landing massive military loads on austere and forward sites. The winning of the logistics airplane contract had become a major Boeing objective.

Commercial airline thinking was turning also in the direction of larger aircraft, though by no means of the size conceived for military use. New longer-body versions of both the 707 and the Douglas DC-8 were under study by the two companies, to reduce the seat-mile cost on routes where traffic was heavy. At the other end of the scale there was getting to be enough business on feeder lines and short-range routes to constitute a considerable market—the area that was being invaded by the new twin-jet Douglas DC-9. Boeing, in its struggle to launch the 727, had been in no position to think of a still smaller plane, but now Jack Steiner's engineers were coming off the 727 ready for something new to tackle. Steiner discussed the situation with Maynard Pennell, who was likewise interested, but Douglas was now a year and a half into the DC-9, and British Aircraft Corporation three years into the BAC-111. Those airplanes had been sold to most of the major U.S. carriers. Of the big four airlines only United and Eastern were left uncommitted.

"This looks like one program we could miss," Pennell lamented.

But Pennell agreed with Steiner, as did Bill Cook, that the possibility of an entry into the two-engine field, even at this late date, should at least be thoroughly explored. Steiner went to talk with John Yeasting about it on April 21, 1964, taking along a handwritten note on which he had jotted down the arguments for and against.

In favor of such a project he listed 1) engineering manpower availability, not only as a result of the 727 completion but also because the supersonic transport was in a state of suspension awaiting FAA determination of the next move; 2) the fact that the SST, if undertaken, would be a long development, not expected to load the factory until several years later; 3) the uncertainty as to the outcome of the CX logistics transport competition; 4) the tendency of the DC-9 to grow into a larger airplane, nearer the 727; 5) the apparent size of the potential short-range market. Against such a project were 1) the fact that the competing DC-9 and the BAC-111 were so far ahead in the twin-jet field; 2) the possible problem of work overload if Boeing should win both the CX and the SST at the same time, which did not seem likely to Steiner, and 3) the question of investment risk in a new small-jet program.

"We'd have to start a study immediately to get ahead of a United Air Lines decision on the DC-9," Steiner told Yeasting, pressing his point. "I've been wondering, John, in case the SST is delayed and we aren't able to win the CX program, if we might not be sorry we hadn't taken advantage of this chance?"

Yeasting said he was frankly skeptical. But he recognized that there could be a large market, and that time for action was going by fast. He agreed the question should be studied.

That same afternoon Yeasting had a scheduled meeting with Bill Allen and brought up the proposal. "I think it would be worth our putting up a half million dollars to take a ninety-day look at it," Yeasting recommended. "I don't believe there is one chance in ten that we can come up with anything that makes any sense, but I think we ought to do this to make sure. The DC-9 doesn't have leading-edge flaps; we may be able to pick up some other advantages by reason of our later start." Allen concurred and the Model 737 program study was begun, May 8, 1964.

When the ninety days of investigation were up, Yeasting was highly interested. He told Steiner he thought the program began to "make some sense."

A question as to where best to locate the two engines was being resolved between Steiner and technology chief Joe Sutter. Steiner had proposed aft engines, Sutter wanted to try them on the wings.

"I think this may be a different situation than we had with the 727," Sutter said. "This time we'll have two big engines on a small airplane. They may be big enough by comparison that the engine effects will be clear of the wing." In the 707 the engines had been put forward in pods partly to avoid interference with the wing airflow, but this had not been practical on the 727. Sutter added, "We won't have as high a Mach number on the 737, so the engine effects won't be as much of a problem anyway."

Steiner put competitive teams to work on the two alternatives. Meanwhile he was seeking the means to greater seat-mile economy, proposing to gain it by employing a wider body than the DC-9 or BAC-111, to seat six abreast. Ultimately the results of the two quests coincided. Wing-mounted engines would permit the wider body, whereas aft engines would be in its wake. They found they could save 1,200 pounds on the forward-engine version and use it to get larger engines, the same as in the 727, together with the wider body. It worked out better all around.

International sales manager Ken Luplow had been talking with Lufthansa in Germany about the 737. It was peculiarly suited to German needs, he thought. Whereas most of the European countries had a single predominant center, Germany had a number of major cities so spaced as to generate much short-haul traffic. To serve this need Lufthansa first wanted an airplane of no larger than fifty or fifty-five passengers to supplement its 727s, replacing its propeller craft. But as traffic increased on the routes it found that it could use a 70 to 80-passenger cabin. The wide-body 737 began to fit. Luplow could see the chance of Lufthansa, already a valued customer, introducing the 737 in Europe and at the same time reaping for itself the advantages of the new airplane's commonality with the 727.

Domestic sales manager Clarence Wilde had been working extensively in the meantime with United Air Lines. Both Lufthansa and United, because of competitive pressures, were forcing an early decision. The 737 presented a clear dilemma by the fall of 1964. Its cause would be lost if the program weren't undertaken right away, but with the market so far gone it would be too much of a gamble to start the program without substantial orders. Yet John Yeasting was becoming more and more convinced that the 737 was needed to round out the Boeing jet family, and Connelly and Sanborn, concerned with future sales, were pushing him. "If our customers have to go to the DC-9 we'll start losing them for the 727," sales director Sanborn kept saying. A Boeing-Douglas battle was shaping up all over again.

The decision was once more before Bill Allen, a decision even more uncomfortable than with the 727. On that occasion there was the prospect of 80 starting sales, and no other American competitor in the field.

At Allen's request finance vice president Hal Haynes was studying the money problem. The company was now committed to three major competitions. A 4,272-page study document had been submitted to the Air Force September 14 on the CX heavy logistics transport—an airplane longer than a hockey rink and twice as wide as a moving van. That contest was continuing under the new designation of "C-5A." The FAA had eliminated North American in the supersonic transport competition and was putting up 75 percent of the cost of another step of design development by both Boeing and Lockheed—Boeing with the variable-sweep arrow wing, Lockheed with the delta. The Aero-Space Division was competing for a still-uncertain Air Force manned orbital laboratory, the purpose of which would be to put men and instruments into orbit to determine their utility in space. All three competitions were mountainous challenges. Haynes, as finance officer, had to keep the company in a position to move into at least one of these programs, as far as capital requirements were concerned, if it should win.

He was assuming that if the program to be won were the supersonic transport, it would be mainly financed by the government, but even then there would be major company obligations to be undertaken in the way of facilities and other support. Already more than $20 million of company funds had gone into the SST development. To undertake a 737 program would add to the burden of unknowns, but Haynes told Allen that he thought it could be financed on top of at least one of the other three programs.

November 9, 1964, the 737 case was presented to the Board. But there was not the basis for a go-ahead. Allen decided they should make an intensive sales effort to get United, Eastern and Lufthansa together, hopefully for 80 to 100 airplanes, in order to lessen the risk.

By January, 1965, no such solution appeared possible. Instead, a crisis decision was on hand. Lufthansa was ready to buy, insistent on a Boeing "yes or no" before delaying longer its decision on DC-9s. No other customers were ready. A Boeing board meeting was scheduled to be held in New Orleans on February 1. Ken Luplow kept Lufthansa tenuously on the line.

26

In New Orleans for the Board meeting, the directors saw at the Michoud plant the staggering immensity of the boosters that would shoot man to the moon—not man but three men with all the paraphernalia for existence in a hostile, unworldly non-atmosphere, and the means to get home again. The dreamy Mississippi River rolling by could bear mute testimony to the prodigious jump of progress in transportation capability that was now almost casually taken for granted. A little more than 150 years earlier the first steamboats had begun coming down-river to New Orleans. At first scoffers had said they would never be able to get back up the river against the current, but in 1815 one of them made it all the way back to Pittsburgh. Now the Michoud plant was building a device powerful enough to push that steamship, fully loaded, straight up and into orbit around the earth.

The growth in scope of corporate commitments seemed to Bill Allen almost as huge. The question before the Board was whether to sign a contract with lone Lufthansa and risk a monstrous loss if the 737 program didn't go, or take the chance of losing Lufthansa and defer the decision longer. At the meeting Allen, Yeasting, Wells discussed the outlook. Allen said he had talked with Bill Patterson of United and Floyd Hall of Eastern. United was not ready, but Eastern expected to make a decision by late

February. Allen expressed reluctance to go ahead with Lufthansa until he knew the outcome with one or the other of these two.

But there was a feeling that Lufthansa was the key sale to launch the program. Directors William Reed, George Weyerhaeuser, D. E. Skinner and others spoke for going ahead. "Don't you think we'd be taking a bigger chance by holding off than by going forward?" they asked. "If we have a good airplane and there's a market for it, we ought to take the risk." Lowell Michelwait had just returned from a meeting with officers and directors of Western Airlines and reported that Western was a top prospect for the 737.

The fortifying circumstance was that airline traffic growth was bounding. The decision was reached; the 737 program was authorized.

In Germany chief executive Gerhard Hoeltje of Lufthansa was concerned as to whether Boeing really meant it, that it was going ahead. An hour before the Lufthansa board meeting to approve the airline's 737 purchase, on February 19, 1965, Hoeltje confronted Boeing's Ken Luplow in an outer office. "I've just had a call from Douglas. They say Eastern is going DC-9."

Luplow was shocked. He didn't think Eastern was committed; there had been some favorable indications from New York, but Hoeltje was obviously upset, not wanting to be left alone with the 737. Board members were arriving for the meeting, those who knew Luplow repeating the same question, "Will Boeing definitely go ahead?"

Luplow felt he was running out of capability, at his level, to assure them. He got vice president Bruce Connelly on the phone—it was 10:00 A.M. in Cologne, 1:00 A.M. in Seattle. All were gathered around as Luplow explained the situation to Connelly. "Mr. Hoeltje would like personal assurance from you."

Connelly gave the assurance and Hoeltje repeated it to the others. Afterward Hoeltje, edgy and short of time, asked for a set of 737 display cards Luplow had arranged to be available for the meeting. The cards had just arrived in a large leather case with a combination lock, but with no clue to the combination. Executive offices were not equipped with hammers and chisels; nail files wouldn't work. There was a new crisis until a janitor was located.

The meeting convened, then broke for lunch with the verdict: Lufthansa would buy twenty-one 737s. Then, within a week, there was dismaying confirmation that Douglas had come up with a changed DC-9 and obtained Eastern Airlines' contract.

The health of the 737 program now rested precariously on a United Air Lines sale. The emphasis was on the wide body with its six more seats than the DC-9, and the advantage of commonality with the 727. Douglas, on the other hand, talked earlier availability, and featured its five- instead of six-abreast seating.

Yeasting and the whole of the Commercial Airplane Division management were in on the effort. They were caught off-guard to learn the scope of United's planning. Based on good current business, a healthy growth outlook and a decision to be all-jet by 1970, United was ready to take giant steps. If it were to wait for the 737 there would be a serious hole in its equipment program.

A whole new approach was begun, a proposal geared to the five-year equipment program, accompanied by displays and demonstrations to show the competitive superiority of the 737. It was concluded that the key to the sale would be in meeting United's combined requirements for two-engine and three-engine planes, substituting an over-supply of 727s on favorable terms or on lease until the 737s were available.

"Suppose we give you the right to turn back the extra 727s in 1969 or 1970," Bruce Connelly proposed. "Then it will be our gamble. On the other hand the traffic may grow enough by then that you will need them." The United people thought the arrangement deserved consideration.

Bill Allen came to Chicago, but there was no commitment on United's part. The airline called a special board meeting in New York for April 5, 1965. Domestic sales

manager Wilde inquired if he should be on hand and was
told it would not be necessary. That could be interpreted
either way. Everyone was left on edge.

Chairman Patterson held a press conference after the
board meeting and the announcement was out. United
was placing a mammoth overall order: forty 737s, twenty
727s, six "quick change" 727s arranged for easy conversion from passengers to cargo and twenty-five additional
727s on lease. It would sign options for thirty additional
737s and nine more "quick change" 727s.

It was also purchasing nine Douglas DC-8s, with options for more. The aggregate amounted to nearly half
a billion dollars, the largest commercial airplane order in
airline history.

In the enormous relief and jubilation that broke upon
Seattle that day John Yeasting confessed to Steiner, "It's
the first time I've felt comfortable since you brought that
darned piece of paper to my office a year ago."

While the sales effort had been going on, another development was also bearing fruit: the long effort toward
obtaining all-weather landing capability. Boeing and the
Bendix Company had been working together to perfect a
system to reach the goals that electrodynamics manager
Ray Utterstrom had set. A 720 airplane had been assigned
to the tests. On March 3, 1965 the Boeing-Bendix all-
weather landing system was FAA-approved with the first
license in the world to carry passengers automatically
to touchdown. It remained for individual airlines and individual airports to qualify with equipment and training
necessary to permit operational certificates. With experience, a step at a time, the FAA would lower the minimums required, first to 100 feet, then to 50 feet ceiling.
There would be more investment required for the new
landing aids, both on the ground and in the air, but the
greatly-needed day when airline operation could be free
of weather interruption was coming gradually into view.

With the 737 program launched the pending outcome
of the three major competitions for government programs

—the giant C-5A logistics transport, the supersonic transport and the manned orbital laboratory—became the all-consuming questions of the year 1965. In the trade press speculation as to which company would get which program had become a favorite game. Generally Boeing was put down as winning the supersonic transport, with Douglas and Lockheed each favored to win one of the other contracts. But Bill Allen felt there were equal reasons for Boeing to try its utmost to win each: the SST for continuance of the Boeing commerical line; the C-5A because the company needed to get back in the military airplane business; the MOL because it was the main new opportunity in space.

Allen asked Secretary McNamara, "Is there any reason the same company could not win more than one of these?"

"None at all," the Secretary assured him. Allen impressed on the entire management that the task was to make sure they *merited* winning the competitions. "The period we are now in may be one of the most crucial in the company's history," he said in a general management meeting. "Boeing is so structured and sized that it requires a number of major programs. We have set ourselves a course which requires that we excel in the fields in which we have entered. In these Olympic games we are in, there is only one medal to be won in each event—the gold medal. It cannot be won except by long and thorough preparation in every detail and, most important of all, the purpose to win. In our business there is no other way; a course of mediocrity is without a future."

In the SST competition a new phase II-A comprehensive report had been completed with high enthusiasm and submitted to the FAA. The body had been re-shaped, its capacity increased, the aerodynamics improved. "A 30 percent improvement in seat-mile costs has been achieved and substantiated by wind-tunnel test results," Pennell reported to the FAA. "The airplane will have lower seat-mile costs than subsonic transports on all but the shorter ranges." Following up the submittal Allen urged that the

FAA authorize prototype construction for one or both of the competing companies before the time lead of the European Concorde was further increased.

"We have come down an orderly path to this point in the airplane's development," he said. "We do not propose any rush into production; rather we propose that the program should proceed to the next orderly step—prototype construction, testing, proving, gaining of actual flight experience."

But a new speculation was rampant in Washington, casting doubt on the SST's future. The question was raised—might a 750-passenger commercial derivative of the C-5A logistics transport bring airline fares down so radically as to make the supersonic transport non-competitive, washing it out? The bold projection of a 750-passenger airplane was granted as problematical, though Boeing's own studies showed a promise for something in this direction. But Allen stood steadfast behind the SST, as did the FAA.

"If we assume a commercial version of the C-5A we still find economic justification for building the supersonic transport," Allen said in a speech in Washington. "They will serve different purposes in the market."

The FAA decided to continue the SST competition between Boeing and Lockheed into a Phase II-B to further develop the designs before determining on a prototype. There was still no agreed plan for financing a construction program.

Nor was the probable outcome by any means clear in the Air Force manned orbital laboratory competition. The MOL was in some ways related to an earlier manned orbiting research laboratory project, sponsored by NASA, in which Boeing and Douglas had each won a first-phase study contract in 1963. Much work had been done, under that contract and since, in bioastronautics, space power, solar panels, meteroid research, all the problems of keeping man alive in space, but Douglas had won the second-phase contract—the preliminary design phase, and had proceeded before Boeing with the establishment of a new space research center. Subsequently the NASA program was suspended. When the request for proposals on the Air Force MOL was finally issued in January 1965 everyone knew that the contest would be close and hard fought.

While the three big races were in progress, and two new ones added—one for a long-cruising Voyager spacecraft to land instruments on Mars, the second for an advanced air-to-ground missile—other projects were coming to test. At White Sands missile range in New Mexico on February 25, 1965, the first HiBEX—the experimental missile with the incredible blink-of-the-eye acceleration that the Advanced Research Projects Agency had sought —was fired. It did what it was supposed to do, streaking to the sky so suddenly that its report had the sound of a sonic boom. Its solid-state electronic equipment was so constructed and packed that it was still in working condition after the missile had smashed to the ground. HiBEX program manager Elliot Mock grinned to explain why. "We had to make it tough. In this thing the shock of take-off is greater than the shock of crash-landing."

Put together by a small team of hand-picked engineers in the thirteen months since the contract was formally signed, HiBEX was, Mock thought, an example of what could be accomplished by a free-wheeling group given a challenging task with minimum paperwork.

Another small group under Doug Graves, manager of space propulsion development, was designing a solid-rocket upper-stage booster called "Burner II" on an Air Force development contract that had been won. Straightforward, lightweight and simple, it was designed to feature low cost and high reliability in potential application to a variety of different military and NASA booster systems.

In the Minuteman program, Wing V, buried across the landscape of Wyoming, Nebraska and Colorado, was delivered to the Air Force in June, twenty-six days ahead of schedule. On August 18, Minuteman II, the advanced Minuteman which would go in Wing VI and would gradually be adopted for earlier wings, was launched. There was reason to be pleased over the whole result of the

Minuteman effort. Turn two keys and the missile would go. Where there had been such difficulty getting the previous generation of missiles "in the green" for operation the Minuteman readiness record was running ninety-seven and ninety-eight percent.

For Wing VI Boeing had received a contract to install the electronic security system as it had on Wing I, this work on the intervening wings have gone to an electronics firm. There was satisfaction in the renewed assignment. The Boeing Wing I system had been experiencing only a fraction of the "nuisance" false alarms of the other wings. The long struggle to perfect that system had been rewarding.

There was another extension in the supersonic transport competition. In August 1965, President Johnson approved a plan to contract with both Boeing and Lockheed for continuing design and test work, short of actual prototype construction, for a period of up to 18 months. As before, the contractors would bear 25 percent of the costs, subject to repayment if the program were dropped. But a decision was expected momentarily from the Air Force on the manned orbital laboratory. Questions of financing this program, in light of accelerating costs of the Vietnam war, had been holding it up.

On August 25 the MOL announcement was released. Douglas had won. The keen disappointment was only offset by the hope that a C-5A decision, expected soon, would favor Boeing. Washington rumor had it that the Boeing C-5A proposal was receiving the highest rating technically, but that Lockheed was low on cost. "T" Wilson, spearheading the Boeing entry, was hopeful that the "cost effectiveness" on which they had concentrated— the calculation of military operating cost over a period of years against the work the airplanes could accomplish— would outweigh the higher purchase price.

As tensions peaked in the C-5A, a labor negotiation with the International Association of Machinists was reaching a crisis in September 1965. The company had long held to the philosophy that personnel promotions, and layoffs in event of reduction, should be based primarily on a merit rating system, just as it sought to win product competitions on the basis of merit. The union, on the other hand, wanted seniority to be the primary guide. Lowell Mickelwait, vice president for industrial and public relations, and his negotiating team, had been in almost continuous session with the Union negotiators, but there was a deadlock on the issue. September 15, the union went on strike.

It was while the plant was idled by strike, with only engineering and administration and minimum forces working, that "T" Wilson, September 25, walked to the main switchboard of Plant 2 with a typed announcement in his hand, and a heavy heart. His hurt voice came over the public address system:

"I regret to report that Boeing has lost the C-5A competition. The award was made to Lockheed. It is an understatement to say that we are disappointed; however, we are not disappointed in our people. In my opinion they prepared an outstanding proposal. What we learned in preparing it will be applied to our other business efforts."

The word was that Lockheed had bid low by $250 million, a price advantage so great as to offset any claimed operational advantages of its competitors. The question of whether or not the price was "realistic," which had become so contentious in the case of Boeing's low bid in the TFX competition, did not enter. Based on that experience the Pentagon had devised a "total package" plan requiring bids to be made to cover follow-up production as well as development and initial quantity. A Douglas engineer commiserated, "All the time Boeing and Douglas were knocking themselves out on the design of the airplane, Lockheed was sitting back and asking itself 'What does it take to win?'. It found the right answer, 'Price.' "

But Lockheed had its plant ready to take on the C-5A upon the cutback of its preceding C-141. There was difference of opinion as to whether it had priced sacrificially to get the contract.

"It's possible to arrive at Lockheed's price," Howard

Neffner, Boeing vice president—government contracts, explained. "First you lay out a probability curve on what the cost will probably be. On the basis of this you chart a curve showing the amount of probable profit and loss at various prices. Then you pick an amount of income you propose to bid for—say it is 90 percent probability of a 10 percent profit, or 70 percent probability of a 2 percent profit. You'll find that a small difference in the choice of profit makes a big difference in the price, by a ratio of about 6 to 1, because of the sharing of profit and loss under the incentive-type contract. So it becomes a question of how badly do you want the business."

The union strike was ended by agreement to jointly study the employee merit rating system for an additional period of six months. Discussions of the C-5A loss continued depressingly, but only for a brief time. An extraordinary thing was happening. Airline traffic growth and forecasts were causing a sudden swell in 707, 720, 727, 737 orders. More and more airlines were coming to the kind of conclusion that United Air Lines had reached about the future. Orders were pouring in, in advance of a forthcoming Boeing price rise that would take up some of the increase in cost of labor and materials. The company's problem was suddenly one of steeply increasing delivery schedules and expanding the plant to handle the business.

Meanwhile at Vertol, which was fully recovered and moving ahead aggressively, the Army and Navy had asked for delivery schedules on Chinook and Sea Knight helicopters to be doubled to meet the urgencies of Vietnam. The Vertol plant would likewise have to be further expanded. It was considered fortunate and timely that the improved financial resources of the company, particularly as a result of the turn in commercial business, put it in a position to make these moves.

The airline traffic rise and the talk about a possible European manufactured medium-size "air bus" had engendered a new long-body version of the 727, to be used on higher density routes. But the plans to offer a stretched-body version of the 707 had not worked out to the point of generating enthusiasm. Douglas was meanwhile cashing in on sales of its long-body version of the DC-8. In the light of that discomforting fact the question of a Boeing product for the future big-carrier business loomed large and important.

Joe Sutter, the chief of technology, was one of those ready for the question. "The happy thing is, we do have something good to sell," he reported to engineering director Dick Rouzie.

In the weeks before the C-5A decision, when everyone was tight with attention to that primary goal, plus the proposed long-body 707, the 737 and the long-body 727, Rouzie had concluded that Sutter's staff was the only one free to start on a new tangent. Sutter felt then that the long-body 707 was becoming unlikely, with Douglas already holding such a lead. It was becoming challengingly evident also that there was too great a time gap between the latest 707 models and the still-distant supersonic transport. The long-body DC-8 seemed to Sutter an interim solution—the end of a line of growth. But any new product to supersede it would have to come fast, before the airlines had stocked up too far in the future with long-body DC-8s.

On the other hand the giant C-5A, so arousing to the imagination when considered for airline use, appeared too large a jump. It was primarily designed for military use. But the C-5A technology was available as a starting point, along with bundles of market studies that had been made when possible C-5A commercial derivatives were being explored.

By using the new C-5A engines they could get a 25 percent reduction in fuel consumption. By using the improved leading-edge and trailing-edge flaps that had been developed for the 727 and 737, and the further high-lift studies culminating in the C-5A proposal, they could get the big airplane into existing airports. The use of these features would in turn allow a thinner wing and greater sweepback for increased performance over the 707. It only remained, Sutter thought, to work out a configuration that would have the right combination of passenger and cargo capacity, and the proper flexibility for application to different routes. He had set his men to that task.

When the C-5A program had vanished and the post-mortem executive conferences were convened, Sutter's project, designated as Model 747, was immediately in the spotlight and elevated to major status. Sutter was made chief engineer—Model 747, and given the full green light to acquire people left from the C-5A project and elsewhere, to bring the new design forward, all haste.

The more they worked on the 747, in versions from 300 to 400 passengers, the better it looked. Burgeoning passenger traffic and the even greater potential growth of air cargo would require it. Conversely the economics of such an airplane would permit both passenger and freight traffic to grow more, Sanborn and Connelly felt, in analyzing the sales outlook.

To John Yeasting the 747 was an extremely exciting prospect, but also a frightening one. It would take an investment of more than $500 million, which pygmied the investments so painful on the 727 and 737. Furthermore there was a time squeeze that was nothing less than excruciating. The product would have to be started almost immediately, in order to have its heyday of sales before the advent of the SST, and to offset the trend to long-body DC-8s. But the business opportunity was there. Pan American, TWA and other airlines were interested. Joe Sutter had a confident air: "The 747 or something like it *has to happen,*" he said.

Bill Allen, thumping with the impact and challenge of what was suddenly taking place, turned on Yeasting and Connelly in his office the morning after the October 1965 Board meeting, at which nine-month earnings were reviewed. "I woke up this morning in a cold sweat. That 747 of yours! Here I've been going all over the country saying how impossible it would be to undertake the supersonic transport without government support. This 747 will cost us half of what the SST development would cost."

Sales-minded Bruce Connelly gave him his infectious

Irish grin. Allen, too, was secretly eager, but the questions were enormous. "I've never seen a time when the decisions were so crucial and the stakes so high," he said. Not only had the stakes, in truth, become immense, but it was necessary to ante for the next game before the results of the last were known, and once a commitment was made it was not possible to back out, because of the very size of the stakes. Then there was the revolting consideration of what would happen in the event that a serious economic recession should catch such a commitment in midstream. Allen and his staff wrestled with the weight of the problem as Douglas, too, began talking of a DC-10 in the same size category as the 747, and Lockheed, with the C-5A, was making up its own commercial mind.

But first there were the problems to be met in the expansion of business on hand. Lowell Mickelwait and engineering vice president George Martin turned to the formidable task of recruiting the needed employees. The Wichita Branch, under vice president Ben Wheat, would have to carry a large part of the load of manufacturing the 737. Vertol helicopter schedules were again stepped up. Plans were made for plant additions in the Puget Sound area on an unprecedented scale—in Seattle, Renton, Kent and at Auburn in the Kent Valley south of Renton, where vice president Tory Gamlem was to manage a new Central Fabrication area.

Plant expansion authorized during 1965, amounting to $165 million, had already reached six times the average level for preceding years, and the 1966 expenditure would exceed that. In a little over two years the plant facility was being doubled.

All this would have to be paid for out of earnings in the next several years, a fact that added its own insistence on the validity of future business decisions.

The giant 747 was not the only determination to be made. The small gas turbine business, nurtured and built over a period of seventeen years, was at a point where a major new investment in product development and plant facilities would be required if the company were to go after the large-scale automotive and special power fields that could justify mass production. An outlay of some $80 million would be needed in the next several years, perhaps more. A decision had to be reached.

Other fields were candidates for increased attention. The Advanced Marine Systems branch under Airo Gonnella had obtained a Navy contract for a big new gunboat with sub-surface foils, to be powered experimentally with the underwater pump-jet that had been developed with the "Little Squirt" on Lake Washington. An association had been formed with an Italian firm to seek other hydrofoil work. The Voyager spacecraft competition, slowed by shortage of federal funds, was being pursued along with other advanced space proposals. Missiles were getting new emphasis in the renamed Missile and Information Systems Division, headed by vice president Bob Jewett as Tex Boullioun moved to vice president—assistant general manager of the Commercial Airplane Division.

Doug Graves, working on missiles and rockets, wanted to pursue aggressively the space propulsion business, with new high-energy fuels, on which much work had been done at the company's recently-acquired test site in eastern Oregon. "But we can't just declare ourselves in the business," Graves said to Jewett. "We have to develop the technology." That, too, would take money, as would new military airplane development programs under way—vertical take-off developments, a high-performance fighter. In the fighter field there was collaboration with the German firm of Bölkow on developments for possible NATO use. Boeing had acquired a part ownership in that firm, one of the moves by which the director of international operations, Jerry Kane, had sought to internationalize Boeing's future.

Whole new fields of activity were being explored by a small Aero-Space office devoted to the broadening of future applications of technical talents and systems management capability: mass ground transportation, oceanography, salt water conversion and water management—vast markets that might some day be invaded by Boeing.

Choices had to be made. Bill Allen shook his head almost incredulously at the aggregate of possibilities. "Our opportunities have outstripped us," he told administration vice president Jim Prince in reviewing the alternatives. "The possibilities of our present technology have gone beyond our economic ability to deal with them." It was true of the company; it was true of the nation as a whole, but it was an attractive kind of problem to face.

Allen was invited by George Mueller, head of NASA manned space programs, to a gathering of industry presidents at which ideas were sought on projects that might follow the Apollo mission to the moon. He asked George Stoner's counsel.

"I think the real challenge of space is going to be on our earth," Stoner said.

"What do you mean by that?"

"Space is a tremendous vantage point, with a country-wide—a hemispheric field of view for surveillance of earthbound affairs. The visible spectrum is only a tiny part of what we can use in seeing from up there. That space is filled with all kinds of reflected electromagnetic rays—radio, infrared, x-rays, a whole invisible spectrum that can be measured with sensors for useful purposes."

Allen pressed him to be more specific.

"Weather forecasting is one obvious example," Stoner said. "It may be possible to determine the location of such things as oil fields or mineral deposits, or the best place and time to plant corn and wheat. We don't know what all. We intend to find out. By selecting the right place in the spectrum you can make the ground talk to you. There are the problems such as smog and air traffic control to be conquered. There is military surveillance. The second big use of the space around the earth is for communication. Surface cables have very severe limitations, especially when you get to the saturation point on traffic. They're hard to move; it's hard to reconnect the ends to new sets of subscribers. Space systems can carry an unlimited amount of traffic and be totally flexible."

Allen was first to be called upon in the NASA meeting, his name beginning with "A." He gave a full run-down of these and other approaches on which Stoner's men were working. Other industry representatives spoke of further orbiting laboratory programs, of explorations to Mars and other planets, manned and unmanned. A Chrysler man more boldly called for space technology to control the weather, to turn deserts into verdant vales. He did not profess to know how it might be done. Allen regarded the sessions a totally stimulating ten hours.

In Seattle there were still the hard present-day choices of where to put money and manpower. A comprehensive survey by vice president Malcolm Stamper of the gas turbine question was before the Management Council. It had been determined that the alternatives were to go all-out with a major commitment to develop an expanded business, or to discontinue it. The field was one in which other manufacturers were well qualified. The prospects were encouraging but not compelling. The skills and the funds that would be required could be used to advance the other programs of the company—commercial, military and space—possibly to help make feasible the 747. The difficult decision was made in January 1966 to proceed with an orderly phase-out of the gas turbine business upon the fulfilling of existing commitments.

The 747 decision, immensely more consequential, was up next. In preparation for that decision the 747 development task was being attacked with full organizational strength by Joe Sutter and his program organization under Jack Steiner, newly-named vice president for product development in the Commercial Airplane Division. The company was moving to triple its authorized number of shares of capital stock, expanding its financial base to meet the opportunities ahead. The supersonic transport development was being given new major emphasis by the creation of a Supersonic Transport Division headed by vice president Maynard Pennell and acquiring new key men from throughout the company. "T" Wilson, as corporate vice president for operations and planning, was assigned to give overall direction to the program.

Through February and March of 1966, barely more than a year since the plunge into the 737, a commitment on the giant 747 program was pressing hard upon Allen,

Yeasting, and the board. Pan American Airways was taking the lead among prospective customer airlines, its chairman Juan Trippe seeing ahead a whole new era in world transportation. Not only would the 747 cut direct operating costs per seat mile by 30 to 35 percent, suggesting sharply lower fares and cargo rates; it would also be faster than existing jet transports, hitting 625 miles an hour, and more comfortable, with its extraordinary cabin volume.

April 13, the suspense was broken. The Pan American board voted a record-shattering $525 million order for 25 of the airplanes, two of them to be all-cargo versions, the rest to carry from 350 to 490 passengers each. The contract would permit withdrawal on Boeing's part by August 1, if necessary for business reasons, but only with heavy penalty. The 747 became a program—unprecedented, exacting, potentially huge.

Boeing was approaching the close of its first 50 years of operation. The curtain on that remarkably eventful span of years would be drawn, only to open again on what already promised to be an even more momentous second half-century. The 747 venture was pacing the period ahead. Close behind was the supersonic transport, still more exciting in prospect.

"The undertaking of the 747 program does not in any way diminish our interest in, and our devotion to, the supersonic transport development," Bill Allen told the 13,000 members of Boeing management. "The SST has its own bright market potential for the future. We have stepped up to the 747 opportunity because this portion of the market has become more immediately available. The SST will reach its production stage at a later date than the 747 and will provide a logical sequence of work as a portion of the world airline fleet requirements move up from subsonic to supersonic speeds. It continues to be one of our prime new business objectives."

Allen stressed the tremendous business risks in undertaking the 747 program which, unlike the supersonic transport, would be wholly privately financed—"risks several times greater than in any of our previous commercial ventures." But equally large, he said, were the prospects of reward, "given the same dedication of effort that has marked our other endeavors up to this time."

A giant surge of new enthusiasm was building at Boeing. There was a spirit to move strongly and responsibly forward into the new markets that progress was creating.

27

The organization that had gathered around the name and ideals of William E. Boeing was pausing to look at itself in its fiftieth year. It was a company, not altogether unlike other companies in its industry, that had built up an enormous capability. Not always had the business gone in the direction toward which the company had set its will, but always something had been learned. There was humility enough to see that, and there was always a roaring spirit of rebirth.

Just what the future footsteps would be was hard to say. The company had gained a reputation as a large and powerful organization in a dynamic business. "Boeing has so much technical capability it's frightening," one Pratt & Whitney man put it. It was an organization perhaps not quick to change direction, but when it moved it moved with resolution.

"It is more the elephant than the rabbit," said Dr. Nate Krisberg, head of its Aero-Space technology. "This may have its advantages. The company doesn't leap from precipice to precipice; it moves in seven-year strides. When it takes one of those steps, you may expect something big. It has the capability to work out a solution to a large national problem."

But it had also moved like a rabbit, as the brilliant footwork in Elliot Mock's HiBEX experiment would attest.

Because the corporation had become so self-conscious about its almost total dependence on military business in the years when it stood preeminent in that field, it had set its sights earnestly on the commercial target, and moved in that direction with all of Bill Allen's determination. Now it had become so successful in commercial transports that the newest concern was over the regaining of a proportionate place in the military and space side.

Yet the Boeing role in military defense was large. "T" Wilson, who had steered the Minuteman, regarded the long tradition as unbroken. "Boeing has always supplied the strategic weapon that obsoletes its own," he said. "The B-24 did not replace the B-17; it took the B-29 to replace it, and then the B-52 to replace that. The B-58 and B-70 were intended to replace the B-52, but neither has done so. To the extent that any strategic weapon has replaced the B-52, it is the Minuteman that has done it."

The company had been late in entering upon the exploratory aspects of space. It had regarded itself as being at the forefront of the advance of technology with the Dyna-Soar, while holding to the Air Force tradition of wings, but it had passed by for a time the staking of its claim in the NASA satellite domain. Still, it had come out with the managing contractor role in Saturn and as such had an awesome responsibility—that of launching the prime of American astronauts and the flag of the United States on the nation's pioneering voyages to the moon.

But there had been the lost competitions—hard losses. Most Boeing people were inclined to take these philosophically, after the first pang was passed. "You can't win them all," observed Vernon Crudge, a Boeing consultant, at his view window in New York's Rockefeller Center. "If you are looking at it from the standpoint of the country as a whole, that becomes a merit rather than a demerit."

George Schairer took a like view. Admitting that the prolonged paper competitions were rough, he saw no grounds for complaint. "The TFX was a very much better airplane at the end of the fourth round of the competition. Both competitors' airplanes were immensely superior to the ones they had a year earlier. The result of these paper competitions is tremendous progress, just as the competition between Boeing and Douglas for the airline business results in tremendous progress. It's a good system for the country. It's good for Boeing."

Bill Hamilton, after the C-5A loss, had looked out across Elliott Bay from his Developmental Projects offices in an uptown Seattle building, as had Bill Boeing some years before, contemplative and optimistic. "It is disappointing when you don't get to do the job, but you have helped advance the 'state of the art.' When we have lost, we haven't lost face, because our proposals have been highly regarded by the people doing the evaluation. We have done a lot of imaginative work with good people. Every time we have lost, we have been solid enough, and strong enough, to pick ourselves up off the floor and do something else in place of it, and make a success of it. We will turn the C-5A into a successful 747, the TFX into a successful SST."

If so, it would mean a still greater emphasis on the commercial manufacturing side of the business unless there were a like expansion of space and defense work to keep up the balance—and a much larger total establishment. The question was being asked, how much new emphasis might these latter fields receive?

"This is one of the company's dilemmas, trying to chart a course with all the opportunities. The airplane business is so good that it makes other decisions tougher," said Dr. Dick Montgomery, director of military systems, at his office in the Boeing Missile Production Center in South Seattle. Montgomery was anxious to give more emphasis to electronic "information systems." "Space Systems are all essentially information systems," he contended. "It's true also of missile systems. How hard can we go after these? Do we have the energy, the muscle, to push them?" He was winning his battle with the establishment of the Missiles and Information Division. But he added, "there is a big potential also in the undersea business. We are doing things in the atmosphere and outside it with systems that are closely related to what could be done under the oceans, and in ocean surveillance."

Said Aero-Space operations vice president George Snyder, "We have to try to key our activities to product areas which we recognize as areas of opportunity."

Jim Prince had the task of helping Allen to juggle the organizational and investment implications. "The biggest fact is that our commercial business has exploded," Prince said. "We were pretty slow in realizing what it is doing to us—the tremendous expansion it has forced in facilities." But Bill Allen had made it clear that the company was committed also to extending its defense and space business. "We are in a position to move to a plateau of attainment far above our best dreams of several years ago," Allen told the staff.

It was mere months since the concern in Boeing had centered on heart-breaking losses of competitions. "I am more impressed," said Wes Maulden, "T" Wilson's planning director, "by the momentum and stability of things than by the change. Each time you think a loss is catastrophic, you find it need not be the case. You have set up a momentum that you can capitalize on and increase. Our real problem is to be flexible enough to take advantage of the experience and other opportunities. There is no reason why we can't double our volume of business."

That brought to the surface again the question of how to win government competitions which had become so evidently a matter of balancing technical competence and cost. Maulden expressed his concept. "A cost estimate is a probability. Pick a high enough figure and the probability of coming out is one; pick a low enough figure and the probability is zero; in between is where the risk game is played. Each manager throughout the organization should take onto himself some of this risk. If he is secure, setting a high enough estimate so he won't *ever* overrun his budget, then he isn't going to have a budget, because he won't have a program."

But did the experience of competitions mean that technical excellence should be sacrificed for cost? Few were willing to say the company should retreat from its quality tradition. In space the need for infallible reliability had brought the requirement for engineering excellence and manufacturing quality to its highest point. "More and more we have to manufacture under hygienic laboratory conditions," said Dean Stowell, who had been directing Aero-Space central manufacturing operations. "It is a whole new frontier. What used to require inspection, then quality control, now requires what we have renamed Quality Engineering and Control. The work has become so sophisticated that we have to engineer a whole new technique to cope with it. We are using an entirely new brand of employees."

If the reliability requirement was true of space, it was equally true of missiles. One misfiring, and the whole thing was lost; it could not be brought back and fixed. So, too, had utmost reliability become more and more mandatory in commercial transportation, with the growing congestion of traffic, the coming of all-weather operation, next the advent of 400-passenger airplanes and 30-mile-a-minute supersonic transports.

"The philosophy of doing an outstanding job technically has gotten us a long way," said Doug Graves, who had been asked by Wood to head an Aero-Space task force to study pricing techniques. "The last thing we want to do is default technically. But we have to insist on cost-effectiveness trade-off studies in every organization, including manufacturing, to find the most economical way to do the job and still do it right. We have to do both."

"The undercurrent of thought here all the time has been that the competition should be for the best airplane," George Schairer put it. "But what is the best airplane? The government says that in deciding which is best it will give consideration to cost factors as well as performance factors. That shouldn't trouble us. We've had no trouble winning commercial business on this basis."

It raised the question, what was the basis of Boeing's remarkable rise in the commercial transport field. Bruce Connelly had an answer. "We've tried to build a team that is customer-oriented. We came to a realization that, if we were going to succeed in the commercial business, the important ingredient was the customer. We can't let the airline say—as it sometimes has—'the only time you are interested in our problem is when you're trying to sell us a new airplane.' It has taken us a long time to recognize the customer's problems, most of all his financing problem. Now his point of view is beginning to percolate through the whole organization."

Airplane engineering vice president Dick Rouzie named another ingredient in the Boeing transport ascendancy. "I think it was partly a matter of timing," he said, "crucial and rather fortunate timing. We had a line of products, in well-chosen varieties, early enough so that we were slightly ahead of the competition. There was a time when we didn't know whether we would come out or have a major debacle on our hands; then the curve started turning upward. Our product was a little further along in the difficult period from 1959 to 1962 when the airlines were going into debt; we got ourselves over the hump and when the traffic came we had something they needed. I feel deeply thankful, almost reverently so, for the business we have. I can't help but think, 'if the airlines are putting that kind of confidence in us, we had better not fail them.' "

Something significant had been happening in Boeing. It was a company that had gained, by reverses and successes, a certain humility despite its size. It was developing into a new kind of organization. With further homework it could be well on the way to qualifying for the term "great." It was a company in mid-passage, its future paths still uncharted in many fields. But one trend was clear. It had moved in a large way into a market to meet civilian needs, a market based in the major, civilian sector of the economy, where once it existed principally in the government-procurement sector. Even in space, it was beginning to view the future market from this new standpoint.

"We are feeling the effect of a translation of science

from war to peace," product research director Ben Ruffner said, even while Boeing B-52s were pounding the targets of Vietnam and Vertol helicopters were becoming the work horse craft of that difficult war. "Boeing has gone the farthest in this civilian direction of any of the aerospace companies, while still carrying forward and increasing the capability to deal with military defense needs." He added: "Many of our choices ahead will not be known until we see the effects of further application of the technology being developed."

"The name of the game is going to be transportation—protection, peace, transportation," said consultant Vernon Crudge. Boeing's business was essentially transportation. Airplanes, helicopters, missiles, spacecraft, hydrofoils were all transportation vehicles. Other types might ensue.

Then what was the future of transportation? Joe Sutter saw it filled with continued growth. "The economy of the world is better. The economy of the airplane is better. People are just learning how to travel."

Airplane sales director George Sanborn was still more enthusiastic. "We are just on the threshold of the airplane business," he said. "It's a baby yet. It's a very young industry. Communication is becoming extremely important in the world. We are just starting on supersonic transportation; we still have ahead hypersonic, then space travel—rockets. All these are yet to come, because what we are selling is speed."

But wouldn't the time come when people would not care about getting there any faster?

"Yes," said Sanborn, "when it's instantaneous."

Engineer Bill Hamilton could see the time when the vertical or short take-off transport—the "V/STOL" on which his group had been working, could be considered commercially. The prospective CX-6 military V/STOL would open the way to extraordinary troop and supply mobility in the field, as the C-5A was opening it between America and distant lands, he felt. It could combine the functions of smaller C-130 transports and trucks, and it could move to inaccessible areas as could helicopters, but with airplane speed. If it could take off vertically it could double its payload by using a short, 1,000-foot runway, which would bring it into the realm of possibility for commercial use, operating from city center to city center, up to 1,000 miles, at airline speeds.

"It's going to come," Hamilton predicted, "both for military and commercial use, but the big market in the future will be commercial. Apply the new 747 technology to V/STOL and with a few more improvements we are going to get very impressive efficiencies. When you combine that with the capability of landing in a few city blocks, the V/STOL will grow like crazy."

But there would also be the need for fresh attention to existing airports and new airports to permit the handling of the air traffic and the ground passenger and cargo movements in the wave that was ahead. "We have only scratched the surface of man's ingenuity in more efficient methods of handling cargo," Bruce Connelly said. There would be the call for systems engineering, ground and air together, as in a Minuteman program.

Further in the future was the space transport. Every step of aviation was a step in its direction. Even the SST at 66,000 feet would be down to about one-twentieth of sea level atmosphere. The United States had been thrust into space almost without intending it, but it now possessed the technology for space travel. Crude and expensive as it might be the basic platform of knowledge existed from which to launch new work toward improvement in purpose and economy. George Stoner was pointing his people in this direction in their study of new uses of space.

"The Boeing Company, in the venture I am starting you on, has one advantage," he had told them after the manned orbital laboratory competition was lost. "We are not involved, so we are not biased. We are in a position to get at fundamentals because we haven't an axe to grind. I want you to do just that. I want you to take a whole fresh look at space."

Stoner's engineers were reassessing the separate elements of space transportation: acceleration, re-entry, space propulsion, structures, configurations, reusable launch.

Extending the work of one NASA contract study an intriguing design project was continuing on an orbiting space telescope that could give astronomy a quantum jump forward. The optical requirements were formidable. From earth the atmosphere so cluttered the view as to excuse imperfect optics; the clear medium of space called for lens fidelity of a much higher order. But more challenging still was the means of holding the telescope motionless in space to gain a crystal-clear image. A man's heartbeat in the spacecraft would be enough to disturb the perfection of that image. Structural designer Dave Bogdonoff found the answer in a device for disconnecting the telescope from the spacecraft, suspending it in total space-quietness for the critical moment of telescopic photography.

Such efforts were justified only in terms of business prospects five to ten years out. Yet that fact in itself lent importance to the present beginnings. New needs would appear. Tex Johnston, heading the combined Minuteman and Saturn test operation at Cape Kennedy in Florida, was urging the filling of one need that seemed to him imperative, for a craft that would be capable of quick dispatch and return in the event that space rescue missions were required. Johnston had headed the Dyna-Soar program after Stoner moved to Saturn, and he was not forgetting its implications for such craft in the future. Nor was he forgetting his days as head of flight test. "The astronauts up there need a sure way to get down," he kept saying. "Someday someone is going to get stuck up there, and there'll be hell to pay. There's a real requirement for fast-reaction equipment to get up and back—a space logistics device. It has a tremendous potential."

That device could be a cousin to a rocket transport. "All of us instinctively believe that the development of the airplane does not stop at Mach 3 or any other number," said Harry Goldie, now Aero-Space director of product development. "Rocket or supersonic ramjet transports would bring the Dyna-Soar technology back."

But the technology of the Dyna-Soar days had already advanced to make possible new approaches to the aerospace craft. Much more was known about heat-resisting materials. Max Braun, who had helped solve the structures riddle of Dyna-Soar, was working on the use of materials that would perspire, like skin, but remain intact at 3,500 degrees Fahrenheit. More discoveries were sure to come.

The whole approach to new materials was through improved understanding and control of the crystalline internal structure of metals. Metallurgist Mose Disotell in the supersonic transport program had been leading one major study of it through electron fractography—using electron microscopes to see the behavior and fracture of materials under heat and strain, and under salt and humid air. Certain atoms would arrange themselves in particular ways in the crystalline structure, causing brittleness. Disotell and his men were learning which alloys of titanium to use and which not to use in the SST. They had been learning also, through several years of development, how to improve light-weight honeycomb structure, and to make use of plastic materials that would serve better than metal for many purposes. They were learning how to join metals together without welding, diffusing one into another, to provide better joints and simplify the manufacture.

The work on missile and space devices was hastening all this understanding, so important to progress in commercial products. It was significant that the biggest new happenings in science were at the infinitesimal end of the scale, in the very atomic heart of materials. An extraordinary fact, little appreciated by the public, was that the primary rewards of space—with all its vastness of magnitude—were in the forcing of greater laboratory development in the microcosm of the tiny invisibles of electrons and protons and atomic interaction. The electronics of control and the physics of materials, both vital to safety and success in the sky, had a common meeting ground in the laboratory, it was becoming ever more evident in the work of both the Boeing Scientific Research Laboratories and the new Boeing Space Center.

A great part of this meeting ground was in the realm of solid-state physics, concerned with the changing of the atomic structure of materials, for it was as a result of work in this region that the fragile vacuum tube of electronics had given way to the transistor, and then to the reduction of the whole of circuitry to microscopic proportions, to be buried in a pea-size solid so it could be packed off to outer space. "The implications of this microelectronics really staggers the imagination," said Harvey Gunning, Aero-Space director of management integration. "It can go into all kinds of fields. It will make possible a computer on your desk no bigger than a book. It can improve communication equipment of all kinds, and the cockpit aids to the airplane pilots. It doesn't weigh anything; once it's made right, it's fantastically reliable in operation. It should ultimately be cheaper than present equipment."

Even the probing for new forms of power, which might hold the key not only to frontiers of space but also to the vast work of Earth, was taking place in a realm closely related to solid-state physics—the plasma physics realm. There was an excited mingling of search and discovery in these two camps in Guil Hollingsworth's Boeing Scientific Research Laboratory. The plasma physicist's experiments were endeavoring to chase electrons and neutrons into the desired places in the super heat that transformed a solid or a gas into an electrical conductor, as do the flames of the sun. One goal was to be able to contain this fiery action by magnetic means. Once this goal was practically attained it could be possible to tame the wildly anarchic power of the H-bomb and to use hydrogen, the most plentiful material in the universe, as fuel for the work of man.

From the invisible atom to the largest, most powerful vehicle in the world, the giant Saturn with its 7,500,000 pounds of thrust, was the span of the work of Boeing in its fiftieth year. And the two extremes of pursuit had this goal in common—the search for knowledge that would make possible another step of progress and then another, as the steps had already come one upon another with almost unbelievable haste in a mere fifty years of earth time.

28

Saturn as a Boeing program was nearing the billion dollar mark. The work assignment had been expanded to include ground support and testing and system engineering and integration of the entire launch vehicle—a role not unlike that which the company was handling in Minuteman. At Marshall Space Flight Center in Huntsville, Alabama, the initial flight model of the Saturn first-stage booster, jointly built by Boeing-New Orleans and Marshall, was ready for its proving run. Tied to the ground in Marshall's massive anchored test tower of steel and concrete it was taking aboard the equivalent of 59 tank cars of liquid oxygen and kerosene, and responding to a thousand check-out commands from the shepherding blockhouse 750 feet away.

At the banks of control consoles in the blockhouse, combined NASA and Boeing teams were as gravely attentive as if for the first Saturn V launch that would follow in mere months at Cape Kennedy. Everywhere white and green lights on the boards were reporting the preparatory steps. The test director at the master console had at his fingertips the lighted switch panels of count control, firing sequencing and firing command. Within quick reach a fist-size red button marked "Panic" had its sobering connotations.

Abruptly the countdown stopped at minus ten minutes, a panel flashed the announcement that firing preparations were incomplete, then a second light came on to trace the trouble to a stuck helium valve. But at full pressure the valve came free and the countdown continued. At minus 90 seconds the whole operation went over to automatic control, a click-click of pre-programmed electronics opening and closing the valves and switches. A back room full of recording devices was measuring power levels and pressures and temperatures on electronic tape, on oscilloscope viewing plates with their bright lines jumping and twitching, and on tracer strip charts rolling out the conditions against 58 critical red-line limits at which cut-off monitors would shut down the test.

A Niagara of water was now rushing down the flame deflector at the base of the stand and flowing away in a temporary river. A tell-tale jet of escaping vapors from the liquid oxygen tank suddenly vanished to indicate that the safety valve was closed and the pressure would build rapidly to force the propellants toward the engines. The periscopes and portholes in the thick blockhouse walls were full of eyes.

A count zero a red burst and a quick-enveloping flash were followed by a demon downrush of flame from the thirteen-foot mouths of all five nozzles, walls rumbling, steam and flame and smoke roaring to the ground and boiling wildly to the sky. It was a continuing awesome outpouring of searing power, consuming 200,000 gallons of propellant per minute. There was the power of 150 diesel locomotives in the mere pumps that were delivering the fuel to the combustion chambers of the five rocket engines. Then, at an appointed 40 seconds, it all stopped, clipped off by the eyeblink cutoff valves that responded in a fraction of a second. It was power that could be tamed.

The Space Division now had 4,500 engineers and technicians working under Huntsville manager Bernie Beckelman, providing technical support to Wernher von Braun's NASA forces in the multiple tasks of preparing Saturn for its momentous moon mission. They were devising the automatic check-out and launch control equipment; working at means to assure equipment reliability; building up the aggregations of computers that could simulate the flight mission and compute all the changing conditions to be encountered at the speed of the rocket itself. Already von Braun was considering other mission possibilities to follow the moon explorations. The Saturn could truck extra power packages into orbit to be linked together to provide a vehicle capable of manned fly-by missions to Venus or Mars, or of taking a crew of eight, plus all the needed supplies for a year-long excursion with stopover landings on Mars.

For more immediate attention NASA was soliciting industry proposals for further study and equipment planning on the advanced Apollo applications that had been the subject of the meeting Bill Allen had attended. In the NASA Washington headquarters, it was former Boeing man Ed Gray who was propounding the long-range possibilities, as director of advanced manned space missions, giving heed to administrator James Webb's directive that the scientific and technological proceeds of NASA programs be made available for prompt application to the nation's industrial and civilian needs. Gray was asking for study on far-reaching applications in the vein of which George Stoner had spoken, seeking new ways of meeting the great problems of humanity—how to obtain the food, the natural resources, the water, the oxygen supply needed for the exploding populations of the nations, how to help those populations to learn to live together in peace with the aid of universal communication.

Against these and a host of other potentials, a Boeing team at Huntsville was working with the IBM company on a competitive proposal for the sophisticated equipment that Saturn could put into a future sky for such purposes. A whole new horizon for the scientific community was being sighted. In fact it appeared possible that the limits would not be in technology so much as in the capacity of scholars in the realms of economics and the humanities to cope with a deluge of data never before available about the earth and its life-supporting elements, and to learn how to select from this and utilize it. It could

mean new work for the universities and research institutes
of the world.

But the Saturn-Apollo had first to be put into the sky.
That comprehensive endeavor was giving rise to the bil-
lion-dollar NASA spaceport called Launch Complex 39
at Kennedy Space Center, Florida, where the combined
talents of 25,000 corporations were coming into focus in
the largest peacetime program ever undertaken. There in
the titanic tension of count zero would come the test of
tens of thousands of specialized responsibilities, directed
from Washington by the same man as had said of Minuteman, "We'll take the bold approach"—General Sam Phillips, now head of the NASA Apollo Program office.

The rapidly growing contingent of Boeing engineers
and planners at Cape Kennedy under Tex Johnston
would not only bear the burden of seeing that the Saturn
booster's 900,000 potent parts were ready to respond to
the call that all the world would be watching. It would
also be giving support to the whole of NASA's Florida
technical establishment which had the task of integrating
all the industrial efforts that must go together to make a
successful launch.

Already the preparations were reaching realistic mission stage. The massive vertical assembly building, largest-
volume structure in the world, with doors big enough to
admit New York's United Nations building intact, was
ready to receive three of the 363-foot-high Saturn V's
fully assembled on their mobile launching stands. Each
of the mobile launchers was itself a 34-story skyscraper
of steel on a battleship-construction base the size of a
baseball diamond. Ready also was the crawler-trans-
porter, a strong-backed turtle on multiple tractor treads
that could walk under the whole top-heavy 5,500-ton
load and carry it like a balanced pencil down the three-
mile crawlerway and up the concrete incline to Pad A on
the edge of the Atlantic.

Back at their safe three miles were the firing rooms,
each of four a theater full of operator electronic consoles,
row upon row numbering into the hundreds, with great

view windows and four overhead 10-foot TV screens to
bring closeups of the climactic events at Pad A.

Amidst these gigantic works it was not difficult to imagine the day of embarkation on what President Kennedy had called "a great historic journey" in which "we
are all partners." The mobile launcher would stand astride
the grand canyon of firebrick and deluge nozzles that
formed the flame trough of the pad. Atop the launch-
umbilical tower the three chosen astronauts would cross
over the dizzying footbridge to the Apollo command capsule at the peak of the pylon of power, casting parting
glances at tiny figures 380 feet below.

It was possible to picture the thunderous ignition, the
launchtower arms pulling away, the 3,600-ton loaded
Saturn lifting up on its five columns of rushing flame,
gaining momentum and gradually accelerating to its racing rocket speed of vertical ascent.

But it was less easy to imagine, until the moment should
come, the tremendous import of each so-long-planned response of that equipment once it was out of sight and on
its lone way. To the intrepid trio would come the strange
sensation of exit from all that means earth. There would
be the dropping of the giant first-stage booster after just
150 seconds of ascent, at 39 miles altitude, then the separation of the North American-built second stage after its
390-second burn and the attainment of 100 miles of altitude. The first burn of the Douglas third-stage booster
would be followed, according to plan, by a circling in
"parking orbit" around the earth to provide time to
check all the systems and calculate the precise moment
for winging out on the wide trajectory to the moon;
then would come the re-ignition of the third stage for
the adventurous acceleration to escape-from-gravity velocity.

At 180 miles out, while racing moonward, it would be
necessary to make some rearrangements that could be
accomplished only in the weightlessness and freedom
from air resistance in space. The metal surrounding the
spiderlike lunar landing device must be dropped away,

the pointed Apollo command module freed and turned around with its maneuvering rockets, to be mated nose-to-nose with the lunar excursion module. Then the expended third stage booster would be abandoned and the Apollo would be prepared to use its own aft rocket for the mandatory slowing-down process required to get into orbit around the moon.

But that next maneuver would remain a long contemplation during a three-day journey through friendless space, a journey which could well give rise to profound thoughts about being and the universe, and about the enterprise of man on the parting planet with the continents and oceans and clouds wrapped around.

Three mid-course corrections of direction, prompted by urgent coaching from the computer-working crew at Houston Manned Space Center, would perfect the lunar aim as the target orb grew gradually into giant close-at-hand reality and the earth behind diminished in size to become a hanging ball. With the great moon looming collision-close, there would be the vital business of braking from 6,000 miles per hour to lunar orbital velocity of 3,600 miles per hour at an altitude of no less than 60 miles from the moon's surface. Through the nose of Apollo at that point would squeeze the two excursion volunteers into the spider-legged lunar landing module, to check its systems, and if all was well, to cut loose and make a scanning orbit, then slow with retro-rockets at the right point to settle onto the weird, crisp landscape of moon.

One man would stand watch while the other, in space garb, ventured forth on foot, heeding the Houston instructions not to stray more than a quarter mile from the tenuous base. Only radio contact with the orbiting Apollo and thence with Houston on remote earth would cut the sharp sense of utter aloneness in such a place.

But the critical test would still be ahead—the checkout and lift-off, leaving the lower portion of the lunar excursion module behind; the accurately-calculated rendezvous with the Apollo passing over in orbit; then the detaching of the excursion module and the departure with lunar escape velocity on the tangent precisely timed to end at earth and not at some vacant point in the sky. Finally would come the most crucial test of equipment and mathematics of the entire heroic expedition—re-entry.

Because they would have a 24,000 mile-an-hour re-entry speed from space as compared with 17,000 miles an hour from previous earth orbits, a "corridor" of entry only 40 miles wide and 30 miles deep, beginning at about 80 miles above the earth, would have to be hit and maintained to regain the earth's surface. Too steep an approach and the spacecraft would plunge into the atmosphere so rapidly as to consume itself in heat; too shallow an approach and it would bounce off that atmosphere and lose the earth for the wastes of space. The correct angle of entry would be about 30 degrees, at which the heat shield would reach a permissible 5,000 degrees Fahrenheit. Even so in the compacting thin atmosphere a short way out in front of the racing spacecraft—but not touching the craft—the heat of colliding molecules would reach a frightful 100,000 degrees, nearly ten times the temperature of the surface of the sun.

At 140,000 feet altitude the mission would be counted all but won, the spacecraft slowing normally in the friction and pressure of the atmosphere. At 50,000 feet drogue chutes would be deployed to slow it further. At 15,000 feet three great parachutes would blossom out to carry the Apollo to the surface of the sea, and its three occupants to the astounded hearts of America and the world.

There would be the sighs of wonder and of praise. There could well be a breath of thanks to the hundreds of thousands of engineers and builders whose equipment had worked according to plan throughout the journey.

Chief of all, there would be the sense of a new dimension gained. If man could do this, what could he not do? As ever, another reach of opportunity would seem to be just at hand. But as always before, there would be the urgent need for Vision to point the way.

INDEX